Imprimi Potest: Donald P. Mulrenan, S.V.D.
Provincial Superior
Techny, Illinois, USA

Nihil obstat: Rev. Robert C. Harren
Censor Librorum

Imprimatur: + George H. Speltz, D.D., Ph.D.
Bishop of St. Cloud

St. Cloud Chancery
St. Cloud, Minnesota 56321
June 24, 1980

Publisher: De Rance, Inc.
7700 West Blue Mound Road
Milwaukee, Wisconsin 53213/USA

Distributor: The Human Life Center
St. John's University
Collegeville, Minnesota 56321/USA

Printed by: Isseisha, Tokyo

Produced by: Family Life Association, Tokyo

Designed by: Graphic Design Office M2, Tokyo

Coordinator: Fr. Anthony Zimmerman, S.V.D., S.T.D. Tokyo

Editor Part 1, Experience: Fr. Zimmerman

Editor Part 2, Sciences: Francois Guy, M.D. Grenoble

Editor Part 3, Theology: Fr. Dionigi Tettamanzi, Milan

Italian, Spanish, French, German, Polish, and Japanese language versions will be published simultaneously or in the near future.

Complimentary Copy, Not for commercial use.
Printed in Japan
Library of Congress Number: 8Ø-688ØØ

NATURAL FAMILY PLANNING

NATURE'S WAY - GOD'S WAY

FOREWORD

During the past twenty years there have been many significant advances in natural family planning. Scientific advances have given new reliability to natural family planning methods. New educational techniques have made it easier to train large numbers of couples. And the apostolic zeal of trained couples, as well as that of doctors, counselors and many of our priests and religious has placed this information at the disposal of increasing numbers of married couples who grasp the basic insight of the Church's teaching.

Yet, despite this progress, a great number of married couples hardly know the basic techniques of natural family planning, and many more are lacking in confidence because they remain unaware of the dramatic advances that have taken place.

This book can serve a very useful purpose in bringing to those who are uninformed a basic knowledge of Natural Family Planning. And, as many of the experiences described in the first section show quite clearly, it can also provide information and assurance that will give new confidence and hope to couples who wish to use the natural methods reliably and effectively. The first section presents the personal witness of married couples who utilize the natural methods, as well as couples involved in the promotion and the teaching of NFP.

But the book is not intended simply as just another instruction manual to be given to couples who wish to fulfill their responsibilities in terms of marital intimacy, childbearing and childrearing in fidelity to the Church's teaching. It is intended for a large audience, that is, for pastors of souls and for those associated with them in the pastoral care of families—physicians, educators, counselors, catechists, and especially those couples who are actively involved in NFP promotional and educational efforts. Thus, the second part of the book provides information on the scientific studies that verify the reliability of NFP, and the sociological and behavioral data that provide a sharper insight into attitudes, values and educational approaches. Part three presents the witness of the Catholic tradition, with particular focus on the teaching of recent Popes, the Second Vatican Council, and many Bishops Conferences throughout the world.

In addressing questions of marriage and family life, Popes Paul VI, John Paul I, and our present Holy Father, John Paul II, have repeatedly drawn on two major themes of the Second Vatican Council—conjugal love and responsible parenthood. The human love of married couples must be rooted in the source of all love—God Himself. For this human love serves the practical purpose of binding the couple together in a relationship that is faithful, unifying and fruitful. At the some time, this love reminds us of God's love for His people—His divine love that stands unshaken and undiminished even when mankind is weak, unfaithful or neglectful. That is why marriage connot be viewed simply as a useful, practical, contractual agreement. It must be understood as "the wise institution of the Creator to realize in mankind His design of love" (*Humanae Vitae*).

For a marriage to develop, succeed, and be fruitful, the special love of married partners must involve a relationship that is mutual, generous, affectionate, and expressed in a variety of ways that bind a couple more closely to each other (*Humanae Vitae, 9; Gaudium et Spes, 49*). This love cannot be selfish, self-centered. It must be outgoing. It should make a couple sensitive to the needs of family, friends and neighbors. The love of Christian spouses should have an outreach to the farthest horizons to embrace others who need compassion and care, giving them the awareness that God's love is mediated through those who have a vital experience of His loving presence.

In the vast majority of cases, as love continues to grow, the couple, looking beyond themselves, take up the privileges and responsibilities of parenthood. But parenthood should not be left to chance, for cooperation with God in the initiation of new life requires courage, commitment and generosity. Responsible parenthood in the spacing of births and the size of the family is based on the married couple's sense of personal security and their faith in God and His provident care. "In a word, the exercise of responsible parenthood requires that husband and wife, keeping a right order of priorities, recognize their own duties toward God, themselves, their families and human society" (*Humanae Vitae, 10; Gaudium et Spes, 87; Populorum Progressio, 36-37*).

Natural family planning should be seen primarily in the context of conjugal love and family life, not simply as another method of fertility control. For, as numerous couples have told us, NFP is not simply another birth control technique. It involves a fundamental approach to human sexuality that places conjugal intimacy in the larger context of marital rights and responsibilities. It fosters marital intimacy and sexual self-mastery. It preserves an openness to life and a willingness on the part of the couple to share life and love with their own children and with generations yet to come, and it prepares a couple for the generosity and self-sacrifice that are necessary in so many other areas of married life.

Openness to life and the extension of love to others must be the dominant qualities for a successful and happy marriage. Yet maintaining the openness to life brings its own share of problems and tensions. We live today in a world in which the child is often looked upon as a burden, rather than a benefit. Each birth is analyzed in terms of the economic cost, without any measurement of the intangible benefits that accrue to parents, to the family itself and to society. The love of children that leads to parental generosity and sacrifice is often constrained by a propaganda effort which has arbitarily decided that the two-child family should be the norm for all couples.

In his encyclical, *Humanae Vitae*, Pope Paul VI showed himself to be compassionately aware of the contemporary difficulties encountered by married couples. The Holy Father urged them "to conform their activity to the creative intention of God, expressed in the very nature of marriage and of its acts, and manifested by the constant teaching of the Church" (*Humanae Vitae, 10*).

With pastoral concern, Pope Paul recognized that observance of the Church's teaching sometimes appears to be difficult or even impossible of achievement, and that it would not be practicable without the help of God (*Humanae Vitae, 20*). However, the Holy Father also recognized that couples can achieve self-discipline and self-mastery by basing their efforts on their mutual love and their faith in a God Who is love, Who understands their struggles and readily forgives their failures, and Who continually extends to them the treasury of graces obtained by Christ and mediated through the Church, in word and sacrament. He said especially to priests: "Teach married couples the necessary way of prayer and prepare them to approach more often with great faith the Sacraments of the Eucharist and of Penance. Let them never lose heart because of their weakness" (*Humanae Vitae, 29*).

In this same vein, Pope John Paul II has noted that "parents may meet with a certain number of problems which cannot be solved without deep love, the love which also comprises an effort of continence. These two virtues, love and continence, appeal to a common decision of the spouses" (John Paul II to CLER and FIDAF, November 3, 1979).

We must also remember that the achievement of conjugal chastity is a process in which a couple, little by little, are able to order and integrate their many feelings and inclinations to the point where they achieve harmony and peace. There is sometimes the frustration of failure, and the tendency to give up. But this is the very time when Christian spouses call upon the graces of the marriage sacrament and move forward toward the perfection of their love for one another and the deepening of their life in Christ.

Once again, Pope John Paul II, recognizing the difficulties that married couples face, reminds us that while "decisions about the number of children and the sacrifices to be made for them must not be taken only with a view to adding to comfort and preserving a peaceful existence" (John Paul II, Respect Life Homily, Washington, D.C., October 7, 1979); at the same time, "it is necessary to use every possible means to provide practical help for couples to live this responsible parenthood." For the Holy Father notes "that what is at stake is the good of families . . . . and provided that an appeal is always made to the virtues of love and continence, it is a question of the progress of human self-mastery in conformity with the creative plan" (John Paul II to CLER and FIDAF).

This book, then, is a valuable contribution to the increasing literature on Natural Family Planning, seen in the context of Christian marriage and family life. For it is only when we acknowledge the twofold destiny of men and women–natural and supernatural–that we are able to deal with the wonders of childbirth and parenting. As the Second Vatican Council reminds us, "Everyone should be persuaded that human life and the task of transmitting it are not realities bound up with this world alone. Hence they cannot be measured or perceived only in terms of it, but always have a bearing on the eternal destiny of man" (*Gaudium et Spes, 51*).

It is my hope that this book will be circulated widely and read attentively so as to expand awareness of the reliability and value of the natural family planning methods. Moreover, it should help pastors, educators and counselors to motivate married couples toward achieving deeper marital unity, responsible parenthood and Christian perfection.

Terence Cardinal Cooke
Archbishop of New York

PREFACE:
THE SIGNIFICANCE OF THIS BOOK

So swift, devastating and apparently irresistible has been the assault on the family that most attackers, and some defenders, have failed to notice a powerful ally moving to the family's aid. It is *Natural Family Planning.*

One reason for this oversight is that Natural Family Planning has long been an object of concentrated scepticism, not to say scorn. Hence any examination of it must first face the question: Does it work? To answer that question is, broadly speaking, the function of this book. To anticipate the answer: Yes, Natural Family Planning works very well indeed.

Nor does it work on only one level, that of *reliability* (as it is usually called). Even contraception will work there. Natural Family Planning works on deeper levels, levels from which spring the highest aspirations and most lasting gratifications of men and women: self-possession and mutual respect, harmony with nature, honor for God's laws, simple happiness.

These are bold claims, admittedly. Yet how fully experience bears them out will be evident from a reading of the first part part of this book.

In fact the entire book can be viewed as an examination of the workings of NFP (to give Natural Family Planning its shorthand form). The first section, drawn in large part from the experience of couples and of teachers, shows chiefly *that* NFP works. The second part, the scientific part, shows *how* NFP works; this scientific section adduces and examines the physiological realities NFP utilizes. The third and final section of the book shows *why* NFP works; this theological part makes clear that NFP is in full harmony not only with the laws of nature but with the law of God.

Because men and women find their highest happiness and fullest liberty in obeying God and His less forgiving steward, nature, NFP becomes for many husbands and wives a liberating way of living their married life. For those who turn from contraception to NFP, it is a deliverance.

Why then the mockery? Why is NFP the butt of so many bitter and scornful jokes? The short answer, and perhaps the deepest answer, is that NFP is a reflection of God's Law and hence a prime target for the world's contempt. Consider the well-known jest:

Question: What do you call a couple who practice periodic abstinence?

Answer: Parents.

The pointed suggestion of unreliability is false, though this is not well understood as yet even in Catholic circles. Still, there is a significant truth to the suggestion that the husband and wife who practice NFP are likely to be parents, either already or one day in the future. For this likelihood there are several reasons.

Spouses who practice NFP know that parenthood is a normal part of marriage and a natural aspiration of husband and wife. Setting themselves afloat on the currents of their destiny, they share it in a way that recalls the root meaning of the old word *consort.* Yet they also feel themselves master and mistress of that common destiny.

This is a paradox made fully convincing only by experience, lived or conveyed. To convey such lived experience is one of the aims of this book.

A second reason why husband and wife practicing NFP are likely to be parents is a matter of physiology. The woman who practices NFP does nothing to endanger her fertility, or for that matter to endanger her health. This is in stark contrast to the woman on the Pill or the IUD, who runs multiple risks to health and indeed to life itself.

Our third reason has an axiomatic ring to it. It is that NFP, by definition, is a method of *family planning.* NFP is not just a way of *postponing conception*, though of course that is one of its uses. It is also a way of *achieving conception*; in fact it is the only method of family planning that can help couples to have children.

Thus Natural Family Planning restores the meaning of *family planning.* Whereas that term has been a euphemism for contraception, or at any rate has been applied only to the restriction of conception, it now means just what it says: *a method for planning families.*

Experience has brought to light a fourth and fundamental reason why couples who practice NFP are likely to be parents. It is that the very practice of NFP, through its motive principles and continuing momentum, helps bring a man and woman to a fuller understanding of human sexuality and of its fulfillment in the child.

Furthermore, it helps bring the spouses to a fuller understanding of one another. Such understanding is reached precisely because NFP is a cooperative venture: the very requirement of full mutual consent prompts husband and wife to examine, together, their reasons for embarking on NFP, their individual and joint needs.

Another characteristic found among spouses who adopt NFP, especially among those who choose NFP over contraception or worse, is a newfound sense of self-esteem. NFP not only *demands that the partners be able* to abstain, but often *shows them that they are able* to abstain.

Paul VI speaks to this matter magisterially in *Humanae Vitae*: "To dominate instinct by means of one's reason and free will undoubtedly demands asceticism in order that the affective expressions of conjugal life be according to right order. This is particularly necessary for the observance of periodic continence. Yet this discipline, which is proper to the purity of married couples, far from harming conjugal love, rather confers upon it a higher human value. It requires continual effort, but thanks to its beneficent influence, husband and wife fully develop their personalities and are enriched with spiritual values."

This "continual effort," this "discipline," is by all accounts incompatible with a merely temporary arrangement; so are the commitment and consideration essential to such discipline, and hence to the success of NFP. This is one reason why couples in such temporary arrangements who begin the practice of NFP may soon find themselves exchanging vows before a priest, and why some teachers of NFP insist at the outset that the first thing necessary for NFP is marriage.

The discipline necessary for NFP also helps explain why organizations that teach contraceptive techniques find NFP uncongenial and are unable to teach it successfully. Contraception-oriented organizations, however, move easily enough into abortion, and historically have become advocates of abortion; that reveals much about the moral thrust of contraception, just as the virtual absence of abortion among couples practicing NFP reveals much about the moral thrust of NFP.

All of this experience—the inability of organizations favoring contraception and abortion to teach NFP, the tendency of unmarried couples who undertake NFP to seek God's blessing on their union, the practical need of marriage for the success of NFP—all of this experience should help put to rest the understandable fear that NFP will become just a physiologically safe way of avoiding the responsibilities of marriage, or a way of avoiding marriage itself. In theory it might; in practice it has not.

NFP does more than demand marriage. It has a way of enhancing it, as we have seen. It does this by bringing to the fore not abstention but the virtues that abstention demands. Now the chief among these is love.

Abstention makes of this virtue a necessity, as indeed it is for the whole of marriage. But the abstinence integral to NFP demonstrates the utter necessity of love with a force and starkness rarely met elsewhere in marriage.

The point is so critical it requires repetition. That love is the most important virtue in marriage is a truth so obvious and so often repeated it has become banal. But the indispensability of love in overcoming the importunings of wounded human nature impresses itself on the minds of those practicing NFP (yes, even when a couple is trying not to avoid conception but to conceive a child!). To put the matter bluntly, even unfairly: NFP shows us that only love can overcome lust.

But love overcomes all things. The love brought to the fore in NFP proceeds to permeate the whole of marriage. To realize what this can mean to a marriage we need only recall St. Paul:

"Love is patient; love is kind. Love is not jealous, it does not put on airs, it is not snobbish. Love is never rude, it is not self-seeking, it is not prone to anger; neither does it brood over injuries. Love does not rejoice in what is wrong but rejoices with the truth. There is no limit to love's forebearance, to its trust, its hope, its power to endure" (I Corinthians 13, 4-7).

A marriage permeated with such love seems less human than divine, and so it is. Any wonder, then, that spouses who have come to NFP from contraception think they have come out of the house of bondage? That some speak in exalted, perhaps even extravagant terms? That NFP might even come to be considered the only way of living married life?

We know the mind of the Church on this matter. The popes, while clearly approving and repeatedly encouraging NFP, do not lose sight of the principle that (in the words of Pius XII) "the right deriving from the contract of marriage is a permanent, uninterupted and not intermittent right of each of the parties, one to the other."

Pope Pius made that observation in his landmark speech of 29 October 1951 on the morality of limiting the use of marriage to the wife's infertile periods, that is on the morality of NFP.

He noted: "Now upon married couples who perform the specific act of their state, nature and the Creator impose the function of providing for the conservation of the human race. This is the characteristic function, from which their state derives its peculiar value, the *bonum prolis.*"

He proceeded: "From this positive obligatory function it is possible to be exempt for a lengthy period, and even for the duration of the marriage, if there are grave reasons, such as those which not infrequently occur in the so-called 'indications' of a medical, eugenic, economic and social kind."

This was Pius XII's solution to the "serious question" he had posed at the outset, of "whether and how far the obligation of ready disposition to serve motherhood can be reconciled with the ever more widely diffused recourse to the periods of natural sterility (the so-called agenetic periods of the woman) which seems to be a clear expression of the will contrary to that disposition."

Less than a month later he returned to this question of the limits of recourse to the infertile periods. He began by speaking of big families: "Because the primary office of marriage is to be at the service of life, Our chief gratification and fatherly gratitude go to those generous spouses who, for the love of God and with trust in Him, courageously raise a large family.

"On the other hand the Church knows how to consider sympathetically and with understanding the real difficulties of married life in our days. Therefore in Our last talk on conjugal morality We affirmed the legitimacy and at the same time the limits—in truth very wide—of a regulation of offspring which, contrary to so-called 'birth control,' is compatible with God's law."

Paul VI formulated the teaching this way in *Humanae Vitae*:

"If, then, there are sound motives for spacing births, motives deriving from the physical or psychological condition of husband or wife, or from external circumstances, the Church teaches that it is then permissible to take into account the natural rhythms immanent in the generative functions and to make use of marriage during the infertile times only . . . ."

So broad are the moral limits of NFP that some hold couples may presume they stand within them simply because they live in a certain kind of society, such as one ruled by a ruthlessly antinatalist regime, or even a modern industrial state. So broad are these moral limits that some hold husband and wife can justifiably begin their marriage with the practice of NFP precisely in order to master the method should the need arise, especially since difficulties may be encountered in learning NFP after childbirth. (Few would question the wisdom of teaching a young couple awareness of their fertility from the outset, even before marriage.) Other questions concerning sound reasons for restricting the use of marriage to infertile periods remain to be resolved.

Whatever theologians may argue in these matters, whatever common conclusions they may reach, whatever the Magisterium may eventually decide, one thing is clear: NFP has already proven itself. It has shown itself sound on many levels, such as the moral, the physiological, the psychological. This in turn has proven a strong reinforcement for the Catholic doctrine on marital chastity. It will probably prove a strong reinforcement for the whole body of Catholic doctrine.

In the recent past, criticism of the Church's teaching on contraception promoted a critical reappraisal of the Church's teaching on many other matters, including her very authority to teach. In the near future, appreciation of NFP will prompt an appreciative reappraisal of the Church's teaching on married chastity, and inescapably of her authority to teach. The stone which the new builders rejected, which was a stumbling-block not only to the world but even to the household of faith, bids to become a cornerstone of a renewed faith.

This book is an attempt to hasten that day's arrival. To the contributors, all of whom have generously and genuinely expressed their views, go the thanks of the De Rance Foundation.

Fr. Anthony Zimmerman
Coordinator of the Book

TABLE OF CONTENTS

PART 1: EXPERIENCE

PART 2: SCIENCES

PART 3: THEOLOGY

APPENDIX: ECCLESIASTICAL DOCUMENTS

EXPERIENCE

Editor's Introduction

AUTHENTICITY IS THE KEYNOTE

Originally the section of this book dealing with experience was to have come last, after the sections on science and on theology. But we soon recognized that readers would prefer first to make sure that Natural Family Planning was more than a theory, that it can be lived in the lives of real people. So the section on the experience of Natural Family Planning now has pride of place.

In order that readers might come into the most direct contact possible with the contributors, we did relatively little editing of this section. Some contributions have a literary polish; others are artless and unadorned.

The first-person accounts in this section come from a sufficient variety of conditions and cultures to convince readers, we hope, that Natural Family Planning can take root anywhere. You will be led into the lives of couples in a Communist country and in the United States, in Calcutta and in Tokyo, in the city and on the farm. Seasoned teachers reflect a cumulative experience of centuries, among thousands of couples in countries of wide cultural diversity.

No attempt has been made to present these contributions in logical order. Readers can leaf through the first section at random. Yet I hope they will keep attuned to an element common to all these contributions: it is the sense that NFP people are *good* people.

Fr. Anthony Zimmerman, SVD, STD.
Editor, Part I, *Experience*
Tokyo, March 17, 1980.

PLANNING SOMETHING BEAUTIFUL FOR GOD

Mother Teresa

The need for a reliable method of NFP among our people in Calcutta has been so great that the work of the Missionaries of Charity led by Sr. M. Paulette has grown beyond all expectations.

At present about twelve thousand couples are successfully receiving instruction and have been able to rear their families in dignity and happiness.

At the same time our educators and social workers, who are concerned with the total sphere of family welfare, have felt the need for guidance in other areas of family life such as the care and development of the child and the harmony of the parents.

Natural Family Planning involves acceptance by the couple of a way of life of conjugal harmony and devotion to their children, which makes of their life something beautiful for God.

The child has been created for great things, to love and to be loved—to be God's gift of love to the world today. Through this child God keeps on loving the world.

To be fully the child of God, the child needs our love and care. To harm the child is an act against God's creation. That is why it is one of the great evils to murder the child in its mother's womb.

The family needs the child. For the family the child is the sunshine of God's love, the hope of eternal happiness.

God bless you.
Mother Teresa M.C.

—From the Foreword to the handbook Natural Family Planning and Family Life Education, Missionaries of Charity, 54 A, Lower Circular Road, Calcutta.

Editor's Comment:

The latest count of her activities shows how serious Mother Teresa is about promoting natural family planning among the poor. Sister Paulette writes from Calcutta that there are 108 centers in that city, with 120 educators; and 20 Sisters are in the field. They are trained and then sent to different parts of India to do the work. From 400 to 500 new cases are accepted each month.

I am especially gratified that Mother Teresa expressed so well the spirit of NFP, which is neither anti-population nor anti-child.

Our purpose is to help families, not to help governments carry out demographic policies.

In 1967 the Missionaries of Charity received as a postulant a young Indian girl from Mauritius who had been well trained by two top specialists, Drs. François and Michele Guy, in the practice of the symptothermal method of birth control.

She started with seven couples in the Bedford Lane Area, who are still using this method today. It has brought real stability to their lives, and they are very happy and grateful for it . . . .

In September 1969, under the guidance of Mother Teresa, the Sisters visited families of all creeds, as they believe that every woman has a right to know the natural method which would help her to plan her family. During their visits the Sisters were able to meet both husband and wife. They showed them how the marvelous work of God is to be found in both of them. They taught them the anatomy and physiology of the female genital organs. They took pains to explain the fertile and infertile periods in the woman's cycle, and how she can detect these through self examination and the use of the thermometer.

The Sisters visited that particular area every morning and evening; they met satisfaction as well as discouragement, but their faith and hope have helped them to eventually achieve success. The language was an obstacle. Also, couples cannot understand how Sisters can speak about such matters since they are not married. The people are now greatly edified and encouraged with this ray of hope.

The couples are amazed at how simple the method is. Once they know how to read the charts and to interpret their cycles, they become self-reliant, and the Sisters move on to guide other families. They have found that they have awakened in the husbands a greater understanding for their wives, and a renewed love now develops between the couples.

In many cases the husbands are the ones who take their wives to the center, since the women generally feel shy. The trust of the husband in the Sisters is such that he will ask the wife, every week, what advice the Sister has given. He will mark down the temperature in the chart for the wife. It is so nice to see them both sitting on the floor to write in the charts. Having learned it together, they in turn help other couples in the compound, teaching them the method.

Many people wonder how poor couples can exercise self-control for more than one week. Yes, they do it; it is possible. It is, after all, their own choice. Some abstain for twenty days a month; others for one, two, and even three months. From our experience we find that it is more difficult for an educated couple to abstain than for a poor and illiterate couple. Why? Perhaps because the wealthy and educated couples have more comforts, and are more inclined to enjoy the good things of life.

—From a report of the Missionaries of Charity in Calcutta on promotion of family life.

We are talking of peace. These are things that break peace. But I feel that the greatest destroyer of peace today is abortion, because it is a direct war, a direct killing, a direct murder by the mother herself. We who are standing here—our parents wanted us. We would not be here if our parents had done that to us. Our children, we want them, we love them. But what of the millions? Many people are very concerned with the children in India, with the children in Africa, where quite a number die of hunger. But millions are dying deliberately by the will of the mother. And this is the greatest destroyer of peace today. If a mother can kill her own child, what is left to prevent me from killing you and you killing me? There is nothing . . . .

We are teaching our beggars, our leprosy patients, our slum dwellers, our people of the street, natural family planning. Our poor people understand. I think that if our people can do like that, how much more can you and all the others do. These are people who have nothing to eat, maybe they have not a home in which to live, but they are great people. The poor are very wonderful people . . . .

—From Mother Teresa's Nobel lecture. Stockholm, December 11, 1979.

A GIFT THAT LASTS

George and Sylvia

Sylvia: George and I have been married 21 years, and we have seven children. Many people ask why we teach NFP when we have seven children. It happens that we changed to NFP about four and a half years ago when our youngest child was born. (Notice that I didn't say "last child was born"!)

George: When we teach NFP, we don't let anyone know that we have seven children until we've locked the doors!

We have a program of four meetings. The first is designed to teach couples when they are in phase three, that is the infertile time after presumed ovulation. We teach couple-oriented fertility-awareness, since this is a couple's responsibility, not that of one part of the couple. Still, the first meeting is taught almost exclusively by the husband. It's the easy part of the program.

The second meeting is about defining the pre-ovulatory infertile phase of the cycle. Then we follow up on how the couple has been doing during the first five weeks; the meetings are five weeks apart.

The third and fourth meetings are a sharing of experiences with the couples about our own lives, and about their experiences during the previous two months. Some accuse us of now talking people into the idea of having another child, saying it isn't the worst thing to happen in the world. And I think that is so: to have another child isn't the worst thing in the world. Isn't that right, Sylvia! *(Laughter from the audience.)*

Sylvia: We were married 17 years and had seven children when we started looking around for something to help us limit our family size. At different times when the children were being born I guess I thought about some special kind of contraceptive; but I know that George believed in living by the Church's teachings, so I decided that in order to keep our marriage as happy as it was, I should go along with his beliefs. Then, just about the time our seventh was expected, I noticed an ad about an NFP program in the Trenton Diocese, and I made a telephone call arranging for us to attend.

George: Our seven children were a result of practicing rhythm. We're the people who gave rhythm its bad name! But while we practiced rhythm as ineffectually as we did, the decision about whether to abstain or not to abstain was always Sylvia's. *She* made the decisions. Now we went to the Trenton meeting to see whether we could learn something which would give us a little better track record than this rhythm had done. And true to form, *she* made the decision to go there.

The most enlightening thing I witnessed there was that the husband gave most of the instruction. So here we had a husband involved in what for us had been a one-party responsibility.

And it was a surprise to us that we gained confidence in the method so fast, after only two or three cycles. I think that the key to this was that we had something we could see, and that we could both share.

Also, we now discussed sex much more than we had done before. I guess that after the first meeting, on the drive back home, we discussed sex more than we had done in the previous 17 years of our married life.

Sylvia: When I think about NFP, I think about abstinence, because that is what NFP really is. You cannot use NFP unless you abstain. Many people think, "Why bother? That's not necessary any more." But we think fertility is a gift from God. And we don't think that any mistake was made. With NFP there is no need to alter our fertility; we can arrange to live in harmony with it.

Being aware that *now* is the fertile time, and choosing to abstain during it, can be beautiful in marriage. Love can still be expressed, verbally, physically, and emotionally. This can be a very secure time, knowing that you are loved as a person, and that this love will not now result in intercourse. Living with this awareness of our fertility and knowing the wonderful powers we have to create a new life has enhanced our belief in God as the Creator of life.

George: On the way over tonight, Sylvia said to me, "You have to say something nice about abstinence tonight." It isn't the first time she told me that. "The whole method is dependent upon abstinence," she said, "so we have to talk about it."

Now, as I say, I'm a little bit uncomfortable with discussion about abstinence. To say something nice about abstinence is like saying something nice about your mother-in-law. It's just not done. But I've been thinking about why I'm uncomfortable in discussing it, and I began to realize that you cannot talk about abstinence alone, out of context. Abstinence cannot be separated from sexuality. It doesn't stand on its own. It's part of God's plan for sexuality.

Abstinence gives us a challenge. It prolongs, excites, and fulfills our sexuality. It makes it worthwhile. It makes this gift that God has given us last.

—Given at a workshop on NFP at St. Mary's Abbey, Morristown, New Jersey, Jan. 23, 1979.

PRIEST TO PRIEST

Fr. Denis St. Marie

Priests are good guys. We are priests because we had high ideals and were willing to work hard to achieve them. We may not all be intellectual giants, but you couldn't be stupid and get through theological studies. The priesthood is a fine profession of men who have chosen a life of service. But why are so many of us apathetic to NFP?

Happy priests enjoy most working with families. As a matter of fact, whatever be the apostolate of the priest, it has some connection with the family. After all, everyone is somebody's child, if not a mother or father or sister or brother. Priests understand the importance of family life. Families and their problems are usually the chief interest of priests.

If it is true that most priests work closely with families, it is likewise true that they live vicariously many of the problems of those families. Not the least of those problems is child-spacing.

While it is said that some priests feel pity for those who practice NFP, more priests don't know what the letters NFP stand for. What is sadder still, perhaps, is that those who *do* know what NFP stands for equate it with the "rhythm method" and dismiss it forthwith.

Many priests doubt the value of natural methods, and most are quite unaware that there is any natural method besides calendar rhythm. This is not because priests are ignorant or malicious, but more likely because they have been kept uninformed or, worse, misinformed—often by the same laity they are trying to help.

During the past two years I have travelled to more than fifty different dioceses in Central America and Mexico, as well as the Caribbean. I have been giving talks as "priest to priest" on family planning and the teachings of the Church, with an explanation of the artificial as well as the natural methods of family planning. My faith in priests has been more than vindicated.

I have yet to find a diocese or group of priests who were not grateful for the opportunity for a patient and detailed discussion of family planning. It would be edifying for the laity to see the genuine interest priests have in problems of child-spacing.

Very often, the comment of priests is that they never heard these things. They ask, "Why haven't the doctors explained these things to

Fr. St. Marie is a priest of the Diocese of Cleveland. At present he is attached to CENPAFAL, the Latin American Episcopal Conference.

us?'' (Doctors often lament that the priests have never explained to them the Church's teachings either.)

At first I was a little confused at the apparent opposition that I received from priests when I gave my conferences. They seemed to argue as though they were opposed to the teachings of the Church, especially *Humanae Vitae.* Then, little by little, I discovered the tremendous loyalty of priests to couples they so wanted to help. Their opposition grew mainly from a helplessness they felt when confronted with such big problems among so many couples. Like the couples themselves, they didn't see how they could possibly observe the Church's teachings. Also, no one was taking the time to explain the problem, the "why" of the Church's teaching and the "how" to solve them except through artificial methods.

Priests all too often labor under the prejudice that natural methods simply do not work. In many cases in the past, they promoted the "rhythm method" and they now—as the wry joke has it—have many children named after them. The laity convinced them that abstinence was all but impossible for normal, healthy couples. How strange that priests who live a life of abstinence didn't seem to recognize that that notion doesn't jibe with their own personal experience. (If the priest only knew just how much abstinence married people really do practice, he might feel himself less a hero.)

When the priest knows of no effective alternative to artificial methods, he may be inclined to keep silent on the Church's teachings. He asks himself: if he has nothing *good* to announce, what right has he to denounce the bad, particularly when the motives are so good? He sees the problems of the couples, and perhaps being a little weak in faith, he keeps silent on the Church's teachings.

But priests are good guys. They would like to know that there is an effective alternative. They appreciate an updating on the artificial methods, how they work, and what is their morality. So many think that the pill of today is the same pill they studied about in the seminary. They may think they can still suggest it for the regulating of the menstrual cycle, as if it had that effect. The IUD and the effects of sterilization all seem to get confused in their mind with the myriad of opinions and propaganda they hear each day. It is hard to distinguish a contraceptive from an abortifacient from sterilization.

It is true, but sad, that many of us priests have not kept up with our studies since we left the seminary. Parish duties are so demanding that we priests often find ourselves neglecting many areas of study. Unfortunately the progress of NFP over the past twenty years has been one of those areas of neglect.

Why are we priests not more interested in NFP? One of the answers is that the laity have not told many of us just how good it is, how many wonderful secondary effects it has on their family and on their marriage. At one conference for priests a teaching couple on NFP so infected the priests with their joy and enthusiasm for natural methods that the rest of us speakers became superfluous. In years gone by the laity convinced priests that the rhythm method would not work. Now, the laity can convince priests that newer methods do work, and work much better.

Laity working in NFP are doing a great service to the Church and to family life. They need and deserve all the support they can get from their priests. It is sad to confess that sometimes those same laity, instead of receiving support from priests, receive misunderstanding and opposition. But with more updating of information among the clergy, it will become clear just how grateful priests are for such help from their parishioners.

My approach has been to teach the negative first. We explain the theology of each artificial method and the harm it causes to marriages, to health and to family life. Then we teach our experiences in working with the World Health Organization's five-nation field study of the effectiveness of the ovulation method. We explain to them that the couples in the El Salvador part of the study were illiterate, undernourished, unmarried and often unhealthy or lacking the blessing of a sacramental marriage. Despite the adverse circumstances, every participant in the study there was able to identify the couple's fertile time in each cycle.

When we tell priests that the World Health Organization, in its preliminary report, indicated that it was as effective as or superior to any artificial method, they are startled and elated. They realize that there is an alternative they can practice, and while it isn't the easiest method it surely is the safest. I try to convince priests that if poor folks in the rural areas of El Salvador can make the method work effectively, the folks in their parish can do the same.

We priests are interested in the problems of family life. We are interested in the joys and successes as well. Teach us, and you will find us more than interested in NFP.

A PHILIPPINE EXPERIENCE

Sister Helen Paul

The question is asked whether NFP is only for white, suburban, upper-middle class people, or for ordinary folk. Let me speak from the experience I have had in the Philippines, and also in the Archdiocese of Newark.

I believe that NFP as an educational program, is applicable and valuable for couples everywhere. I believe that NFP can give a couple fertility control, whatever their purposes may be. It can do much more than that: it can build the marriage relationship through sharing the responsibility for the gift of fertility, and through the development of mutual respect.

The reason I believe this is related to the experience of teaching NFP on the Island of Mindanao in the Southern Philippines, in the Province of Bukidnan. There I had the opportunity to observe marvelous growth of persons, an increase in marital harmony, in from 4,000 to 5,000 couples whom we were able to reach with this educational program, over a period of eight years.

There were farmers, fishermen and others. I'd say that the farmers and fishermen were 95 percent, the engineers, nurses, doctors and such only 5 percent of the population. We began the program in an effort to help families with an average of eight children per family. With an income of $1.00 per day, it was just impossible to feed, educate and clothe them properly.

We went to the homes, taught them personally rather than in groups. Those teaching them were their social equals. The couples succeeded in controlling their fertility and much more, as the report of the employer indicated: population growth diminished, and a remarkable improvement in the law-and-order situation in the camps of the laborers was noticeable.

The thing that impressed me most, and keeps me interested in this program today, is the fact that it's a beautiful opportunity to observe persons grow. A change seems to occur in an individual's self-image, the way a man sees himself as a man. He becomes a person aware of his dignity, a person worthy of respect; a person who can expect respect from his peers, from his wife, and his children. His personal discovery of self-control in his sexual life opens up to him the opportunity for change in other areas: gambling, smoking, alcohol. It is interesting that a change in an individual's self-image opens to him a possibility for change in many other areas of life.

The children used to comment about the change in mom and dad. No more fighting at home, they say. And when this happens within a home, the children apply it in their own relationships. We see this change in behavior of children because of the change in the parents.

Here in New Jersey I was delighted to meet couples who have the *patience to try* NFP. I believe that this is the key phrase for success: the *patience to try.* It takes only a very short time to discover that you really *can* manage this system, which is not at all as complicated as it may seem at first. And these couples have not only tried it themselves, but they live it each day, and have gone on to promote it among others, to share the values that they have discovered enhancing their own marriage.

In our work for the Newark Archdiocese, we have made efforts to reach the foreigners. We have learned that here too, as in the Philippines, the large gatherings are not the acceptable way to reach these people—Spaniards, or Cubans, or South Americans. They need the privacy of person-to-person approach. But I am very confident that there too, as in the Philippines, within six months they will have the courage and enthusiasm to go out and speak publicly of fertility control as a couple.

I believe that American Society needs a challenge. I believe that couples need to be challenged to try NFP. Marriages today are in dire need of assistance. One of the strongest ways to assist marriage is for the Church, doctors and others to offer couples the practice of NFP.

I believe that if couples are encouraged to try encouraged by their clergymen and their doctors—then NFP is for all couples, regardless of their standing in society. I believe that *not to challenge them* is to underestimate their potential, that God-given potential which lies within each person.

—Given at a workshop on NFP at St. Mary's Abbey, Marristown, New Jersey, Jan. 23, 1979.

MAURITIUS: NON-CHRISTIANS FIND NFP SATISFACTORY

Bishop Jean Margeot of Port-Louis, and Doctor Pierre Piat

The movement *Family Action* was established on Mauritius in 1963 to help Catholics at a time when a major campaign for population control was being mounted by the government.

In 1960, Professor Tittmus, an English expert who had been invited to make an official report on the population situation, sounded the alarm. Following upon the eradication of malaria and improved sanitation, population was showing a marked increase. Faced by pressure for birth control, we felt obliged to give suitable guidance to our Catholics, who form 40 percent of the population.

A. 1. *Family Action* thus originated from a desire to help Catholics use natural means when practicing birth regulation. It is paradoxical that right from the beginning even until today, 15 years later, 45 percent of the registered users of the natural method as promoted by *Family Action* are non-Catholics: Muslims, Hindus, and others. This indicates how wrong many international demographers are when they label a natural method of birth regulation "Vatican Roulette."

2. Our experience in Mauritius also calls into question the widely held cliché that the sympto-thermal method is practical only for an intellectual elite. A very large percentage of our users have only a certificate of elementary school; 16 percent have never been to school at all; 4 percent are totally illiterate.

3. Is a natural method impractical for newlyweds? Many engaged women follow their sympto-thermal chart for several months before marriage. Our experience indicates that after they marry these remain far more faithful to the method than older couples.

4. Is it a method that cannot be followed for a long period of time by couples? Here again we have in our organization couples that have followed the method faithfully for 17 years. We have several cases where women users have become in turn educators of their own children. The passage from one generation to the next comes quite easily.

5. Are artificial methods more efficient than the natural ones? We wonder about the good faith of those who keep people confused between the ineffectiveness of the Ogino (or calendar) method, and the high effectiveness of the sympto-thermal method, which rests on newer scientific data. We also observe a tendency to attribute failures to the method and not to the real source, namely the negligence of users, or a lack of sufficient information. Apropos to this we might add that an astonishingly large number of couples have been coming to us during

the past several years, after having abandoned use of the pill.

B. The sympto-thermal method is not taught as a mere technique to avoid pregnancies. We have always put the stress on education of the couple for total married life. We stress the following points.

6. When teaching the STM our educators are careful to make women aware of their biological systems. Women thus gain much self-knowledge. They learn what is happening within themselves. Husbands then become more attentive to the entire personality of their wives, and realize that biology is an important factor.

In this manner, education of the couple fosters deeper human development. Our experience has taught us that an important dimension is neglected if a woman is taught only to record and interpret a chart without giving her a more rounded biological education.

7. We have been trying to help the couple discover the human dimensions of the sexual act as an expression of the total person. It is impossible to teach the STM without evoking in the couple *a deepening of the quality of their love.* We have noticed profounder dimensions of communion via the sexual act in many couples. In some cases, the sexual union has remained superficial, mechanical. We tried then, via the occasion of abstinence which the STM requires, to help them discover that the higher quality of the less frequent unions can be made to compensate for the lower quantity. We have invited the couple to see the sexual act as a means to reach in depth the "personal core" of the partner. The periods of abstinence are in no way presented as times when affection is not expressed. On the contrary, when exercising tenderness and affection in lieu of sexual activity, many couples have rediscovered carnal harmony and sexuality as an expression of mutual giving of self.

8. A final important concern is the relationship between love and the gift of life. *Family Action* has always insisted that the child should not be presented as a potential danger. The effort expended in the exercise of continence reminds the couple of the indissoluble link between the gift of self and the gift of life, and awakens an awareness of that link.

Seen in this context, the sympto-thermal method, as promoted by *Family Action,* is not simply a technique for birth regulation. It is seen as a means of deepening the dialogue between the partners at all levels. We could quote a great number of witnesses from among couples of Mauritius, Christian or Hindu, Muslim or Buddhist, very rich or very poor, who now live out their conjugal relations in a much improved manner because they have adopted the sympto-thermal method as a *way of living* their love.

Bishop's House, Port-Louis
February 12, 1980

"WE ACTUALLY FELT DESPERATE"

John and Jeannie

Jeannie: John and I have been married for six years and have three beautiful children: Chrissy is four, Mary is two and a half and Jimmy is one. So right after Jimmy was born, John and I thought seriously about birth control, more than we ever had before.

There are still many fertile years ahead of us. The costs of raising the family are constantly increasing. We were also worried about our ability to cope with the situation of more than three young children just as this time.

We actually felt desperate. Ever since we were married I was either pregnant or nursing, and I felt that I needed a break, both mentally and physically. We had to do something—something that works and that is reliable.

John: To give you a better understanding of our dilemma, let me tell you a bit about our background. I was raised as an Episcopalian and converted to Catholicism just before I married Jeannie. Jeannie was raised in the Catholic Church all the days of her life, in a very strict atmosphere concerning the teachings of the Church.

After we had thought about and discussed all the methods of birth control available to us at the time, we decided that I should have a vasectomy. I pushed this on Jeannie for several reasons. First, it was effective and safe; but more importantly, I would be having this done to my body, not to hers. We were having enough internal strife and grief and guilt feelings as it was and I figured that she will feel less guilty if I had it done to my body. I felt that I could live with myself and God, and rationalize this major decision.

Jeannie: Because I still was not sure that this was the right thing to do, we asked our parish priest to come to our home and talk to us about birth control. We asked for the Church's views on birth control and we were looking for guidance. Father explained that every couple has a unique situation and that we would have to search our own minds and souls for the answer to our particular situation; and that what we felt was right with our conscience would be okay with the Church.

We understood Father's problem of trying to meet the needs of his parishioners and at the same time to follow the guidelines of *Humanae Vitae.* We found that we could just not live peacefully with ourselves by following this rationale. We also feel certain now that if Father had been aware of NFP, he would have told us about it then.

John: After Father left, we still had no firm resolution about the

Church's requirements, and I proceeded with making an appointment with a urologist to have the vasectomy performed. When I told Jeannie that she would have to come with me to the doctor's office in order to sign the papers stating that we understood that this was an irreversible precedure, she became afraid. She just could not face the fact that we were never again going to have the chance to have children. She felt as though she was selling her soul to the devil.

The following Sunday I read a notice in our Church Bulletin on NFP. It caught my interest and I showed it to Jeannie; she felt as though this must be a message from God. So we signed up and went to the series of four classes.

Jeannie: It was the best thing that we ever did. We found the answers to all our problems. NFP is safe and effective; and even more important to us, it is safe in the eyes of God. John and I share the responsibility of planning our family. And NFP has made us much more aware of God's law in our lives. We realized that we had been getting caught up excessively by material considerations when trying to run our lives and plan our family; actually it is God who rightly has the final say in everything, even in planning families.

John: NFP has changed our lives in many ways, all for the better. We have become much more sensitive to each other's thoughts and needs; this refers not only to sexual matters but to a whole range of things in our relationship. NFP involves *both* of us, and so we both have a share in the responsibility and in the understanding of its use.

We have found that abstinence is not a concern or problem at all, and that it has definitely made intercourse more meaningful. In fact we might say that we have discovered that "Abstinence makes the heart grow fonder."

Jeannie: John and I have also discovered a new respect for life itself, because we are no longer afraid, and we find ourselves in complete control over planning our family. We no longer have that desperate feeling that we had before we came into the knowledge of NFP. In fact, we are now looking forward very much to having another child. As you can see this is really a complete turnabout from the way we felt before.

A QUARTER-CENTURY OF NFP EXPERIENCE

H.P. Dunn, M.D.
National Women's Hospital,
Auckland, New Zealand

My first paper on NFP appeared in 1956.[1] It dealt with 156 couples using a simple rhythm system with a fairly satisfactory success rate—approximately five pregnancies per 100 woman-years. The method failure rate of those who kept strictly to the method was only three.

Since then I have instructed thousands of couples in modern variations of NFP. In my latest report,[2] 600 successive cases were analysed. Over the years I have seen great personal, marital and spiritual benefits flowing from the use of NFP. At the same time society has gradually become aware of the hazards and disadvantages inherent in conventional contraception. These I have outlined in a recent pamphlet.[3]

At first sight it may seem strange that the medical profession in general has not espoused NFP, since one of its basic duties in the field of promoting good health should be to teach the principles of physiological living. NFP is the perfect physiological way of life in the area of sexuality for those who wish to avoid pregnancy either temporarily or permanently. But to achieve these ends the profession tends to adopt means that are surgical (intrauterine devices) or pharmacological (the pill), and its mind seems closed against the efficacy of modern NFP.

NFP is incompatible with artificial contraception, sterilization and abortion. To abandon all these may be too high a price for the secular humanist physician to pay. Sexual freedom has been bought at a tremendous cost: the destruction of individual lives (in abortion), of personal sanctity, of innumerable marriages, even of society itself.

Here are advantages peculiar to NFP and to no other method of regulating conception:

1. It preserves normal intercourse.
2. It is esthetically and ethically acceptable to all peoples and to all cultures.
3. No drugs; no inherent dangers to health.
4. No cost; no equipment.
5. Responsibility for family planning is shared equally by both partners. In every other method the onus is placed on one partner, usually the wife. NFP embodies the ideal of equality of the two sexes.
6. The marriage is strengthened by the necessary self-control. Other contraceptives eliminate the need for sexual discipline; this makes the marriages vulnerable in times of stress.
7. NFP is not detrimental to the unmarried because it is not an inducement to promiscuity.

8. There is an inexorable progression from contraception to sterilization and abortion. NFP users are not subject to this rule.

References:

[1] Dunn, H.P. "The Safe Period", *Lancet* (1956), *2*, 441–442.

[2] Dunn, H.P. "Natural Family Planning", *N.Z.Med.J.* (1975), *82*, 407–408.

[3] Dunn, H.P. "What's Wrong With Contraception" (1979), The Word Publishers, Box 66-018, Auckland, N.Z., pp. 20, 75c.

THE MYTH OF SPONTANEITY

Fr. Gilberto Gomez B.

1. In my pastoral work with many couples, I often find that they seek advice to solve the problems of conscience they have when they need to space their children or when they cannot have any more children for health reasons, financial constraints or other motives. When I tell them about natural fertility regulation they raise many objections, but I also hear many answers. This pastoral dialogue allows me to learn a lot about the couples' lives. Perhaps I learn more than I can teach them. And I use what I learn to help other couples discover better ways to conduct their marriage in accordance with God's plan.

2. One of the most frequent objections, especially from young couples, when talking to them about natural fertility regulation, stems from their fear that periodic continence will suppress the "spontaneity" of sexual relations. They feel that periodic continence will force them to "plan" their sexual activity. And they don't want to lead a "planned" sex life, because they would have to give up the charm of "spontaneity". When they refer to the "spontaneity" that should exist in sex, I have tried to figure out what they mean when they use this word. When they feel that periodic continence impoverishes their relationship, because it deprives sex of "spontaneity", I realize that they consider something to be "spontaneous" when it isn't planned, when it is immediate. They believe that something "spontaneous" is more sincere. And by "planning" intercourse, the act loses freshness, sincerity and naturalness.

I have been able to discuss this concept of "spontaneity" with other couples. And I have been able to discover that, in contrast to the immediacy involved in the idea for some couples, others find that it provides for free and conscious choice. "Spontaneous" is not only what I do at a given time, guided by the impulse of desire, but "spontaneous"—and more humanly "spontaneous"—is also what I don't do and leave for later, for a better occasion, when circumstances are more suitable.

This other way of understanding "spontaneity" comes from couples who seem to understand their sexuality in a new way, more as a language than as a function. They understand then that this language has many expressions, and that the more expressions it has, the richer is their relationship.

They understand that "continence" does not stand in the way of

Fr. Gomez is engaged in pastoral work in Latin America

"spontaneity" but quite to the contrary, continence challenges them to develop other expressions for that language, where the physical relationship is but one expression. And that this relationship will be all the richer when they experience it within a context of frequent expressions of tenderness, both verbal and non-verbal.

Thus continence assumes the sense of silence, of the silence needed to make room for dialogue and to transcend the spoken word. In fact, there can be different types of silence in a relationship. Silence can be:

–The silence of denial: when one person refuses to speak to the other, rejecting his presence, his self.

–A listening silence: to receive the other person's words, to let them become part of oneself. Without this silence dialogue becomes two simultaneous monologues.

–The silence of contemplation: when words aren't needed and the other person's presence is enough. It is the silence of ecstasy which is not emptiness but plenitude.

Thus periodic continence must be experienced like the listening silence and, eventually, as the silence of plenitude, when affection and love find in the partner a language so rich and so constant that the genital relationship is not necessarily required.

The couple is aware of its many bonds and strives to consolidate them through many channels–verbal, non-verbal, internal and external. And the genital relationship occupies a position of honor, but not of exclusiveness.

Couples then understand that the sexual relationship is much richer than the genital relationship, and that it cannot be ruled by immediacy, but that, like all human actions, especially if they have to do with interpersonal relationships, must take into account time and circumstances. In a certain way it has to be planned; in other words, it is necessary to foresee the best time, the best conditions of environment and privacy. And one of these conditions, for a couple who presently are not in a position to procreate, is that fertilization must be impossible at that time.

A couple told me, "Do you think it's a lack of spontaneity when we plan our family birthday parties? Not at all!" To prepare for a couple's union is not depriving the relationship of spontaneity. Quite to the contrary–it is making the sexual relationship a truly free choice for both partners.

THREE DECADES OF PROMOTING NFP

Fr. Paul Marx, O.S.B., Ph. D.

My three decades of work with couples in the NFP apostolate have been most rewarding, leaving me with great joys, positive memories, and happy experiences. I find that couples practicing NFP are very happy couples.

Calendar rhythm was much more successful than most people seem to realize today, that is, provided the method was understood properly by the couple using it. True, irregularity of cycles increased the amount of abstinence required. But I learned early that the amount of physical sexual activity in a marriage is by no means an index of the happiness and joy of the couple. The humanist psychiatrist Erich Fromm has observed that love is not the result of sexual satisfaction, but sexual happiness is the result of love.

As a celibate, I wondered why couples who deeply loved each other found continence not to be a major problem. The paradox was illuminated when a young husband told me, "Father, if husbands and wives really love each other, they will know many ways to express love." I began hearing couples talk about the courtship and honeymoon phases during each menstrual cycle. Some husbands and wives used to say that the practice of rhythm was "exciting" and even adventurous.

In the early days of NFP the occasional pregnancies that occurred contrary to plans were accepted as proof that God, after all, was in charge; that was a time when children were always considered a blessing from the Lord. Couples who wished to avoid a pregnancy but experienced one nevertheless often felt that God wanted them to have this special child who, properly raised, would honor Him for all eternity. Besides, children are meant to make saints out of their parents.

It became more and more evident that Catholic couples who practiced rhythm were by no means at a disadvantage compared with those who resorted to condoms, diaphragms, spermicides, and withdrawal, all of which had and still have high failure rates. Contraceptive practice is often accompanied by impulsive intercourse. (Also the abortifacient Pill and IUD, which came to the scene later, have high user-failure rates.)

In many discussions with contracepting non-Catholics it came home to me that contraception does not promote good marriage and family life; actually it unleashes the sexual instinct, to the deterioration of the relationship, and leads to aberrations like spousal exploitation, fornication, adultery, perversions, sterilization, abortion, and eventually euthanasia.

On the contrary, NFP enhances the communication of the couple, asks no more of the wife than it asks of the husband, produces a healthful insight into the real nature of marital sexuality, love, and biblical two-in-one relationship; not least, NFP occasions a sexual maturity and bond that contracepting couples often fail to achieve.

It continues to be a joy to see NFP couples become the natural teachers of sexuality and NFP to their own children; the parents are virtuous models of authentic masculinity and femininity. Because they are basically pro-life, NFP couples come to the defense of the unborn. Experiencing the benefits of NFP, these couples also applauded the wisdom of *Humanae Vitae*. I might add that in thirty years I cannot recall a couple who began their marriage understanding and practicing NFP who ended up with a separation or divorce.

As I look over the past now, I recall that those married couples who struggled with their sexuality, and who sometimes endured lengthy periods of abstinence, often had children who opted for the religious life or the priesthood or both. In general, the children inherited from their parents a respect for the sources of life. The couple who make sexual technique their top priority appear to have a difficult time achieving true happiness in marriage.

Abstinence does make the heart grow fonder. In the process such couples enrich their "love-making," since continence itself is an eloquent expression and proof of concern and love for one another and for their family. Besides, as Gerald Vann has written, "You don't make love, love makes you."

Periodic continence can enhance affection. I vividly remember the wife who told me that every night she falls asleep in her husband's arms. Another said, "I have the proof of my husband's love in his willingness to abstain for my sake and that of the children."

Then there were the wife and husband who argued vehemently with me in defense of the legitimacy of contraception. Afterwards the wife told me privately, "Father, if I see my death coming, I surely want to confess to a priest how many years I have contracepted." It appears to me that popularity-seeking priests who try to assuage consciences in this area, against the teaching given to us, do not succeed.

Actually the qualities that make a marriage successful are the same as those that enable couples to practice NFP successfully. When a marriage goes bad, many priests blame the Church's birth-control teaching, whereas what is really at fault is the marriage relationship. As Mormon sociologist Reuben Hill has remarked, sexual intercourse is a brutal truth session, reflecting the couple's total life-pattern together.

Still, real difficulties in promoting NFP also come to mind. I have always been amazed that so few married couples and also so few priests understand the God-made human reproductive process. The human reproductive system is astonishingly unique; it is quite distinct from that of the brute animal. I regret very much that the Church, in most places, does not routinely provide engaged couples with information necessary for NFP.

The popes since Pius XI in 1930 have given us valid instructions about guiding couples concerning the practice of NFP. In 1951 Pope Pius XII spoke out twice and strongly in behalf of NFP. In the encyclical *Humanae Vitae,* Pope Paul VI urged us to engage in this important apostolate. The present pope has several times stressed its importance, as in his talk of November 3, 1979, to the International Federation for Family Life Promotion, and Centre de Liaison des Equipes de Recherche.

The practice of NFP, in so many cases, helps to build beautiful families and saves them from the horrendous sexual abuses that are sapping the foundations of the West. Thank God that we are now, after all these years, moving into an age when bishops are providing full programs for marriage instructions, including NFP, in their dioceses. I look for a better world and a much healthier and more vigorous Church, with married couples who are proud to implement in their lives the teachings of this Church, radiating good influence over the entire human race, illustrating once again that the Creator of Man and of sex has also shown us how to live out our lives beautifully.

Rev. Paul Marx, O.S.B.
Human Life Center
St. John's University
Collegeville, MN 56321

Fr. Paul Marx, O.S.B., Ph. D., is Founder and President of the Human Life Center at St. John's University, Collegeville, Minnesota, USA. Leading figures gather annually at this Center for the Inter-Symposium on Natural Family Planning to teach and discuss the latest developments of all the approaches to NFP. Father Marx has acquired vast experience during 33 years in the area of NFP, pro-life, and anti-abortion and anti-euthanasia. Among his confreres he is sometimes called "Father Rhythm." He has visited 50 countries working in this apostolate, and has published widely. He is publisher of the INTERNATIONAL REVIEW OF NATURAL FAMILY PLANNING.

FAMILY LIFE EDUCATION IN KRAKOW

Dr. Wanda Poltawska
Psychiatrist at the Institute for
Theology of the Family in Krakow

I. Introduction

Even as I started my career as a psychiatrist in 1951, I became committed to pastoral work for families. My work at that time was in two areas:

1. As a specialist in the psychiatry of youth I worked in a dispensary for deprived children and young people, and I was obliged to start family consultations for the parents of these children.

2. Experience indicated to me that the majority of the difficulties had their source in the affective and sexual areas of life, both among adults and among children. For that reason I became a sexologist.

II. Method of Therapy

It became evident very soon in the course of my work that these people were in conflict with themselves and with their environment. I have therefore elaborated my own method of psycho-therapy which I have called the *Objectifying Method*. After practicing the method for several years I found an adequate theoretical basis for it in the philosophy of Cardinal Karol Wojtyla, as explained in his book *The Positive Person*. The author develops a concept of the integration of the human personality through positive action; passive integration does not exist.

As my work along this line developed it became more and more clear to me that to help people effectively we must show them precisely what it means to be a human person and what is the destiny of a person. It was at that point when I organized courses for basic theology and for moral teachings. That is how the Institute for Theology of the Family in Krakow took its beginning. It now has two branches, one for lay people and another for priests. There is a two-year study program, including theology, pastoral medicine, biology, anthropology and others.

III. The Problem Areas

Experience indicated that the majority of the conflicts had their source in a collision with ethical norms. People, including believers, do not know how to bring their personal lives into harmony with ethical norms. The essential values, such as human life, fidelity, monogamy, the sacramentality of marriage, chastity before and in marriage, and the rest are all in present danger. It has become clear that in addition to theology, foundations in Christian anthropology, in sexuality, in a knowledge of the natural methods of family planning are all necessary.

IV. Pastoral Procedure

We switched priorities from therapy to prevention, since it is clear that the cause of marital conflicts is very often found in a lack of proper preparation for sacramental marriage. For this reason we are working more and more in the area of marriage preparation courses. The Bishops of Poland have issued special instructions for this, which I follow. Personally I also give courses to students, organized at the parish level.

Details of procedure differ from parish to parish. But all of this is organized as an activity of the Church. In Poland, participation in marriage courses is obligatory for those who apply to receive the sacrament of marriage. In addition, it is required that the future bride and bridegroom together attend a course arranged by the Center for Marriage Consultation, to learn the natural family planning methods before their marriage.

V. Activities at the Center for Marriage Consultation

Besides my work as professor of pastoral medicine, I continue to carry on the work of Objectifying Therapy at the Center for Marriage Consultation. This is done in collaboration with a priest. Certain problems cannot be solved except in the confessional.

In the course of time it has become evident that the entire question of pastoral family work and education of couples is really a passing on of ethical norms. When I started this work it seemed to me it would suffice to teach the natural methods of family planning in order to make the dramatic sins—killing children and contraception—disappear. But now I am convinced that the solution of the problem is not in the methods, but in an authentic vision of Christian and human sexuality.

God, in creating man, endowed him with sex; he has given man this body, and fertility as an aim to be reached. It is in this reality that the solution must be found. A man who fulfills his life in accord with the plan of God is at peace, and achieves full integration of his personality, which is called holiness. He achieves the essential purpose of his life. But the man who does not understand what is the function of the body, of marriage, and of the family, destroys himself.

Consequently it is not in biology that the solution is found, nor even in theology. The solution is found in faith, and in a deep personal contact of man with God. To find God in oneself and in others is the true goal of life and of every action in the family. The sexual act of man has its origin in the mind of God, and it is precisely this dimension which needs to be re-discovered. We must make the entire realm of sexual life into something which is also spiritual. Each sexual act is not something which is confined to the body alone; it is an act of the totality of the human person. This person is created as an image of God, and he will find himself again only in God.

Experience acquired during many years of work in family-life problems convinces me that the heart of the problem is not so much planning the family as planning collaboration with God who is Creator of man and of the family.

Editor's Comment:

Dr. Poltawska has provided us with testimonies of couples who have found peace and growth when using natural family planning. Some of these testimonies can be found in this book. She has made a study of 200 cases of couples treated at the Center for Marriage Consultation, which has been published in a Japanese version. Many of the marital problems had developed when the couple were using *coitus interruptus*, without suspecting that this was the real source of the troubles: pathological fear of children; frustration and depressive reaction on part of the woman; indifference to sex or frigidity; anger and even violence on part of the man; and a gradual death of the love-relationship. Then less frequent intercourse or even a complete halt; perhaps unfaithfulness; then divorce.

Therapy came through insight into the problem, then re-building the love-relationship through the art of natural family planning, through loving during periods of abstinence as well as during sexual intercourse.

Here are conclusions reached by Dr. Poltawska from her studies:

1. Contraception does not forestall abortion. On the contrary, abortion is the consequence of a contraceptive attitude. When contraception spreads, the number of abortions increases.
2. Contraceptive intercourse generates neurosis.
3. The clinical picture of conjugal neurosis caused by contraception differs with man and woman. Hyper-sensitivity and aggression increase in the man, and depressive states in the woman.
4. The contraceptive attitude destroys love, leads to unfaithfulness and brings on disintegration of the marriage.
5. The only correct solution of the problems of human fertility lies in the use of periodic abstinence, on the basis of biological methods.
6. Complete sexual abstinence undertaken solely on account of fear of a child is not the correct solution and aggravates the conjugal conflict.
7. Periodic abstinence may evolve into a contraceptive attitude if the couple does not learn real unselfish love.

"WE DIDN'T WANT TO SAY '*NO*' TO EACH OTHER"

Michael and Marilyn

Mike: We both went through Catholic grade school, Catholic High School, and then chose Catholic College; so we were brought up as Catholics and it was very important for us to do things as Catholics should. We married in 1966, after graduating from college.

One of the first choices we had to make was the question of birth control. In 1966 there were two possibilities open to us as I recall; one was the pill, the other was rhythm. Our conscience told us that the pill is not for us, so we decided instead to try rhythm. And that is exactly what we did for the next several years: we *tried* it, very sporadically. And so by 1970 we had three children. Then we decided that we had better figure something else out. Although we love children, we didn't quite figure that we should have so many in so short a period of time.

Marilyn: Mike's father is one of 18 children; and my mother is one of 8; so after we had the 4th child, we realized that this could go on and on . . . . I remember one night Mike and me sitting down and wondering why rhythm didn't work for us. And why I was saying *no* to Mike only because I was afraid to become pregnant.

At that point in my life I wanted never to say *no* to Mike. I wanted our relationship to be so close and saying *no* should never be a part of that. We had a beautiful marriage; people used to come up and say to us that we had such a terrific marriage. We really relished in one another; we loved one another so much and we wanted to be one. And yet it was like choosing between the devil and the deep blue sea because on the one hand we wanted so much to be lovers, and on the other I was saying *no* to Mike constantly because I was afraid to have a baby.

We decided then, in 1970, to use the diaphragm. We reasoned that I would then never ever have an excuse to say *no* out of fear of pregnancy. It seemed—intellectually—that this would work, that it was a good thing for us as a couple. We could then have what we thought was the totality of relationship: we could have intercourse every night if we wanted.

So we thought; but there were those little gnawings. Our innermost core is Catholic, as we said. Using a diaphragm was going contrary to that. There was something inside which said: "There has to be more than just this."

Mike: It was disturbing for us to discover that we were not peaceful now. We had asked ourselves how we could find peace; we chose this method to find it; yet peace was not ours. For the next several years we struggled tremendously; we more or less intellectualized, saying, "This is great, not saying *no* to each other; we must love each other very much." We went through this for two or three years, fooling ourselves, not being peaceful at heart.

About that time, while we were looking around trying to find something else, we met some friends who told us about NFP. They invited us to a meeting and we went to look and listen. We decided to try it. That decision has made a tremendous difference in our lives, up to the present.

One quality about NFP is—abstinence. As a couple we would like to address ourselves to this subject; we think it is the greatest thing going.

Marilyn: When I first heard that *abstinence* is involved in NFP, I said, "No way! I do not want anything to do with *abstinence* because I don't think that it is *natural* for a married woman to say *no* to my husband. That is *against* nature," I said. I don't want to agree with anything that was going to keep me from fully satisfying both myself and Mike for even a short time during the month.

Mike: In the course of time we realized that what we had tried to avoid in our quest for oneness, in our search for peace and love; what we had discounted and turned away from, was to become the very thing which has the most value for us. Now we are looking to abstinence, to NFP, to gain real freedom in our lives. NFP allows us to decide when we want another child. It *is* freedom. Right now we have five children, but we're open to having another. NFP allows us to make the decision when we wish.

Marilyn: I decided to try NFP because of the testimony of couples, the testimony of priests, and because I trusted Mike. I was in quest of peace, and willing to try anything. I wanted to experience again that feeling of peace as an "innocent" Catholic, a person growing up in a Catholic environment and in harmony with it. I wanted that peace of mind, that peace of heart again, and so I tried NFP. And I want you to know that it works; it is like having my cake and eating it too. I know that I now have peace. I am living Catholic values. And I'm also never saying *no* to Mike. Abstinence does not mean that we say *no* to each other. Our abstinence is so fantastic that we are able to say *yes* to each other in its practice. Our creative sexual love-making is so beautiful; during this abstinence time every other part of our lives is enhanced.

Mike: It was kind of surprising to me to realize how much I had been performing. I used to think that I had to perform while making love. It now occurred to me that we could make love without having intercourse. I realized that Marilyn loves *me*, not just "performer me," and not just for all sorts of pleasure. She loves *me*, because I'm *me*, and I'm *her husband.* That is great peace, deep security. That awareness has helped me to change quite a bit over the past several years. To be loved as a person is the greatest benefit that I have personally gotten out of NFP.

Marilyn: We also realized that this oneness that I was looking for with Mike is not just an end result; it doesn't just come because we have intercourse. That is not the oneness that I had been seeking all these years. I had thought that it was the act of intercourse which satisfied me and which satisfied Mike. And it *is*, most certainly; I am not denying that. But all the little unions that go before this totality of union, these are the things that enrich us; the tenderness to each other during the other twenty three and a half hours of the day; the sensitivity to one another; the touching of one another; the just being fully aware of the presence of one another; that kind of oneness was not there before. It came when we realized that nothing was taken away from us by abstinence with NFP; rather, new things were added to us. All these onenesses that went around intercourse, before and after intercourse, all of the little unions that we had with one another—these were the things which fulfilled our lives. That was the oneness in our sacramental relationship, the satisfaction which we were searching for. So we really do have our cake and eat it too.

Mike: We have come up with a new definition of abstinence; we decided that abstinence for us from now on, is the answer to our search for freedom. Freedom in love-making and in our desire to be one in our coupleness, in our Catholic sacramental life as a couple. And we think that it is so terrific that every couple should have the opportunity of finding such deep-rooted freedom and peace.

—Given at a workshop on NFP at St. Mary's Abbey, Morristown, New Jersey, Jan. 23, 1979.

IS NFP A THREAT TO KINDERGARTENS?

Fr. Anthony Zimmerman

A priest who operates two kindergartens near Tokyo told me recently: "When you teach NFP, please stay far away from here. I want many children for my kindergartens."

The priest's fears are without foundation, I believe. Quite to the contrary, a switch from condoms to NFP would more than likely increase the kindergarten crop.

Admittedly, the condom is not always effective in preventing conception. (As Dr. Wanda Poltawska quipped during a seminar in Tokyo, "The condom is most effective when the woman is unable to conceive.") NFP can easily be more effective than the condom in avoiding conception. Condom-users in Japan, however, almost routinely abort unplanned babies; they will never enter the kindergarten. NFP-users are totally disinclined to abort unplanned offspring. To do so would be contrary to the gentle, considerate, loving philosophy of NFP. Hence, with NFP, a tiny increase in kindergarten enrolment is possible.

More important, familiarity with the fertile and infertile times of the cycle enables some sub-fertile couples finally to have the joy of bearing children. This fact is becoming well known in Japan. More kindergarten children can be foreseen.

Moreover, NFP couples become great lovers, pleased with the family, pleased with the partner, enjoying the neighborhood, happy to be alive, thankful to God. You can see from some testimonies in this book that NFP-users are quite inclined to have a child or two more than they had earlier planned, just because they love has expanded, and because they have serene confidence that they are in control of the birth-control situation. A small increase of kindergarten children is therefore a reasonable expectation.

The Japan situation during the past 32 years illustrates what can happen when governments and mass media over-advertise birth control, especially when the intention is anti-population or deceleration of demographic growth. Statisticians tell us that a billion condoms are manufactured annually in Japan; about two-thirds of these condoms, more than 600,000,000, are used in Japan itself. Yet there are about 2,000,000 abortions annually in Japan.

It is only too easy for governments to ride roughshod over the feelings of parents, to turn their hearts against children, to introduce destructive and immoral practices into the family circle.

If governments constantly urge couples not to have children, many people become confused. One Catholic mother in Japan asked me, in tears, whether it was a sin to have given birth to four children.

It is high time to restore dignity to family planning in Japan. By teaching NFP, we strengthen the role of the parents as the unchallenged master and mistress in their own home. No government agent ranks above them there. We make them free again. We help them plan their families in accordance with their own felt needs. Families should always remain the meeting place of church and society; they should be oases of peace and plentiful happiness in a world which is too often barren, too often disturbed.

As Sirach wrote two thousand years ago:

With three things I am delighted,
for they are pleasing to the Lord and to man:
Harmony among brethren, friendship among neighbors,
and the mutual love of husband and wife (25, 1-2).

Again and again in this book you find that couples who had earlier practiced contraception now feel their love had been dwarfed and mutilated; whereas after learning NFP their love became stronger and more considerate, more attentive, more fulfilling.

We hear that natural family planners are not likely to get abortions or divorces. Is this not a sign that love prevails in their lives? We also know that contraception, where widely practiced, spawns abortion epidemics; and there is a notorious rate of divorce in many contraceptive societies. Is it not a sign that where contraception prevails, love fails?

St. Thomas Aquinas teaches that continence is good for man in his present state, although it would not have been praiseworthy before the fall:

> Beasts are without reason. In this way man becomes, as it were, like them in coition, because he cannot moderate concupiscence. In the state of innocence nothing of this kind would have happened that was not regulated by reason, not because delight of the sense was less, as some say (rather indeed would sensible delight have been the greater in proportion to the greater purity of nature and the greater sensibility of the body); but because the force of concupiscence would not have so inordinately thrown itself into such pleasure, being curbed by reason, whose place it is not to lessen sensual pleasure, but to prevent the force of concupiscence from cleaving to it immoderately. Therefore continence would not have been praiseworthy in the state of innocence, whereas it is praiseworthy in our present state, not because it removes fecundity, but because it excludes inordinate desire (*S.T.* I, 98, 2 ad 3).

NFP should merit the description of "praiseworthy" from Thomas insofar as it is a system of governing desires according to reason. The governance of instincts for the achievement of reasonable ends is a distinctly human triumph, which is not in the slightest manner accessible to our fellow animals. A woman who sees in her husband the exercise of willpower over powerful instincts grows in admiration and love for him. A man who sees the woman as one who loves his human traits more than sexual blandishments, esteems her beyond measure, and tries to live up to her high expectations. He becomes more and more master in his own house, and she becomes mistress in her own self. Freed from compulsion, each enjoys a life of serene dignity, experiencing in created life something of that freedom which God enjoys in His uncreated trinitarian life.

Testimonies also tell us that children coming from families where parents follow the natural way, without contraception, radiate happiness and good neighborliness. The Tokyo priest is well advised, therefore, to encourage NFP near his kindergartens, for more than one reason. In the long run hc may have more children for his kindergartens, and parents and children will both enjoy life more.

WHAT SOME PRIESTS DON'T KNOW ABOUT NFP

Dr. Elisabeth Wojcik

I am a pediatrician, of Polish nationality, living in Vienna. My husband is at the Atomic Energy Office. We have three children. The oldest is getting married soon in Poland; our future daughter-in-law has learned NFP and is in agreement with its principles.

Because a theologian (a friend) writes me his opinion that it is practically impossible for couples to follow this method, I wish to reply to some common objections:

"The sympto-thermal method is too complicated."

It may seem so at first glance, or when reading instructions for the first time. From experience I can say that women understand it very quickly. The combination of the two signs, temperature and mucus, makes it easier to recognize the fertile and infertile times.

"It's a big bother and takes lots of time."

Naturally, measuring the temperature is a bit bothersome, and at the beginning not so pleasant. One gets used to it very fast and it becomes a habit, like brushing the teeth. After some experience, one doesn't have to measure it daily, but only during eight or 10 days of the month.

"It requires leisure and a very regular life."

The "leisure" required comes to this: that a married couple have a room to sleep in. Rising at night to take care of a child is no hindrance. Differences in time for measuring the temperature are of no importance if within a two-hour range. If a woman has night duties, she can measure the temperature in the daytime after an hour or two of rest. During a journey, most important is temperature measurement around ovulation time. But if a woman knows both signs well, she can sometimes recognize the fertile time by the mucus alone.

"Some priests think that temperature measurement is practically not possible."

Many married couples are already using the temperature sign for NFP, and they have no reason to mention this in the confessional. But couples who don't know NFP or who don't want to use it, may tell the priest it is impossible, and talk a great deal about their difficulties.

I have arrived at this position through experience. Naturally it is possible that some couples may have special difficulties with recognizing the days. Then they should seek special guidance.

I don't think that a young woman should learn only one sign at first, and then, if she has difficulties, learn the other sign too after some months. It is so much better if a young woman learns to interpret both signs together from the beginning. In this way she learns her biological signs well; and then after some time she can use the sign alone which she prefers, if she notices that she can get along with only one sign. But from the start, she should learn both signs.

In Austria, NFP is practically unknown among the people. Priests tolerate contraception. Among some persons there is an antipathy against NFP which almost amounts to aggressiveness. Even Catholic publications are wary of NFP.

During the past year, however, interest in NFP among young married couples has spread. The book of the Lutheran Ingrid Trobisch, *The Joy of Being A Woman*, is being read widely. Last year Dr. Josef Roetzer gave three lectures on NFP in Vienna for the first time. I have received approval for two medical lectures for marriage courses in May and June 1980. We should live in hopes!

NFP: AN ART TO BE LEARNED

John Kippley

The title of our manual, *The Art of Natural Family Planning*, was chosen very deliberately. In practice, natural family planning is an art. It involves a certain amount of skill in observing and interpreting the monthly signs. It is relatively simple, but still it has to be learned. It involves the use of reason in the learning process and in making practical judgments. It involves the use of freedom in making decisions about whether to express mutual marital affection in the coital embrace or in some other way.

As in any art, one's practice of NFP improves through experience. It doesn't require any genius to become skilled in this art, but it does require a little practice in the observation and interpretation of signs in order for the couple to feel really comfortable with it.

In a way it is like swimming. The person who says, "I can't swim and I can't learn and therefore I won't try," will never develop the art of swimming with those attitudes. The person who has an open attitude, follows directions, and practices, soon feels comfortable swimming: An art has been learned. So also with NFP . . . .

Many women appreciate the self-awareness they develop in natural family planning. They are able to note physical abnormalities sooner than they would otherwise and thus can seek medical attention at an earlier date. Some women may avoid an unnecessary doctor's visit or surgery. Pregnancy tests can usually be omitted when self-awareness is developed. One woman experienced severe abdominal pain, and upon consultation a doctor scheduled her for surgery. Fortunately, she was able to contact another doctor who suspected ovulation as the cause of her agony. His diagnosis was confirmed by examination and basal temperature readings, and this woman was spared unnecessary surgery and additional hospital expenses.

Some women express a sense of satisfaction from knowing just where they are in their periodic cycle. A former user of contraception told us that whenever her period was three days late, she used to worry about being pregnant. When she started natural family planning, she was very skeptical. Within six months she became very confident. She finds she is no longer fearful when her period begins late. . . .

Women can develop a better understanding of their bodily and emotional states through fertility awareness. A married woman writes: I would like to add a personal vote of thanks as a woman for bringing to me a feeling of true-self. That is, now I really seem to grasp the idea of

what a cycle consists of—all the changes within me that occur . . . .
This is a very deep satisfaction . . . .

From the book The Art of Natural Family Planning. *Used with permission. The book is available at the Couple to Couple League, P.O. Box 11084, Cincinnati, Ohio 45211 USA. The Couple to Couple League is a leading NFP teaching movement in the USA, now established in many dioceses, and in several other countries.*

VIGNETTES FROM POLAND

Family Experiences

I. Sophia and Joseph

My husband has a technical education and is an electrician. I have a primary education, and do the farming. We were married in 1964. I learned the natural method of family planning in 1968 and was very glad about this, since I already had two boys and a six-month old daughter. With this knowledge we could at last arrange our marital intercourse without having to fear a next pregnancy; at the same time we preserved our self-respect, and lived as Catholics.

The first child planned in accordance with the natural method came in 1974, but for unknown reasons there was a miscarriage.

Two years later, in 1976, we planned a daughter; but a son was born in March 1977. We now have four children aged 15, 13, 12 and 3. We do not plan to have more.

Since I have short cycles, we use the second infertility phase of the cycle. In the past my husband had no difficulty in observing periodic abstinence, but of late, we don't know why, it is sometimes difficult.

I work now in the Family Advisory Service of the parish. I think that the married couples, especially the younger couples, should not be left alone and entirely unaided when they practice periodic abstinence. Additional lectures should be organized for them from time to time. Older couples should also be helped in this way, right up until the time they become grandparents. I speak here about our parish and the region in which I live.

II. Stanislawa and Henry

Our housing conditions after marriage were very difficult. We had four sons who were born in 1950, 1952, 1953 and 1955. Family planning, and planning the sex of the child, were unknown to me. My husband did not approve of having so many children and feared that we would not be able to cope with our problems. He had a good job. I stopped working for five years, then I took a job in my profession as a nurse-midwife.

After my third child I looked for some information relating to family planning which is in harmony with human dignity and does no harm. I used the Ogino-Knaus calendar method, and conceived a child, the fourth one. I searched again and learned about the thermal method; I learned fully about this only in 1966. That method was rather difficult and required much sacrifice. My husband was accustomed from the beginning to a comfortable marital life and had difficulties observing abstinence during the fertile period.

In March 1968 I began to teach other people at the Birth Control Center. There were some difficulties about interpreting the signs which indicate the first beginning of the fertile phase; and some women were unwilling to measure their temperature. Then I learned the Billings Ovulation Method which was a great help to me for resolving difficult problems.

I began with myself. We had much trouble in our conjugal life. My husband wanted me to use contraception, considering that I had much medical experience as a midwife. My opinion was, however, that as I teach other people, I must be able to give witness to the possibility of a married life based on periodic abstinence.

On seeing my determined attitude, my husband had to accept this. He soon became convinced of the correctness of my arguments when he heard people talking about the many problems arising from an unhappy married life. At present we both are of the opinion that the solution of the birth regulation problem lies in applying periodic abstinence, and that this leads to moral order and happiness in marriage.

In my married life I always saw the element of natural spontaneity. At the age of 15 or 16, I listened with great interest to the lectures of a priest who explained to us about the order and harmony prevailing in the world; he told us that there are no hopeless situations. I often remembered those words during my life, and in return I want to help other people with that advice. I feel deeply this union of God and creation.

III. Hedwig

At first we made use of the calendar method. Our first child was not planned. It was a boy, born in 1963. We planned the next child who was born in 1966, also a boy.

At that time I heard about the thermal method. I travelled daily to Krakow where I attended lessons to learn the method. That was in 1967. Since that time we apply the thermal method only.

After a longer interval we planned a third child, using the method. A son was born in 1974. My husband dreamt of a daughter. After three years we planned another child, and this time also planned the child's sex. There was only one intercourse, immediately after menstruation. This time we succeeded. On January 28th, 1978, our longed-for daughter was born.

Obviously we continue to use the thermal method. My husband is very satisfied. We cannot imagine another kind of marital union. For some years I had a time of very irregular cycles. The shortest cycle had 28 days and the longest 55. But thanks to the method we were able to have intercourse and to plan the family. I measured the temperature accurately and observed the symptoms of ovulation, so I always knew in which period of the cycle I was at the time.

I consider that the natural methods are the most fitting for man.

IV. Stephana and Bronislaw

At the time of our marriage there were no courses in NFP. We knew nothing about the thermal method, and we did no planning of our children. Within ten years we have five children. I never resented this, and my husband resented it only a little whenever I became pregnant again. But I often thought that if things continue to go on like this our situation would be difficult. Then, when a child was born, my husband's displeasure vanished and he was satisfied.

In 1968 I learned the thermal method. The beginning was rather difficult; I did not have much confidence in it. Besides there were some difficulties about periodic abstinence. After ten years of marital life we suddenly had to adjust ourselves to this change; sometimes the waiting for the fertile time to pass was long. It was not so easy, especially for my husband.

Month by month the method started to work; my husband waited patiently, and at last we got used to it. Within that time we often wanted to have a child, as our situation was a little better. But I had experienced some difficulty before in bringing the pregnancies to term. We have the same blood group "A", my husband Rh+ and I Rh-, so that we were afraid of a miscarriage. At last the longed for day came and our sixth child was born in 1979. We, the parents, and also our older children were very pleased.

We appreciate very positively the thermal method and I want to encourage my children to use it when their time comes. Since the time we used the method, the whole world seemed changed for us, and our mutual love has grown stronger.

The biological method allows us to keep inner peace in the humdrum affairs of daily life. My husband appreciates my work as advisor, as I now work in the Advisory Service of our parish. I do this because I find that our young people need some help and admonition. They should be engaged now already in planning for the family, so that they can create truly healthy families. I know that there is often a lack of common language between the parents and the teenagers. So I do my best to do some good here, to teach them to appreciate the family and to feel responsible towards the Church.

V. OUR CHILDREN HAVE CONGENITAL DEFECTS

Michalina

Michalina, aged 40 years. Adam, aged 43, is a manual laborer.

We have two children now aged 13 and 15. Our children have congenital defects owing to hereditary transmission: under-developed eyeballs and cleft spine with fistula; they are seriously mentally handicapped. When pregnant with my first child I had a miscarriage. The second child also died. The third and fourth are the children now living.

Because of our children's congenital defects, I became interested in natural birth regulation. Since 1968 I have been learning about it quite thoroughly—the thermal method. I made use of the second infertile period. There were great difficulties, because of the long waiting period for the infertile phase. Though it demanded understanding and sacrifice on the part of my husband, we observed the periodic abstinence. The beginning was particularly difficult since I had to get up during the night to look after the children. The charts were less readable then, but I kept them up very accurately.

In 1975 I became acquainted with the Billings Ovulation Method, which was less strenuous and by which we could determine the first infertile phase after menstruation. From 1974 to 1975, we applied a combination of the mucus and thermometer signs. At present the Billings method alone has stood the test in our marriage. This method enhances our marital love which had slackened due to other circumstances, and it also exerts a favorable effect on our mutual love.

During all these years I have been taking advantage of the Family Advisory Service offered in our parish, and I was under the guidance of the same person. Also I profited much from reading books which I borrowed from the Service Center. Thanks to the information and advice there is some order in our family in spite of our handicapped children and other difficulties.

ABOUT BIOLOGY, DESIRE, AND LOVING

Joseph and Arlette D'Sousa

The myth that women are inclined to sexual congress only when they are fertile is in perfect accord with what in Marriage Encounter we term *the world's plan for sex.* When spouses have become disenchanted with each other, when they find they have less and less in common, and when they opt to live a separate, uninvolved life-style, then sex between them becomes more a matter of satisfying a biological urge, one in which each uses the other for convenience, rather than a means of communicating the depth of longing to be totally given to each other, and a celebration of life-long unity.

In such a scheme of things, our Creator has provided that at least once a month at the peak of her fertility, a woman may be reminded by her physiology that she can be life-giving to her spouse, and also be the vehicle of the miracle of new life, carrier of viable cells of life from her husband, in the image of the fatherhood of God. At worst, it is a time when an unloved wife finds the husband's approach least repugnant. In the plan of God, it is a very poor alternative, that new life be generated in circumstances where father and mother are not continually life-giving to each other in the profoundest and most complete expression of love; where by contrast, due to indifference or downright hostility, life is conceived by intention if not in fact, in sin, giving a stark reality to the Biblical phrase, and perpetuating the condition of our Fall.

The mystery of a woman's sexual desire is that it is more closely bound to conditions of mutual affection than a man's is. A woman is capable of going without sexual activity for extended periods, but not without affection. Without affection she becomes emotionally impoverished and spiritually infertile, a condition which becomes increasingly visible with time (see Fr. M. Catarinich's statement in the Sept. 1979 issue of the *Bulletin of the Natural Family Planning Council of Victoria.*)

But when her husband honors and loves her, entering her feeling and making her sentiments his very own, then he has begun to make effective what was our Creator's plan from the beginning, that they should be no longer two, but one flesh. Then she in turn becomes a fecund river of living water for her husband, a continual source of life. And with this spiritual fertility, her body too responds and her soul

Joseph and Arlette D'Sousa teach natural family planning and conduct Marriage Encounter Sessions in India.

cleaves to her husband's soul.

His tenderness to her with physical signs and gestures, which accompany his verbal appreciation of what she has been to him, opens her heart to him and her body like a flower, replete with all the richness of a woman's spirit and her physical being. We would not believe it initially but our experience has time and again proved that the physical desire of a wife, when aroused from spiritual and emotional causes, results in a richness of her inner being, through characteristic reactions, far greaten than any peak of the biological mucus symptom can foster.

Since this happy condition has been observed by us at increasingly diverse times of the cycle, we have no hesitation in stating categorically that a woman in love desires her husband always.

The second myth, that men are never satisfied, is another statement from the world's plan for sex, where relationship is at a discount. It is true that God has endowed man with a desire *to be* always *sexually communicative*; in fact, *this is at the heart of our sacrament.* It is equally true that in a loving way, a woman finds her fulfillment in being always *sexually receptive* to her husband.

This means that we are always responding to each other with the fulness of the being that we are as man and woman at a given time. It does not always mean intercourse, but it always respects our emotional and physical state, even our state of being married or engaged to be married. Who would say that we are not being intensely ardent and responsive to each other as man and woman as we prepare to be married?

In fact it is an impoverishment of our sexuality to think of sexual communication and receptivity only in terms of intercourse. Such an outlook is the greatest contributing factor to a growing lack of apprecia-tion of each other as persons and spouses, the wonder of our being man and woman, and is at the root of a growing disillusionment and staleness in our sexual life.

In God's plan for our sexuality, we feel an increasingly urgent call to return to our first virginal encounter, as He first presented us to each other, pure and spotless and without wrinkle or blemish. It was a deeply sexual and a deeply virginal love which impelled us to say in our hearts as we chose one another forever, "This one, at last, is bone of my bones, and flesh of my flesh" (Gn. 2,23).

And we find that the fulness of our life with each other as man and woman increases rather than detracts from this ideal of virginal beauty. The wonder of a wife's selflessness, her disponibility, her reticence and sensitivity, her feminine care and motherly tenderness, her grace and the delicacy of her particular charm, are unfolded and revealed only under conditions of deep and growing respect daily evidenced by her husband. As he rejoices in the gift of her unique person, her lovely body, her eyes and her limbs turn to him as a flower to the sun. It is no longer a question of his ardor alone; her longing to taste every gesture of his love, her eagerness to experience the abandonment of herself in loving him, is astonishingly equal if not stronger.

Depending on time and place the fulfilling ardor of our love may find expression in various ways and degrees. But at all times we are fully aware of the joy it brings us, and of the promise of greater joy available freely to us at the next opportune moment. And to a husband the uniqueness of his wife's surrender, and her self-abandon in accepting the joy he alone can bring her is the continual evidence of her virginal gift to him, and the means by which she remains his ever-virgin bride.

It is this continuing evidence of her virginal surrender, at all phases of their life and love together, that comes so naturally to a loved woman, and especially her surrender at the peak of her sexual fulfillment, which irradiates their relationship, which constitutes the charm filling the being of this fortunate man, a fruit and a reward of his own selfless love. For this reason we assert that a man in love is always satisfied.

So it should be clear that our sexuality, when expressed in God's plan of love between spouses, is a virginal and sanctifying element of our character. Being completely given to the joy of our spouse and the strengthening of our unity, it is able to give us fulfillment at no matter what stage or depth of expression.

Namely, the joy we feel in suiting our gesture of love to the time and place, never thereby lacking in this life-giving closeness we need so much —whether this gesture is in a word of love, or a touch, or with an intimate caress—our joy is just as complete, even if not as thoroughgoing, as that which we experience in intercourse. In other words, our sexuality has become completely joyful, and eternally fulfilling, because it has become continent.

The key to the joyful expression of our love, whether within the fertile phase or outside it, is continence rather than abstinence. A man is being just as continent when he expresses tenderness for his wife in a crowded bus, or in a park, or yet again at home before their children, or when she is tired or ill, as he does during her fertile period; when respecting her physical and emotional integrity, he causes her (and himself) the greatest joy possible with no possibility of an unintended pregnancy.

The modes suitable to an individual couple to express their tenderness for each other are as varied as two human beings joined into one can ever be. But it begins always with that deep rejoicing in each other's presence that two lovers always have. And with it the infinite modes of verbal and non-verbal expression, little attentions and services to each other that only lovers can render. We have essentially to get back to the days of our courtship to know how to conduct ourselves.

And so, for one couple it may be hand-holding and looking ardently into each other's eyes, seeing as it were our past present and future, summed up in the answering look of life-long devotion. For another, it may be the touch of a gentle hand on a cheek, or on the nape of a slender neck, that conveys volumes. To others yet, it may be the insistent ardent caresses of each other's forms, clothed or unclothed. What matters is that we find the appropriate means to express completely and satisfyingly the ardor of our tender and grateful love.

Though we may hark back to days of our courtship to find modes of showing love which are appropriate to ourselves, yet we *are* a married couple and we *have* a much deeper and more tender intimacy. And as we become more confident and joyous in our continence, we may want to bestow many more intimate caresses.

What we formerly thought of as forcplay, somc kind of a means to an end, now *becomes the play of our* constantly inventive, refreshing and *continent love.* Or even if we do nothing, but hold each other ardently, with the firmness of our virility and the softness of our femininity, we have already communicated to each other in a satisfying manner, the essence of who we are.

The foregoing will have indicated that continence and abstinence are two very dissimilar things. One is positive, the other somewhat negative; one joyous, the other somewhat sad. Continence believes in life and in love and in God's plan for our sexuality; abstinence may be somewhat hesitant if not suspicious.

But for all those who are willing to believe, continence will show that our loving during the fertile and infertile phases is not essentially different, but only in degree. In fact, continence allows us the free expression of our love in just the way we find most fulfilling to our inmost selves.

A PHYSICIAN SPEAKS ON RIGHT TO LIFE

Dr. Herbert Ratner

I was first attracted to the Catholic Church through her moral teachings. What had led some to leave the Church led me into the Church.

Today we see many Catholics who rebel against the teaching of the Church and refuse to accept its guidance in matters of morality. During the visit to Chicago of His Holiness we have even heard a prominent Catholic priest state over the air that though Pope John Paul II had a great message of love and unity, "He really doesn't understand the American Church. It is not the Polish Church."

God preserve us from those who prefer their own concept of the Church and their own infalliblity to that of the Vicar of Christ on earth.

After becoming a Catholic in 1938—and my first assignment by the Dominican Fathers was to conduct a seminar at the University of Chicago on *Casti Connubii*, the great encyclical of Pope Pius XI on marriage—I quickly discovered that under the cultural influence of the puritanism of an Anglo-American heritage most Catholics whom I encountered looked upon the moral teachings of the Church as a strait-jacket which robbed them of many pleasures on earth, a straitjacket which had to be suffered on earth in order to attain heaven. I knew of some Catholic physicians who actually believed that the teachings of the Church handicapped them in their competition with Protestant and Jewish doctors. How short-sighted they were!

In the great controversy raging today, with dissident theologians pitting themselves against the teachings of the Magisterium—a dissidence which seduces and confuses many of the laity—there is a fundamental teaching of our faith which we must never forget.

That our God is trinitarian.

That God the Father, the first Person of the Trinity—who is, in many ways, the forgotten Person in the Trinity—created Heaven and Earth.

Herbert Ratner was baptized in the Catholic faith several years after finishing medical school at the University of Michigan in Ann Arbor. His youth was spent in New York City. His parents were Jewish; his father, also a physician, was a socialist who escaped from Czarist Russia. Dr. Ratner describes his early environment as "liberal and atheistic." He now is editor of Child and Family Quarterly, *and formerly was health director of Oak Park, Illinois.*

As the Credo states: "We believe in one God, the Father, the Almighty, maker of heaven and earth, and all that is seen and unseen."

That, accordingly, the Book of Nature, the book studied by scientists, is a revelation of God, as well as is the Book of Scriptures.

That truths do not contradict one another. God does not tell us one truth in his book of nature and a contrary truth in the Scriptures or through his representative on earth, the Magisterial Church.

That the Church gives us answers which harmonize with nature.

Paradoxically, while some Catholics are rebelling against certain teachings of the Church, feminists, because of bitter experiences undergone in the past twenty years, are beginning to discover the truth of these same teachings, teachings which God mercifully presents to his people on a silver platter.

Let me cite one of many examples. In a column entitled *Hers*, written by women in *The New York Times*, the writer speaks of "The New Celibacy." Apparently, women are discovering that love without commitment, the kind of commitment that goes with marriage, is love not worthwhile. These women reject promiscuity. They find that "lack of sex does not make you blind or ruin your complexion." They discover the benefits of solitude, and say that "solitude grows on you." They develop a deep concern about losing their "new-found, hard-won autonomy." They discover that "The New Celibacy is really a matter of maintenance rather than of abstinence, more of acquiring self-hood than of giving up sex." The writer concludes: "It's fabulous. So fabulous that The New Celibacy could very easily lead to the old celibacy." (Sept. 27, 1979)

We ourselves may add further that The New Celibacy protects women against abortion, venereal disease, the ravages of the birth control pill, suicide and other psychiatric disturbances. The feminists are beginning to discover that their real opponent is not the so-called old-fashioned morality and old-fashioned religion. They are discovering that their real opponent is nature. Whereas God always forgives and man sometimes forgives, nature never forgives. The bitter lesson of repeated human experience is that, when one thwarts nature, nature rebukes, nature retaliates, nature strikes back.

By contrast, the grace which is available to us in the sacraments and the teachings of the Church helps make good the promise of nature. As Saint Thomas puts it, "Grace does not destroy nature but perfects it" (1,1, q. 1 a. 8 obj. 2).

In the light of this, we should never forget—and I direct this particularly to the young—that God has given each of us only one body. It is not a rehearsal body. It cannot be traded in for a new one after the fun is over. So, take good care of the body you have; it is intended to last for a lifetime.

I urge you, therefore, as an experienced physician, to beware of abortion, of sterilization, of the IUD and the Pill (which is chemical warfare against the women of the world, and the tool of social engineers to whom women are expendable). And, more to the point, both the Pill in its current dosage and the IUD are abortifacients.

I would urge you also, as an experienced physician, that if you really love the family—the natural institution given to us by God the Father and the supernatural institution given to us by His Son—you must beware of artificial contraception. As one can readily observe in our society, it has given rise to widespread fornication among the young, an increase in adultery, a tremendous increase in abortions, and a pandemic of venereal diseases and their consequences, primarily, a sharp increase in undesired and involuntary sterility, robbing young women of their greatest creative power, the gift of motherhood.

In closing, I would like to read the pledge to Pope John Paul II of the Catholic physicians of Chicago, which appeared in our diocesan newspaper, *The Chicago Catholic*, of October 5, 1979:

In honor of the visit of Pope John Paul II, we physicians pledge our obedience, support and loyalty, and wish to publicly affirm the following:

1. All life is sacred and given by God.
2. Life is scientifically and medically proven to begin at conception.
3. Abortion is the taking of human life.
4. In our experience, abortion is never a medical necessity.

Furthermore, we pledge not to perform, advise, or refer for abortion; nor will we support or condone the practice of abortion.

One does not have to be a Catholic to be against abortion. Five centuries before the Christian Church came into existence Hippocrates, who read the book of nature well, included the following in his famous Physician's Oath, which most physicians today still adhere to:

> I will use treatment to help the sick according to my ability and judgment, but never with a view to injury and wrong doing. Neither will I administer a poison to anyone when asked to do so, nor will I suggest such a course. Similarly, I will not give to a woman a pessary to cause abortion. But I will keep pure and holy my life and my art.

As we see, Hippocrates not only came out against abortion, but against euthanasia as well. Were there ever a time when euthanasia, or so-called 'mercy killing,' may have been justified, it would have been twenty-five hundred years ago, when the best anesthetic available was a crack on the head with a wooden mallet to render the patient unconscious.

Finally, let me say that these are times for courage and a renewed confidence in and a renewed commitment to God and his representative on earth. This is the meaning of Pope John Paul's visit to Chicago. Do not succumb to cowardly suggestions which omit all appeal to self-discipline. That road leads only to disaster on earth, and jeopardizes eternal life.

Above all, rediscover your love of children. Pass on to your sons and daughters the joys of children and the value of children in marriage. Do not cultivate stinginess in this matter: emulate the generosity of God. The child is a gift both biologically and theologically, a gift in the natural and in the supernatural order. For those of you who are fearful of an unplanned pregnancy, remember that this is certainly not the worst that can befall you. It is not cancer. A child is not only a parent's greatest treasure; it is the greatest gift you can give your other children.

In rediscovering the love of children—and His Holiness has given us so many demonstrations of his love of children during his visit—you will learn to appreciate the great teaching of *Humanae Vitae:* not to shut out the life-giving from the love-giving; to keep integral the unitive and the procreative, the unitive which is for the sake of procreating not only the newborn but of procreating in an environment of love the mature adult son or daughter as well.

"Happy are you who revere the Lord, who walk in his ways! For you shall eat the fruit of your handiwork; happy shall you be and favored" (Ps. 128, 1-2).

Address given at St. Ferdinand Church, Chicago, Oct. 7, 1979.

EDUCATION IN LOVE AND SEXUALITY: A FRENCH EXPERIENCE

Charles and Elisabeth Rendu

Listening to many couples who have consulted us on family planning has revealed that contraceptives endanger conjugal love. After using them for two or three years, women (especially) complained of a cooling of mutual love even though they had at first been happy to be able to prevent too-frequent pregnancies. Their language pointed to an objectification: "During intercourse I am only an object, a thing, a means, at the service of my husband's pleasure." And this attitude prevailed even among couples who continued to love each other.

According to our observations, this attitude developed when intercourse was frequent, regardless of a desire to have a child, or sterility, menopause, and so on.

There must be periodic abstinence in conjugal love even in couples hoping for a child, for an excess of intercourse tends to render the act mechanistic, instinctive, difficult to control. Frequency leads, for example, to rapidity, generally on the part of the man, and a consequent absence of feminine orgasm. The same couple achieve sexual harmony on days when they precede intercourse with a fairly long moment of affective and sensual intimacy, with the act subsequently unfolding at a leisurely pace.

Harmony is achieved, however, only if the spouses, and especially the husband, are able to control the sexual instinct. For it is that instinct, indeed, that prompts them to consummate the union in order to take their pleasure as quickly as possible—each spouse using the other as a means to this end, in an attitude of capture.

True love, sacrificial love, seeks the good of the other and wishes to give of oneself as totally as possible and, in particular, to *give* sexual pleasure. This gift is possible only when instinct is placed under human control, mastered. Then only can it serve true love. Thus, periodic continence is not an optional but a necessary constraint, agreed upon by both spouses.

Dr. Charles Rendu, a specialist in internal medicine who has worked for the World Health Organization, is co-founder of CLER and of Laissez les Vivre (Let Them Live), the French national pro-life association. A life-long student of human love and sexuality, he and his wife Elisabeth, an NFP and marriage counselor, were members of the Papal Commission on Marriage and the Family.

The same constraint applies, indeed, to the control of all instincts: one must learn to limit one's use of tobacco, alcohol, food, and so forth, to avoid gradually falling into behavior detrimental to one's true well-being and that of society. One is a responsible adult only to the extent that he uses reason—enlightened by faith, in the case of believers—to dominate his instincts instead of being enslaved by them. Mastery over instincts is one of the goals of education in general and of sexual education in particular.

In the insect sexuality is totally automatic because its brain is no more than the hypothalamus, a center in which all perceptions automatically induce attraction or rejection reflexes, depending upon the stimulus. Dr. Paul Chauchard, a neurophysiologist, says that if a female butterfly is deprived of its genital organs and a piece of cotton permeated with the odor of its ovaries is placed beside it, the males will try to copulate with the cotton, being completely uninterested in the castrated female.

Complexity of the brain is related to the degree of development of animals. The highest level of complexity is attained in the human being, through the action of his superior, prefrontal brain, which of course receives the signals of the hypothalamus but also is able to reject them if reason demonstrates the necessity for rejection.

Dr. Chauchard thus affirms that in man (as opposed to animals) the brain is the chief sexual organ. Consequently, sexual control "humanizes sexuality" by allowing reason to govern it.

Periodic abstinence from sexual union can become a positive force in conjugal love only if it is lived in tenderness; each spouse using his or her body intelligently to express love. Let there be no abstaining from expressions of love! Sexual abstinence requires sacrifice: love grows with the kiss that is given, not from the kiss that is seized.

And as conjugal love is characterized by bodily intimacy ("two in one flesh"), it is absolutely necessary that spouses live this intimacy with tenderness, every day if possible. These intimate moments of tender exchange are indispensable to the preservation and growth of love. They may or may not progress to intercourse, depending upon whether procreation is desired and therefore upon the phase of the feminine cycle.

Here again, experience shows that if conjugal love is to be nourished and enriched by intercourse, the act must be engaged in with tenderness, in a spirit of giving rather than grasping. At any rate, the sexual control acquired through periodic abstinence enables the spouses to live their bodily union—before, during, and after intercourse—slowly enough to let it be the expression of mutual love instead of the satisfaction of instinct.

To illustrate and supplement what we have said, we wish to quote some statements, selected from among hundreds, from a poll which we organized as members of the Pontifical Committee which studied birth regulation. The phrases are short, since the couples did not have much space to answer the questions concerning the advantages and disadvantages of the STM. It is important to note that these couples had been using the STM for an average of five years (from two to 13 years).

—"Unions are not as frequent but more satisfactory."

—"The joys surpass by far the difficulties which this method involves."

—"Continence . . . . provides love with its full scope."

—"Even if it were possible and 'permitted' we would not renounce periodic abstinence which we consider to be an enriching element, basically on the affective level."

—"Domination of self in one area brings with it a psychological enrichment."

—"A secure method, which renders husband and wife equals in regard to their responsibilities and their satisfaction on the levels of carnal, affective, and spiritual life."

We rearranged the hundreds of answers under these subtitles:

Advantages on the affective level: "A deeper love. Meaningfulness of the effort. It is more natural. The wife admires her husband. Fosters respect for the partner. Improved conjugal harmony. Partners are better prepared for the conjugal act. Discovery of other means to express love. Meaningfulness of continence."

"*HUMANAE VITAE* ONCE SEEMED RIGID, NOW PROPHETIC"

Canadian Couple

As a young married couple, 25 years ago, we, like most Catholic couples at that time, accepted the Church's teaching on birth regulation without question. We had several children in succession, and it was difficult. After the birth of our sixth child we could see that it would be desirable to avoid another pregnancy. It is then that we started, gradually, to discover the richness and truth of the Church's teaching.

We discovered the joys of living our married life in harmony with nature and creation. We knew that regulating births the natural way was accepting the possibility of a pregnancy because the natural methods are human methods with human limitations. We were looking at God's creation, working within that creation. It was saying "yes" to God if he willed a life, the gift of life. The openness to life implicit in natural methods appealed to us. We sensed in our hearts that this was right, that we were not interfering with the fruit of our love.

We discovered that periodic continence, though difficult and demanding at times, enriched our married love. The intermittent periods of abstinence enhanced the marital act when it took place—just as all good things must be used with temperance if the sense of wonder and discovery are to be maintained.

We discovered that natural family planning required all the qualities required of a good marriage—tenderness, affection, deep friendship, self-restraint, fidelity—and that the exercise of these qualities only deepened them. We learned to abstain from the marital act in love, and to enter into it in love.

We enjoyed the equality and mutuality involved in this chosen method, and the freedom implicit in a method which requires self-knowledge and qualities of the heart and mind—all human attributes.

How marvellous for a woman, how indicative of her husband's love for her, that he should take the trouble to understand her fertility and to respect it when a pregnancy would be untimely.

In *Humanae Vitae*, ten years ago, Paul VI appealed to Catholic scientists to develop their knowledge in the field of natural family planning. People like Drs. John and Lyn Billings gave it their whole lives. Because of this knowledge of our fertility we were able to regulate family size without upsetting the normal activities and the hormonal milieu of our bodies. And this knowledge of our fertility has eliminated the need for long periods of abstinence between the ages of forty and fifty. Understanding our own fertility and the delicate hormonal balance within the woman has helped us to understand our persons better.

Humanae Vitae seemed to us rigid indeed, ten years ago. Now it appears absolutely prophetic. How grateful we are to our Church which, as Chesterton stated, is always there to uphold a truth at a time when it is very unpopular to do so.

—"Respectfully submitted to our bishops" by a Canadian couple.

WILL JAPAN FOLLOW THE NATURAL WAY?

Fr. Anthony Zimmerman

Many of Japan's 116,000,000 people have heard of Dr. Kyusaku Ogino's discoveries about the cycle, which were published in 1923. Very many couples also use the so-called Ogino system of rhythm to some extent. Doctors are quick to say that the natural way of family planning would be better for families than artificial ways. Yet there is no systematic teaching of the newer natural ways on a large scale. Before NFP can be widely accepted, certain difficulties and ambivalent attitudes must be dealt with, and the dynamism to make this a national movement must be generated and set into motion. Perhaps the Catholic Church has a unique opportunity in Japan to launch an NFP take-off there, if only the Church itself can generate enough energies within its own ranks.

One of the difficulties in Japan about practicing NFP is that it requires frank communication between husband and wife about the menstrual cycle and sex. They are not accustomed to such conversation. In Japanese society talk about sex is practically prurient; it is equivalent to interest in pornography.

One energetic midwife helps wives get around this difficulty. She coaches them to ask their husbands to explain the meaning of the charts which she has been keeping, saying that they are too deep. The ensuing dialogue opens communications in the area of the cycle and their sex life. The midwife coaches the wives to remind their husbands that neither of them likes the condom, which is a nuisance and costs money, that condom failures mean abortion, which also costs money and causes pain.

Because the mention of sex in serious conversation is considered in bad taste, priests also are reluctant to discuss the subject. Like the priest and Levite of St. Luke's Gospel (10, 31) who hurried past the injured man who had fallen prey to robbers, priests tend to neglect helping those who have serious problems in regard to family planning.

In one large church where marriage instructions are given from a manual, priests skip the four pages devoted to contraception, abortion and NFP. One retreat master told seminarians there are loftier matters for priests to preach about than abortion and contraception, and urged them to avoid such mundane matters.

Some superiors do not consider promotion of NFP to be a suitable apostolate for priests. The Bishops of Japan, however, are supporting the work of the Family Life Association, and the situation among the clergy appears to be changing.

Will abstinence pose a special difficulty in Japan? Some observers claim it will, saying that Japanese will not abstain, hence NFP will never become widespread. It will be confined to Catholics, who "must obey the Church," according to this view. One young doctor spoke up on the subject during our International Symposium on NFP in Tokyo, in October of 1979. Most in the audience were gynecologists, and practically all were non-Christians. Dr. Edward Keefe of New York had finished his lecture on monitoring the cervix, and there was time for questions. "Unless you can perfect the system of NFP to such an extent that abstinence is reduced to only three days, NFP will not go over in Japan," said this young doctor. Doctor Keefe replied that you cannot ever expect to reduce abstinence to three days. It is a pipe dream. He continued that even hormonal tests at home—if invented—would reflect the erratic nature of the progress of the cycle, and be of little more help than the observations women can carry out well right now without such gadgets. Dr. Keefe pointed out that human beings, when they have a compelling reason, get used to scheduling things. Men arise early to go to work, and get there rain or shine; they arrange their work to fit in with mealtimes; they wait for their pay checks; they stand in line for taxies; they arrange payments according to income and don't buy what they can't afford. Drivers stop at red lights, and keep speed laws. When men make up their minds to abstain during the fertile time, this becomes a routine problem, not an anguishing problem. Abstinence is a matter of scheduling intercourse.

In comparison with other nations, the medical world in Japan is definitely favorable towards NFP. But doctors, midwives and nurses look for leadership, for a movement to inspire the people to accept the natural method, especially since it involves abstinence. The problem is more in the area of education than of medicine.

Yet Dr. Shigeru Murayama, in a paper at the IXth World Congress of Gynecology and Obstretrics in Tokyo, October 25–31, 1979, stated that Japanese have little use for the pill and the IUD; the condom and the Ogino method are the staple here. He proceeded to opt for scientific NFP for all Japan:

"The way to promote birth control effectively in Japan in the future is to deepen the knowledge of NFP and to introduce the notion of abstinence."

Dr. Rihachi Iizuka and Dr. Shigeru Murayama, in an article about NFP in the medical journal *The World of Obstetrics and Gynecology* (April 1979, pp. 93–106), asked that doctors take a new look at NFP for general application in Japan:

"We would like now to recommend this method anew and to make people understand it better . . . . We hope to promote NFP in Japan and show its value."

The National Society for Fertility and Sterility with 4,000 gynecologists as members, has associated itself officially with the Family Life Association to work on the scientific aspects of NFP, and to help with teaching. When famous doctors give the lectures to NFP classes, midwives and nurses come gladly to listen.

Infertility specialists may even popularize NFP more readily in Japan, as a means of achieving pregnancies, than those who promote it as a means of avoiding pregnancies. Under the doctor's care infertile couples learn to watch for every clue of a fertile time in the cycle, and schedule intercourse accordingly. Some doctors, and some midwives, are gaining a reputation for successful guidance; clients pass the word along.

Correspondence courses are very popular in Japan. We are ready to test a correspondence course designed exclusively for midwives, public health nurses and other nurses. If we can teach NFP by mail to these we can reach many more of the 16,000 public health nurses and 26,000 midwives than by lectures. Our present priority is to form teachers who can then guide couples. The real test for NFP in Japan will come later. Will couples in significant numbers wish to use it?

One company now sells a million and a half thermometers annually which are specially designed for monitoring the menstrual cycle; other agencies sell an additional half million. This indicates that a vast number of women in Japan are already interested in following the thermal method. If trained midwives and nurses learn to teach the thermal method systematically, adding also training in observing the cervical mucus signs, and a proper application of the modified Ogino "shortest cycle minus 20" rule, then real NFP can finally become available to millions here.

Since the women's thermometer market is so large, competition is also lively. A new thermometer is now being designed which should give an accurate oral temperature reading in one and a half minutes, instead of the usual five to eight minutes now required. This development promises to facilitate temperature taking by NFP users not only in Japan but in the world. It may prove to be a real NFP break-through.

In 1948 a bogus kind of family planning, and an evil one, was promoted via mass media and with social pressures in Japan. It was—and unhappily remains—family planning without God, and with little love. It is family planning which divides couples, which wounds mothers, which occasions two million abortions yearly. This keeps the people away from God. Even Buddhist and Shintoist family prayers have gone into hibernation after the infamous birth control law came into existence in 1948. And the healthy postwar interest in becoming Catholic has declined since the mid 1950s. No one has a right to keep the 116 million Japanese people away from knowing and loving God and Christ, because of bogus family planning.

One Catholic midwife, president of a parish's Catholic Women's Guild, said that women feel very much alone when wrestling with their consciences about birth control. "We agonize with this problem day and night. We live with it all the time." She had taken it for granted that priests would not enter this world, that the women must struggle there alone. When priests arranged for NFP courses in her parish, she said that tears of joy came to her eyes.

Mrs. Takako Honma, President of the Catholic Women's Guild of Japan, and Chairman of the Family Life Association, is giving her full energy to promotion of NFP and family life education. This is so very important for Japan, she feels. Above all, we must help women to stop this killing of babies, which ends their little lives, and sears the hearts of the mothers.

Maybe the Lord is watching and helping the Japanese people in a special way now, as they grope to contend with family problems. Maybe that is part of the explanation for such willingness of so many medical persons—practically all of them non-Christians—to learn NFP and to give a hand in organizing teaching courses. The Hierarchy, and especially the Pro-Nuncio, Archbishop Mario Pio Gaspari, are encouraging us.

Now we hope that the Holy Father will come to Japan too, to bring new spirit into our tiny Catholic body of 400,000, and to open a new horizon to the 116 million Japanese who are waiting to taste deeper joys of human life. NFP will not come automatically to Japan. It will not come without hard work, without much prayer and fasting. But we hope it will take hold here, and that Japanese families will join the fellowship of families everywhere who escape contraception and abortion, and who taste the sweet joys of a harmonious family life which God intends for them.

STORING SEXUAL ENERGIES

Nona Aguilar

Natural family planning providers are beginning to recognize that they are dealing with considerably more than a birth control method. This is because the primary focus of natural methods is the couple—not a device. For NFP to be effective, both the man and the woman must agree to use the method and thereafter they must become—and remain—cooperative partners.

NFP is also uncovering new dimensions in the male-female sexual relationship. One of these facts is that a short abstinence phase seems to enhance, not detract from the relationship . . . .

Like any energy source, sexual energy is more effective if "stored" to be released later at an appropriate time of our choice.

Sexual energy release is most readily triggered by the erotic. But that is also the most superficial "trigger." According to Dr. David Landers, periodic abstinence helps the couple grow so that ultimately the "triggers" releasing sexual energy become the emotional and affective aspects of the couple's love bond. As a result, the erotic gradually loses its position as the primary sexual force. Instead, the *other person*, the loved one, plus the emotions and feelings felt toward the loved one become the primary force . . . .

Certainly one reason so many have become enthusiastic about NFP is that they have begun to master the art of sexual energy control. One woman commented on the positive effects on her marriage:
"When we *can* make love, my husband is more affectionate and tender and gentle. He is affectionate every day and looks forward to when we can make love. I don't feel" "used" anymore and know he doesn't take advantage of sex *or* me . . . .

The technological level: Like contraception, natural family planning is highly reliable when used properly. Unplanned pregnancies are rare and at the same time, the method has no known hazardous side-effects. In other words, from the point of view of sheer "technology" the method *works*; it's effective.

The physical level: I never interviewed an individual or a couple who complained that their sexual relationship had deteriorated because of their acceptance of abstinence. This complaint did appear twice in the

Reprinted with permission from the book NO PILL, NO-RISK BIRTH CONTROL Rawson, Wade Publishers, Inc., New York, 1980.

questionnaires, but couples overwhelmingly report that their physical relationship had improved, sometimes considerably, since relying on NFP.

Certainly one reason for improvement is that the couples are "storing" their sexual energies. As one woman married less than a year said, "Abstinence is the best aphrodisiac." Obviously contraception doesn't involve any kind of storage and may be a factor in the growing problem of sexual boredom and male impotence.

Another matter: Women often felt "used" while using contraceptives, particularly since many husbands tended to forget about "courting" them. Once they learned that their husbands were willing to abstain for a short period of time—in effect, not "use" them, rather, court them—their response became more ardent when intercourse became available again.

The interpersonal level: The human sexual experience is never wholly separated from the personal experience. Moreover, there are many ways to use sexual intercourse. It can be used for exploitation, conquest, humiliation, anger, etc. But ideally, sexual intercourse should be an expression of the deeper human emotions. Love, joy, spiritual closeness, tenderness, and other deep emotions that move men and women are profoundly suitable for sexual expression, although this is by no means the exclusive, or even the best, mode of expression. A touch, a glance, a soft smile may say considerably more.

Most couples understand this instinctively, even though our culture tends to obscure this reality. Still, this instinctive understanding may be one reason why couples are willing to walk into an NFP class: couples already know that abstinence will be involved, but their values are sufficiently developed so that "sex on demand" is no longer an essential value to them. It may still be *important*—but it's no longer an *essential* value.

A young husband's experience shows how he and his wife began to experience natural family planning at all its levels:

> I never thought that after ten years of marriage and a handful of children I would ever feel the yearning for my wife that I had felt when we courted and were first married. I figured that all those old feelings were a part of being young and in love. Being older and loving each other was nice, but there certainly wasn't any cha-cha-cha about it.
>
> I wasn't enthusiastic when we changed to NFP, but we saw no other way. We went to class very, very reluctantly. Me especially.
>
> But almost right away it started happening again: That incredible yearning I used to feel for my wife returned—and not just once in a while: It was there every month. Every cycle gradually turned into

courtship and honeymoon all over again.

We think that the longing and yearning we feel for each other is better than what we felt when we were younger. We both think this is because we've been through so much together by now—childbirth, baby's first steps, family weddings, as well as unemployment, sickness, and other hard times. NFP has become more than a method of birth control for us: It's a life-style.

A woman was ebullient in summarizing her experience of NFP in the couple's life:

Our marriage "began" and bloomed 100 percent after we started using NFP. We felt closer to God and this helped our marriage. We had the phases of courtship and honeymoon and celebrated. We shared my body awareness. We shared days of uncertainty and we shared days of gambling and pregnancy. It was a change from 'I' to 'we.' Our last baby was conceived out of love and with full knowledge that we would conceive. From that moment we could picture the hours and days of growth.

But before NFP I *feared* going to bed as I didn't know my fertility cycle and worried that I might become pregnant. Now I know my fertility signs and feel 100 percent confident in those signs and no longer fear. It is a great relief and a burden off my shoulders. I want more children—but when I am ready and capable.

I would like to make a personal comment at this time. When I first heard about natural family planning, I thought of it as a last resort for couples who simply could not tolerate (for reasons of health) the effective artificial methods. And except for those with moral objections to contraception, it was unimaginable to me that any couple would actually *prefer* a natural method to an artificial one.

Today I recognize that periodic abstinence is not only effective for fertility control, it is also a creative contribution to the human experience. Personally, I can no longer imagine any other love style but this one. It is my hope that this, too, will become your discovery.

NFP COMES TO THE CONGO

Francoise and Zephyrin Goma

Permit us to explain briefly the steps which led to the present organization of the "Foyers Chretiens" movement.

In 1963, every movement of an ecclesial character was suppressed in the Congo. Some people then began activities for couples, at first through visits, common meals, and discussions of biblical texts. By 1970 we began to be aware of the real problems of couples: lack of dialogue; and lack of information about conjugal life.

We organized conferences to deal with these problems. To these we invited capable persons of good will, such as doctors, midwives, social workers, priests, and religious. In 1976, when the pill was being promoted as the only means of family planning, we heard about the existence of IFFLP (International Federation for Family Life Promotion). In 1977 IFFLP organized a meeting in Yaounde for African Movements and Associations interested in family life promotion. At this time the "African Zone" of IFFLP was set up.

Even before the Yaounde meeting, the Foyers Chretiens invited Drs. Michele and François Guy for a formation session in Brazzaville. Since that time the teaching of the natural methods is performed by teams of the Foyers. Our work is done in teams grouped around the parishes. Each team counts six or seven couples. There are actually 17 teams in the country. In each team we have a CIVIC (the acronym for the French of Center for Information on the Conjugal Life). The CIVIC is animated by the team itself, and it is not an established organization. In some parishes, the CIVIC helps couples to interpret the temperature curves of the charts.

When women who do not belong to the Foyers movement come for instructions in the natural method, we require that the husband consent, since we consider the decision about conception to be the responsibility of the couple.

Our experience is still too limited to provide statistical data.

We receive assistance and moral support from a national chaplain, from some religious and some parish priests. However, the local clergy, which should be most of all interested in our action, is not motivated and takes no initiative in the family life movement. Are priests perhaps afraid of moral compromises within the family?

A RAGE AGAINST *HUMANAE VITAE*

Gene and Judy

Gene: We're part of the NFP teaching program of the Newark diocese. The program is growing all the time; at present there are three centers for teaching at Catholic hospitals in the diocese, and in September there will be a fourth.

We are here to relate our own personal experience. We have five children.

Judy: Yes, we have four boys and a girl; the oldest is 13, and the youngest is four, and today is his birthday.

Gene: Maybe we should begin by telling you that when we were married in 1964 there were of course some cultural differences from today. If you were married then and not pregnant in the first year, your parents wanted to know how come. And today if you're pregnant in the first year, they want to know why! Young people who become engaged and get married today have different pressures and problems to face. Let us tell you how we faced ours at the time, and where we are today.

We had difficulty achieving a pregnancy early in our marriage. We attended a rhythm clinic to help us achieve a pregnancy. After two years we had our first child. About 18 months later—we were practicing rhythm now to space children—we had our second child. And after 17 months more we had our third. We were finding out that calendar rhythm was ineffective in terms of fertility control for us.

During that span of five years in which we were having the first three children, Judy also had a Caesarean for the third one, and she had a major gall bladder operation, and several miscarriages. So after five years of this Judy thought that she was kind of moving into the hospital permanently. Then we panicked after these five years of such fertility experience. We projected our fertility into the remaining years and got quite scared when we saw this 12-14-16 child family ahead.

We were experiencing about three to three and a half weeks of abstinence practicing calendar rhythm, and arriving at no fertility control. So we sought the counsel of a priest and a Catholic doctor, and with their support but on our own moral decision, we decided that contraception was the proper choice for us.

And we were delighted—I'll say, I was personally delighted—that we finally found something that gave us the opportunity to have uninterrupted sexual experiences, after coming off the three and a half weeks of abstinence. Judy was taking the pill, as that was the leading contraceptive at that time, towards the end of the 1960s.

I remember particularly well that while Judy was pregnant with the third child, how I was working on one Saturday; I was crossing Liberty Street in downtown Manhattan and reading *The New York Times*, and learned there that the pope had come out with this encyclical *Humanae Vitae.* I fell into a rage.

I was just filled with rage. I could not believe that he had taken such an incredible stand, given the circumstances in which I found myself, with my concerns for my wife and my family. A tremendous rage was in me: at the Church, at the pope, at his stand, at his incomprehensible position, viewed from where I was at that time, in 1968.

We practiced contraception for three years, and at first I was delighted with it, as I said. That lasted about six months, of just sheer romance. But I can tell you that at the end of the three-year experience, we were having less sexual intercourse than we had when we were practicing calendar rhythm. Only we didn't call it abstinence. We didn't call it anything. It just sort of worked its way into our marriage.

We developed—I certainly developed—an attitude of: "If this is always here to be had, then who wants to work for it?" I grew bored with our sexual relationship. It was like lining up 400 beers and saying: "Drink all of them at once!"

I find now, looking back, that I spent a lot of time at Madison Square Garden. And I was constantly inviting my family over. We were playing cards and having a good time in the house. I found a number of ways of compensating for what I now understand was the pressure to perform. I didn't realize this at the time.

Judy stopped taking the pill after three years. We had drifted apart spiritually and psychologically, and the pill was beginning to have a physical impact on Judy. There were contraindications which would take too long to enumerate. So we went off the pill.

We had our fourth child, which we wanted to have. We were dissatisfied with contraception. We went back to calendar rhythm. And 17 months later we had Danny who is four years old today. During that pregnancy we said that there just has to be something besides calendar rhythm and contraception.

As you know, it is difficult to go to your local parish and find the answer to that. We found it in Minnesota. I never thought we would have to go to Minnesota to find the answers, but that is where they were; there and in Washington, D.C.

So we found NFP, and it was the answer to the question of fertility control as well as a way to benefit us physically, psychologically, and spiritually, leading us to a better marriage.

Judy: We have told you how we found NFP. Let me tell you something now of what it has done for us, and why we continue to practice it today.

I think there were two major effects on our marriage, the first being a shared responsibility in fertility control, and the second, better communications.

In the first area of shared responsibility: I guess that without even realizing it I had begun to develop resentment about carrying what I called the "burden of fertility." I was the one who had to have the answers of whether I was fertile or whether not. I had to say *yes* or say *no*.

There was very little verbal communication in the area of sexuality. And in 1971 we made a Marriage Encounter Weekend, through which our communications in general improved tremendously. We were able to deal with our feelings and started to talk to each other differently. Still the area of sexuality was something that if we didn't *want* to bring it up, we didn't have to, and we could avoid it. And that was a difficult area for me to talk about because I came into marriage with certain attitudes and myths about who men are and who women are supposed to be. I had the idea that men were supposed to be very aggressive and women were supposed to be passive, and things like that. It was in this situation that we started to practice NFP.

With NFP came this surge of understanding that Gene was really involved in this whole area with me. For the first time I understood that this is an equal responsibility. It was like lifting a cloud from over my head. It had been a heavy weight that I had been carrying around and I didn't even realize it. This had been a block against building a better relationship, against giving scope to our marriage to grow and become more mature.

Gene: My initial involvement in NFP was doing the charting, that is, taking down Judy's temperature daily and recording her fertility signs. That is the way we teach it, namely that the wife observes her natural signs, the husband charts them, and both together interpret *their* fertility.

When I entered marriage, I thought that Judy understood all about things. I was taught that women were supposed to know all these things, so I thought she did. And I supposed that whatever she didn't know, she could ask her doctor. I didn't realize that both of them had difficulty in this area. But if even *they* had difficulties, *I* certainly had even more. I knew nothing at all about Judy's physiology, and about my own masculinity and how it operated. Now for the first time in my life I was able to participate in an area about which I had been confused and jealous and ignorant.

Judy: I realized clearly that our lifetime commitment, which we made when we got married, served as the solid basis which allowed us to come this far in our life. It was this that enabled us to re-evaluate, and then to begin to make some changes. We were committed to the idea of a great marriage. That's the way we started and that was our goal. And that commitment was what allowed us to have the flexibility to fight each other, and then to keep coming back and to hang in there, and to move to a new point in our life. I think that attitude about permanence and fidelity is really the basis for all the other decisions we have to make in life.

Gene: I entered marriage with the idea that I had to be the performer; that I was responsible for all of our sexual activity in terms of whether it was good or bad. *I* had to *make it good.*

I thought that God looked the other way when we had intercourse. I had no idea that God was really an integrated part of that whole area. I know that's tainted and immature. But that's where I was at the time.

Through NFP, through communicating, by being able to talk with Judy, I came to appreciate a spiritual dimension of our sexual relationship, which I hadn't seen at all before. We hadn't been expressing ourselves. We were afraid, when we first began NFP, even to say the word *mucus.*

Judy: Abstinence helps to uncover some of the other areas of marriage which have to be looked at, but which get iced over frequently by intercourse. You know how we tend to think that if we can have intercourse then everything will be okay again, and we'll feel better tomorrow, and all will be sunshine and roses. But the problems are still there, and we don't face them.

When practicing abstinence and trying to make it a positive and creative experience, many of these issues come to light. A new kind of awareness and sensitivity about each other begins to happen. Oh, we fight, and more than we ever did. But they are like two-minute fights, and things come to light so much faster and get handled so much better. That is because we are aware of the atmosphere we are setting, we're aware of where I am in the cycle, and things like that. It helps so much with the atmosphere in the house, the way we relate sexually, the way we relate with the children, the way I feel and he feels about our own sexuality, about femininity and masculinity.

Gene: I want to say only this last thing: I created an impression, saying that I was filled with rage about Pope Paul and his encyclical *Humanae Vitae.* I thank Pope Paul today. And I thank God for giving him this insight into things. I just didn't understand what he was talking about, until we spent three years using contraception.

HAITI: SOURED ON THE IUD, MOVING TOWARD NFP

Fr. Michael Welters

Action Familiale conducted a survey among 821 couples in June–July of 1979 to learn why they chose the Sympto-Thermal Method (STM) in preference to artificial methods. Their main reason is that the natural method does no harm.

At this time the number of insertions at government clinics of the IUD is minimal: 329 in 1978, and 132 during the first half of 1979. STM-users outnumber them. The pill is also feared. Complaints form a veritable litany. In the city of Gonaives, among the 555 users of the STM, 40 percent had switched to this natural method after experience with contraceptives; among them were 136 former pill-users.

Other reasons for preferring the natural method include: the friendliness of the teachers; reversibility of the method; the perfect absence of expense; and the peace of conscience they enjoy. Pill-users who live where there is no government clinic may have to make a journey to the city to obtain pills. If there are medical complications from pill use, they must pay for treatment. Some doctors refuse to remove an IUD which was inserted by another doctor. The cost of removal in a private hospital runs as high as $10.

People have their own logic about peace of conscience and birth control. "If the artificial methods were according to God's will, then why do they make us ill?" they ask. Baptists and Adventists also say that they find peace when using the natural method.

Couples also tell us that they are happier with the STM because they gain better knowledge about their bodies and their mutual relations; there is an improvement in sexual relations, a deepening of love, an openness to dialogue.

Some specialists claim that illiteracy is an obstacle to NFP. This only shows how little some specialists know. In Haiti, 65 percent of the followers of NFP are illiterate; 24 percent have a few years of primary school; 11 percent have completed primary school.

Effectiveness: Up to now we have not found a method failure of the STM when used according to the formula of coitus in the post-ovulatory period, calculated according to the three CLER (Centre de Liaison des Equipes de Recherches) points. Unforeseen pregnancies occur, of course. Among 1849 couples there were 70 pregnancies in 1979. Perseverance is high: among 1849 couples, only 92 dropped out in 1979 for lack of interest.

Abstention, of course, is the main problem. But the problem

becomes manageable through the employment of judicious means:
—Information about the fertile and the infertile days must be given in a clear and precise manner.
—The educator must take care to listen to the couple, to create a climate of confidence, and to respect the couple's convictions and their gradual progress. Personal rapport between the educator and the husband and wife is of utmost importance.
—The approach should be positive: full of confidence with respect for the child and its value, openness to a deepening of conjugal love, trust in the good will of the partner to live up to expectations. This positive approach achieves better results than talk about overpopulation, the misery of poverty, etc. Although fear may serve as a starting point, it can never become the basis of solid motivation.

Economic deprivation prompts Haitian families to start thinking about regulating births, in almost all cases. But fear does not give continuous and adequate motivation in the long run if more ideal motivation does not develop gradually. The ideal is something deep down in the hearts of the couple, although perhaps dormant; the challenge to the couple and to the educator is to make this ideal dominant.

Truly, the natural way is a method of love. Husband and wife do not know how much they love one another. NFP helps them discover that.

TEACHING NFP IN THE ARCHDIOCESE OF KRAKOW

Eve C.

Since 1969 I have been working in the Family Pastoral Center, in a parish of Krakow, operating a Family Advisory Service by giving lectures to engaged couples. I also do counseling services for young married couples.

Those who come to the Center have either been sent by their confessors or come on their own initiative. They represent members of every age-level and social class.

The problems most frequently met are conjugal conflicts, birth regulation, unmarried mothers, and parent-child conflicts. A frequent question is: "Why doesn't the Catholic Church approve artificial birth control or contraception?"

Each engaged couple, after completing the course, comes to the Advisory Center to talk things over privately. I also encourage the young ladies, even before their marriage, to practice observing their monthly physiological changes in order the better to appreciate their cyclic fertility.

The pre-marriage conferences have a strong religious tone. This is particularly important in view of the inadequate religious instruction young people have. Therefore, I consider it very important that there be frequent and significant contacts between parish priests and the individuals working in the Advisory Center.

Medical doctors who are getting ready for their own marriages and are obliged to attend lectures at the Center feel a bit downgraded, but mainly at the start. They come confident of their medical knowledge; actually they know little about the regulation of births. Nurses are more familiar in this area. I begin the meeting by telling them how happy I am to see the doctors and nurses at the Center because their expertise and prestige adds greatly to the value of the Center's work.

Sexual intercourse gives rise to some problems in any marriage. However, for persons of deep faith, full love, and good will, there is no doubt that the only way is to adjust themselves to the woman's biological rhythm and to recognize that periodic abstinence is a necessity in every marriage, without making too much fuss about the situation.

However many persons are either badly informed or find periodic

Eve C. aged 55, university graduate, professional architect in Krakow. Married in 1950.

abstinence too difficult. They think of it as a "home-remedy" for avoiding pregnancy, which cannot really compare in effectiveness with the advertised contraceptives.

The decision belongs to the married couple. A problem arises when the woman alone looks for this ethical way of birth regulation; frequently women have difficulties in persuading their husbands. It is much easier when they work together on this. Frequently the husband listens to the lectures better than his wife, and is more interested than she in the logical arguments and the scientific information.

Experience acquired in my work allows me to draw the following conclusions:

–It is alarming how unprepared the young people are for marriage. The betrothed should know that the sacramental vow is meant also to hold through times of difficulty. This truth should be repeated in different ways and from different angles. It should be presented to the young at school and at the catechesis, to the betrothed before marriage, and to young married couples who certainly should not be left alone with their problems.

–If the marriage is to last, if the family is to be a good family and is to develop in an atmosphere of love and affectionate friendship, the married couple must know that love requires fidelity, and this is proved during periodic abstinence.

–The activity of the Church, as can be seen even in the Krakow archdiocese, is long-term work which does not give quick results, and therefore deserves priority.

NFP ON THE MOVE: SPOTLIGHT PARAGE

Pedro Richard and Coordinator

1. CENAPLANF in Montevideo

Father Pedro Richards, C.P. who has been active in NFP work in Latin America since 1948, reports that teachers are now being trained for parishes and schools at the Centro Nacional de Planificacion Natural de La Familia (CENAPLANF) in Montevideo, Uruguay. Bishops send capable teachers for seminars to the Center, and thus courses in the O.M. method of NFP are being intensified in parishes and schools of the country.

WOOMB INTERNATIONAL, recognizing the activities of CENAPLANF in various countries of Latin America, made this its representative, with an International Board. CENAPLANF is teaching the O.M. in nine countries, Argentina, Bolivia, Colombia, Chile, Ecuador, Paraguay, Venezuela, and Brazil.

Courses given at CENAPLANF are always of an integrated nature, including: (1) LOVE IN FAMILY LIFE in its physical, psychological and spiritual aspects; (2) SOCIAL DUTIES of the parents as well as the children, toward the making of a BETTER WORLD.

The work was begun in Buenos Aires, Argentina in 1948, when the Ogino-Knaus method was promoted through the Movimiento Familiar Christiano; teacher couples promoted the method in city parishes as well as in the country. From 1955 yearly trips through 19 countries of Latin America were made to teach the method. The temperature method was included in the teaching somewhat later, and about 60,000 couples were orientated. In 1967 a Center was established in Montevideo, which flourished and developed into the Institute of today which teaches family sciences on a university level. In 1972 the switchover was made from the Temperature Method to the Ovulation Method.

A giant step forward was made at PUEBLA in January 1979 when the Latin American Bishops passed the resolution to promote the existence of centers to teach NFP:

611. . . . We must promote the existence of centers where people will be taught scientifically the natural methods of birth control by qualified personnel . . . . *(Conclusions of the Third General Conference of Latin American Bishops.)*

COMMUNICATIONS FROM CENAPLANF

"The ovulation Method is a challenge. Not only does a couple have to learn how their bodies function, they also have to study the pattern of mucus secretions and practice restraint during the fertile periods. This requires some sacrifice. However, most people are willing and able to meet this challenge."

"An often reported outcome of use of the Ovulation Method is a more meaningful relationship and the improvement of communication between husband and wife. The sharing of the intimate knowledge of the woman's menstrual cycle opens the door for better communication in other areas."

"An observer in Central America related that just as the artificial methods have secondary harmful effects, the natural methods have secondary beneficial effects, so much so, that child spacing becomes a secondary effect. The primary effect that he has seen is how it unites the couple."

2. From India

Father Joseph A. Menezes, S.J. writes that the Ovulation Method is slowly but surely picking up in India and the initial results are very encouraging:

"Even our simple rural women with no education are able to follow the OM successfully! Further, in two places we have found to our surprise, that they are able to do so without charting the mucus pattern! But of course they are carefully taught by NFP teachers who visit the couples in their own homes. Here in Delhi there are about 2,000 women using it for nearly two years and there had been only five surprise pregnancies."

Father Menezes is Head, Department of Responsible Parenthood, The Catholic Hospital Association of India. MISEREOR has made a grant to get the teaching started and organized.

Sister Catherine Bernard, M.D., Director of the Tamil Nadu Family Life Center in Tiruchirapalli, South India, reports on a study made of 6,165 acceptor couples of the OM, during July 1978 to December 1979. There were only 38 pregnancies, all of them user-related. [Pearl Index 0.4. This is a fantastic success rate of 99.6 percent.]

Father E. Vincent Gallagher, S.J. writes from the Natural Family Planning Training Programme Association at Patna, Bihar how they give the initial instruction. It is simply this:

1) When mucus begins, then abstinence begins.
2) As long as mucus continues, abstinence continues.
3) When mucus stops, abstinence continues for another three days.

Once a woman becomes an acceptor, she is visited once a week for six weeks. During these weekly visits more instructions are given. Fr. Gallagher made a study in the Hindi speaking region of north India for the 12 months ending December 31, 1979. Of all the 2,888 couples studied, 2,748 (95.2%) used the NFP method to avoid pregnancy; 140

wanted to achieve pregnancy through the NFP method. The success rate for the 2,748 couples who used the method to avoid pregnancy was 98.8%, [33 pregnancies] and the failure rate was 1.2%. Out of the 140 who wanted to achieve pregnancy, 9 (6.4%) succeeded in becoming pregnant. The continuation rate comes to 96%. Father Gallagher concludes with some advice from a veteran of the field:

> "Marking charts was found often to be a hindrance. Hence, whenever marking charts is not a hindrance, charting should be encouraged. But where charting is a problem, such of the NFP users should be allowed to use the method without marking charts."
>
> "There has been too much paper work for the NFP users, teachers, coordinators and directors. The paper work should be reduced by encouraging the NFP personnel to work out a simple way of keeping their records and making their reports so that more time will be available for covering more eligible people to become users of NFP method."

A study by *Dr. Ajay K. Gosh and associates*, National Medical College, Calcutta, India, made with the help of the Missionaries of Charity with the permission of Mother Teresa extended over two years, between 1978 and 1980. Of 700 women approached, 525 accepted. The pregnancy rate in the control group of 500 women exposed to the chance of pregnancy was 31.7 percent. There was no pregnancy in the study group of women following the sympto-thermal method, a success rate of 100%. However, 28 women dropped out of the study due to some personal reasons, giving a discontinuance rate of only 5.3 percent.

Note of Coordinator: When we see these records we begin to wonder what is holding us back, and why have we waited so long. This reminds me of a letter from a person who recently travelled to Mainland China. He lectured to a group of medical personnel there about the Billings Method of Natural Family Planning. He writes: "They were amazed and happy to know it, and they hope that some one can give this teaching more systematically throughout the large cities of China." I ask you simply: Who will do it? NFP is on the move in many places, but in other places pioneers are needed to open the frontier. The initial efforts need funding and will perhaps require much record keeping and paper work. But once NFP becomes known more widely, it can move on its own momentum.

MOTHERHOOD IS GOLDEN; NFP CAN HELP

Erica P. John

The most beautiful name a woman can possess is *mother.* To her is given the precious experience of feeling within herself the stirring of God's most beloved creation, a human life.

Mothers are destined to give new life and to nurture and protect it. Not only does a mother give physical birth, but her welcome and love give her child psychic birth, that is, the ability to experience life in full measure. A child deprived of such affirmation, deprived of joyful interplay with his mother, will achieve something less than the full experience of life and may even suffer psychic harm.

The psychological and emotional well-being of every child is dependent upon his mother's tender love. A child's psyche is unfolding even at birth. This growth is nourished by the mother's unsleeping awareness of her child's psychic and physical needs. A child grows and develops through his mother's continual close physical and spiritual solicitude and through her constant attention and loving interaction with him.

From the moment of conception a child, hidden within the walls of his mother's womb, unknown to everyone and yet very much alive, has the right to live and the right to be loved. God entrusted mothers with this most awesome duty and great privilege.

The process of birth and nurturing should be a great joy for every mother, even though it is very demanding, both physically and psychologically. Thus, every mother needs moral and psychological support from her family; she needs the freedom to give her own very best effort to her new child.

Motherhood is a woman's most important task in her entire life, and yet there is so little formal educational assistance to prepare her for it. Pastors and teachers can be of great service by providing enlightened premarital instruction.

The greatest joy and fulfillment of a woman is precisely in having

This address was first presented by Mrs. John at a Seminar on Family Life Education at Morning Star High School, Tokyo, March 26, 1980. It was adapted for the book during subsequent interviews. The Seminar was sponsored by the Archdiocese of Tokyo, the Catholic Women's Association of Tokyo, Morning Star Schools, and the Family Life Association.

this child – this little one, this miracle of life. Holding her newborn baby is such a stirring experience for a woman that words can hardly express it. Here is this little one, so perfect, so close, so loving – and he is totally dependent on you. There is just nothing in the world that can be more rewarding to a woman – nothing! Not fame, not ability, not money, not acclaim. This is it! She is happy; she is fulfilled.

I think I didn't enjoy motherhood as much as I could have when the first babies came. I was too preoccupied with trying to do the right thing for the child and avoiding mistakes. Later I was more at ease and could enjoy it. It's so tremendous! [Mrs. John is the mother of nine children. – Ed.]

The family within which the mother functions needs strong support from society if it is to remain stable and loving and to carry out its task of supporting new life. So much damage is done to families, and so much injustice to children, when there is a lack of support or a hostile attitude toward babies.

The term "unwanted child" should never be used. The mass media would do well to bury that term, to put it away forever. It is a terrible thing to say, even in the news media. *No child should ever have any doubts!* Every child has a right to be born; every child has the right to be wanted. These rights belong to every human being.

Abortion is unjust and unspeakably cruel. Does the mother choose which of her children she will affirm and love and which she will abort? Does she select certain of her children to love and others to reject? The decision to abort cuts deeply into the true essence and integrity of womanhood itself, and society should never attempt to pressure mothers into such an unnatural, unmotherly, and horrible decision.

One thing to be observed, though, is that mothers should not feel *compelled* to have large families. Mothers are not machines. Theirs is a vocation to be carried out with joy and good order. And that is why NFP is such a beautiful answer for mothers in our day and age. Very often the difficulty is not having too many children, but having them too close together. If they come too fast, one right after the other, the mother finds it hard to cope, and the little ones may feel deprived of enough attention and love. She can't give the growing baby all he needs and deserves before the next one arrives.

Spacing children two years apart, even three, is good. Let mothers have a voice in setting the pace. NFP can remove excessive burdens without removing the delight of motherhood. I am happy to hear that NFP is helping some countries like Japan overcome an abortion problem, but I think that is only the beginning. NFP can help mothers positively, help them to live their vocation without fear. NFP can also help many wives to achieve a desired pregnancy if they are having difficulty. By observing the signs, many subfertile couples can select the best times, thereby increasing their chances to bring a loved one into this world. I think it is good that women of today receive an education in NFP.

The love a mother gives to each new child, this affirmation of his life, is a gift he will always possess, a treasure he can always keep; it can nourish and support him. To see love at work in each new child is a marvel to the eye and a joy to the heart. This love is an energy that is received by the child, to remain as his constant spring of life. Even in old age, people think back on their childhood. They find it easier to conduct themselves as human beings should, easier to be stable, when they always carry about this treasure of love that mother gave them.

Thus life is affirmed from generation to generation, down through hundreds and thousands of years, from age to age. Tragically, the lack of affirmation of life, when a young child does not receive enough love, also passes down through the generations, and with negative results.

The father, too, plays a special role in the life of the child. Children seem to sense this truth better than adults. The mother affirms the child's life, being almost a part of it; the child sees his mother almost as an extension of himself, hardly recognizing her as a separate person. The father, on the other hand, is another person to the child. The father brings the outside world into his life. Everything that is exciting, that is new, that is fun – this the child seeks in the father. Babies laugh with their fathers more than with their mothers. I notice that our baby, upon getting up in the morning, breezes past all the rest of us and goes to father. Fathers make the child feel warm, secure, brave in the world. That is why fathers are so important, and why they should be there for the children. I agree that the best gift a father can give his child is to love his mother, as has often been said. All human relations start right there. What a tremendous benefit it is for the child to experience a warm and cozy life in this nest of love, where father and mother give themselves to each other and to the children!

God has made motherhood so marvelous, so precious! Let's keep it that way. Motherhood is a lamp we must keep lighted so that it can shine for the good of mankind. As Christ said: "No one lights a lamp and puts it under a bushel basket or under a bed. He puts it on a lampstand so that whoever comes in can see it." (Luke 8:16)

EDUCATION OF THE COUPLE AND RESPONSIBLE PARENTHOOD

Maria Teresa Forero de Ramos, M.D.

Teaching Natural Methods cannot be included in antinatalist campaigns as just another technique designed to impede the transmission of life. Periodic continence is a way of life, and should be presented as an element which helps the couple educate their sexuality at the level of sexual control and clear information on the function of their genital organs.

Marriage counselors are mindful that one of the main conflicts facing the couple in their married life is the "quality" of sexual relations. This depends on several factors:

1. *Biological sexuality:* Many couples marry with this concept of human sexuality; they ignore the value of sex because of deficient education in this area. For many of them, sex is simply an instinctive biological function, as seen in animals.

This mistaken notion of sexuality must be clarified since sexuality with human dimensions, above the animal level, allows both partners to fulfil themselves as individuals.

This natural sexual drive between the two sexes can and must be controlled by the intelligence and will which characterize the human being; so it is not a blind force, uncontrollable as in animals. This implies self-restraint, respect for the spouse and self-esteem, all of which result from an adequate sex education.

Living sexed beings can be divided into three levels. Plants have the most elemental level of sexuality; to be fertilized by pollen, the flower opens up, producing a fruit which will provide seed to ensure the plant's survival.

On the next level, animals represent another type of sexuality, mainly characterized by its instinctive nature which enables the male to recognize the female's fertile period to mate with her in order to reproduce their own kind. Thus animal sexuality is successful in conservation of the species.

The highest level of sexuality corresponds to man, the only being of creation capable of loving. This potential develops in accordance with the family and social environment surrounding the individual. Thus love is the distinctive feature of human sexuality, in addition to the human's typical attributes of intelligence and will, which allow the couple to

Dr. Ramos works in Latin America.

control their sexual drive. This is why humans are capable of responsible sexuality. Instinct has to be rejected as an element of human sexuality, as a blind uncontrollable impulse. When a person has experienced human sexuality, he can well understand responsible parenthood, enabling him to be mindful of when and how he transmits life.

2. *Ignorance about the function of the genitalia, and about female physiology:* It is known that men constantly produce sperm, and for this reason they are constantly fertile (except in special cases of infertility). Both sperm and a "viable" ovum (apt for fertilization) are needed to produce a new life. This points to the conclusion that for a pregnancy to begin, intercourse must occur during the woman's fertile period which can be determined by the signs of ovulation–genital wetness and change in basal temperature.

This lack of knowledge regarding the biological aspects of sex is observed during pre-marital courses. It is well known that young couples do not want to have a child right after being married, and therefore resort to contraception, also ignoring the consequences that the use of these methods entails. As time goes by, problems which affect family life begin to emerge. This fact has helped gain many followers for natural family planning, because once a couple has clear knowledge of sexual physiology, they can stop using contraceptives and maintain adequate sexual relations.

When a couple has intercourse, knowing in advance the result of this act, the quality of coitus varies in that the act will not be conditioned by the uncertainty of pregnancy, nor by the use of contraceptives; both partners can give themselves freely, with no restrictions.

3. *Sexual taboo:* This problem still exists in some couples who consider sex to be bad; consequently they commit several mistakes that necessarily affect their married life.

This taboo stems from deficient sex education. Ignorance about these aspects was replaced by the negative concept that sex is something bad. In these conditions, marriage was considered, unilaterally, as a solution to human lustfulness.

This concept has been completely reassessed since human sexuality is part of God's plan, and his making cannot be defective.

These considerations make it possible to understand why natural family planning betters the couple's human qualities. On one hand it helps them know each other better and favors the control of their sex drive, guiding them towards responsible sexuality which in turn leads to responsible parenthood. This is why it was stated right from the start that more than a technique it is a way of life.

LARGE FAMILIES, CHILD-SPACING, AND WHEN TO START NFP

The Coordinator

I have been admonished, warned, reminded, and then re-reminded to tell the readers that this book is not anti-baby, not antinatalist. This book is addressed not to "population problems" but to families. Nor does it adopt a doctrinaire stand on demographic questions.

Thus we shy away from terms such as *regulation of births* which smack of population policy. Rather than speak of "births" we prefer to speak of babies and children.

I suppose everyone in his right mind loves the bustle of a large family. Pope Pius XII spoke admiringly of large families as "those most blessed by God and specially loved and praised by the Church as its most precious treasures." (Address of Jan. 20, 1958.)

When parents omit family planning and accept children as they come, they act laudably so long as this is within the bounds of prudent human foresight. But not every couple can afford a large family, nor is every couple physiologically or psychologically up to it. Such couples laudably employ NFP to tailor the family size to their capabilities. As Pope Pius XII said, the boundaries of legitimacy here are very wide. (Address to Family Front, Nov. 26, 1951.) We do not sit in judgment on which family is better or more heroic.

By providing education in NFP, we respond to the needs of many couples in the world who badly need freedom to adjust family size to their situation, whether in housing, income, health, or ability to cope. We help the father to be king in his house, and the mother to be queen. They are in control. In regard to family size couples are not subject to arbitrary government interference. In this area they are indeed king and queen in their homes. And we say: if they are able and wish to rear a large family, God be with them.

Dr. Herbert Ratner, editor of *Child and Family* magazine, thinks no one can improve on nature's method of spacing births, usually by means of breastfeeding:

> To find the paradigm—the optimum and natural interval between births—one must turn to the breastfeeding mother. Here the average interval between births is approximately two years. Sensitivity to the accumulated wisdom of nature gives us reason to suspect that many yet-to-be discovered subtleties, contributing to the optimum, will relate to nature's spacing.
>
> Artificial child-spacing is a practice which has been extensively

> promoted by birth-control organizations, cultivated and implemented by gynecologists, and seized upon by social engineers .... Instead of wisdom these specialties have substituted myths. (*International Review of Natural Family Planning*, Vol. II, No. 1, Spring 1978, p. 12).

Dr. Ratner then presents reasons why the spacing of about two years, which he calls "nature's prescription," is advantageous:

Nature's prescription not only shortens the obligations of the preschool period, (1) it brings youth to childbearing and the arduous early child-rearing years, (2) it permits children to grow up with more intimately shared lives, (3) it closes the generation gap between parent and child, particularly valuable in the adolescent years, (4) it lengthens the joys of parenthood and grandparenthood, (5) it allows for leeway in case of obstetrical misfortunes and tragic events, (6) it gives parents the opportunity to reexamine their goals while reproductive options are still available, and (7) it rids the couple of fear of an unplanned pregnancy with each love act, permitting them blissfully to ignore birth control for nine years or more during the period of greatest sexual activity. *(Ibid.)*

Not all the experts agree that ignoring birth control early in the marriage is the best policy, especially for young couples. Dr. Josef Roetzer, who has guided couples in the practice of NFP for 25 years, advises young couples to start the NFP pattern of life right away, from the beginning of their married life. It is easier for them to learn the symptoms of fertility and to become accustomed to the NFP pattern of life before the children come into the marriage than afterwards. He advises them to familiarize themselves thoroughly with the NFP system and become confident about its reliability, before they try to achieve their first pregnancy.

Some of his clients cooperate with experiments when they are ready for a pregnancy: before using the days of maximum fertility for intercourse, they try the "borderline days" to locate the boundary line of their fertility more precisely. It they do not become pregnant, they procede to use the most fertile time.

Dr. Roetzer reports that clients are well satisfied with this procedure. Some of the young couples not only wish to "practice" NFP for some months, but wish to postpone the first pregnancy for a longer time because of serious reasons. He made a survey of 86 couples who practiced NFP from the beginning of marriage, some of them for five or six years. He learned that all 86 couples had happily achieved their desired pregnancy within one, two, or three months after trying. (The sample is small and one cannot extrapolate; the odds are against 100% success because of infertility problems.)

Dr. Roetzer is now doing a prospective study on clients which should be of major importance to illustrate how effective NFP can be if it is taught well, and if the couples are serious about wanting to use it successfully. In his retrospective studies, the effectiveness rate is above 99%; and when couples confined intercourse to the indicated high temperature phase of the pre-menstrual time, the record is a clean 100% during 17,026 cycles. When one sees such records, one looks for reasons. Perhaps one big reason is that many of his couples start "practicing" NFP during the initial months of marriage; then the children come; thereafter it is easy for the couple to control fertility for the rest of their married life, as their conditions indicate. They are always masters of the situation because they learned NFP early.

Advising couples to "practice" NFP for at least some months before they try to achieve a pregnancy strikes me as thoroughly good advice in many cases. Our modern age exerts pressures on young people which induces many to marry at an early age. On the other hand, proper housing is not always available to them; and professional education goes on for long years. We must offer help to everyone, also those young people who start married life in circumstances which are not ideal because of social conditions. Surely many young couples search for a sound and natural solution, and they want to stay away from the pill, the IUD, all artificial means, as well as sterilization and dreaded abortion. If they start NFP with marriage, they can learn the system perfectly while marking time until conditions to bear children become favorable for them.

Another consideration favoring early NFP is presented by experienced teachers who say that it may be harder to begin periodic abstinence after ten years of married life, than very early. Couples establish a pattern if they begin right away; the rhythmic "courtship and honeymoon" cycle is viewed as their normal fulfilment of expectations. Whereas couples who have already established another pattern and experienced it for ten or twenty years, have some initial difficulties to switch patterns. It is not a compelling reason, but teachers mention it.

Finally, NFP is hardest of all to learn during the postpartum, when fertility itself, and with it the signs, are being re-established slowly. If couples have all their planned children first, and abruptly begin a "do or die" regime of birth control during the postpartum, tensions rise. It is the custom in Japan, for example, to have one, two, or three children during the early years of marriage, then to stop for good. The two million abortions per year in Japan are, to a large extent, rejected children who were conceived after couples had terminated the planned birth schedule. We look to a brighter future in Japan, when couples will be in control of their fertility because they can easily fall back on NFP when they wish, since they learned it when they began married life.

Some may well question the wisdom of a universal recommendation to practice NFP at the very start of marriage. What seems good in Japan and Austria may not apply everywhere. Perhaps this question merits discussion, study, and research.

When all is said and done, NFP provides couples with conscientious freedom to decide the number of their children. With that freedom they also carry the responsibility that goes with freedom. And man, being prone to evil as well as to good, must constantly stir up within himself the springs of generosity, which may run dry if not refreshed. We must urge ourselves to be generous; we must listen to others who urge us to be generous.

May I close my observations with the words of Pope John Paul II, spoken in Washington, D.C., Oct. 7, 1979:

> In order that Christian marriage may favor the total good and development of the married couple, it must be inspired by the Gospel, and thus be open to new life—new life to be given and accepted generously. The couple is also called to create a family atmosphere in which children can be happy, and lead full and worthy human and Christian lives.
>
> To maintain a joyful family requires much from both the parents and the children. Each member of the family has to become, in a special way, the servant of the others and share their burdens (cf. *Gal. 6:2; Phil 2:2*). Each one must show concern, not only for his or her own life, but also for the lives of the other members of the family: their needs, their hopes, their ideals. Decision about the number of children and the sacrifices to be made for them must not be taken only with a view of adding to comfort and preserving a peaceful existence. Reflecting upon this matter before God, with the graces drawn from the sacrament, and guided by the teaching of the Church, parents will remind themselves that it is certainly less serious to deny their children certain comforts or material advantages than to deprive them of the presence of brothers and sisters, who could help them to grow in humanity and to realize the beauty of life at all its ages and in all its variety.

SCIENCES

CONTRIBUTION FROM THE SOCIAL SCIENCES

Francois Guy, M.D.

In the field of human fertility and its control, the experiments and reflections put forth in the first part illustrate the originality of Natural Family Planning as a means of birth control and suggest a definition at the same time: in different languages, cultures, and countries, it is first of all an *educational approach* that allows every human being, every couple, to *understand* and recognize the reproductive process and therefore to *choose* his behavior, his way of life, without any exterior intervention, and this in relation to his family project and what sexuality—all interpersonal relationships, the multiple facets of the conjugal dialogue; in other words, what human love—means to him.

Precise theoretical and practical knowledge of the biological facts is an essential initial condition: nothing could replace it. But all the groups committed to this point of view have been able to ascertain that this knowledge is only a starting point and that it is impossible to conduct a valid educational project without also considering the psychological, sociological, and ethical factors. This fact has continually forced itself upon all those concerned.

The history of "Natural Family Planning" is to a large extent the history of this realization. Claude Lanctot, M.D., Executive Director of the I.F.F.L.P. (International Federation for Family Life Promotion) or F.I.D.A.F., of Washington, D.C., has described the first phases:

- An initial *experimentation phase,* essentially biological and medical, which, before 1955, grossly defined human-reproduction mechanisms and identified the first practical tests, independent of paraclinic and hormonal investigations: Knaus-Ogino method and calendar; basal body temperature control.
- A second phase of general *maturation or adaptation,* during which representatives of the medical professions joined those of the nonmedical professions to create information-and-help centers, essentially for married people ("couple to couple"). Groups from all continents joined the five pioneers (Canada, Columbia, France,

Francois Guy, M.D., is Master in Science of Education, Technical Assistant (with his wife) of "Action Familiale" in Mauritius (1964-1966); Vice-President of IFFLP-FIDAF; IFFLP-FIDAF Consultant for Africa; Director of I.R.E.C. (Institut de Recherche sur l'Enfant et le Couple, Grenoble)

Great Britain, and Mauritius) and set out, often empirically, programs based first on the sympto-thermal method and then on the observation of the cervical mucus (the Billings "ovulation method").

- The third and present phase is characterized by the spreading and deepening of all activities. The groups are becoming more and more numerous, often with a very modest structure, sometimes situated at a national level. They unite to form the I.F.F.L.P. with headquarters in Washington, D.C., or the W.O.O.M.B. (World Organization of Ovulation Method, Billings) with its headquarters in Melbourne, Australia.

The interest raised by the educational prospects of family planning finds expression in two ways: on the one hand, *financial support* from private organizations, from government structures (USAID, ACDI, SIDA, Cooperation Francaise, etc.), or from international organizations (U.N.F.P.A., etc.). On the other hand, basic research in the biomedical, psychological, and pedagogical fields is on the increase: the regular collaboration, inaugurated in 1976, with the Human Reproduction Department of the World Health Organization is one of the best examples of this.

The second part of this collective book will illustrate some aspects of this evolution: we can sum it up as follows:

- The general orientation will be given in the introduction by Professor Jerome Lejeune.
- The physiological basis and general principles for the tests of the fertile and sterile phases of the menstrual cycle will be described by Michele Guy, M.D., Suzanne Parenteau-Carreau, M.D., and John and Evelyn Billings, M.D.
- Physicians and researchers involved for various reasons in the programs will stress one or the other aspect: in the historical field (R. Vollman), on techniques (Adams, Bonomi, Keefe, Roetzer), research (Prof. Campanini, A. Cifuentes, J. Spieler), or evaluation (Doering, Perez-Sanchez).

Some of the authors do not adhere to the religious beliefs or philosophical orientations that are the basic trend of this book. We have encouraged their participation as evidence of the growing interest in the scientific, nonreligious fields in the educational, ecological approach represented by Natural Family Planning.

We received a more specific contribution from the social sciences, on the psychological level, by Wanda Poltawska, M.D., or on NFP methodology by Claude Lanctot, M.D.

We shall thus have reached our objective: to show, on the fundamental and applied research level, the role played by the social sciences in the development of Natural Family Planning based on the different tests for fertility awareness, and this in a general educational perspective and for the promotion of the person.

THE INSTINCTS OF LOVE

Professor Jerome Lejeune

Recognizing the face of a friend in the midst of a crowd allows each of us to observe that all of mankind is based on the same nature and yet each individual is unique. The reason behind this phenomenon is the fact that the union of two reproductory cells, each equipped with the same chromosomes but with different genes, provides each descendant with an unprecedented grouping.

Both the species and the individual benefit from this: the individual receives his biological personality and the species a practically inexhaustible diversity without disruption of its basic unity. On the other hand, the members of the species are divided into two distinct categories, male and female. It only remains to unite the two and there exists an amazing variety of instincts for this purpose.

Take fish for an example: all the possibilities seem to have been covered, from total ignorance between the two parents as is the case when the male scatters his milt over eggs laid freshly by he knows not what female up to a most elaborate seduction rite observed with the nuptial swim of the male stickleback inviting the female to visit his nest. Even the supposedly impossible exists with seahorses where, after a hurried courtship, the female lays her eggs in the male's ventral pouch where they are fertilized in passing and it is thus the male who is "pregnant" and later gives birth to baby seahorses complete with labour pains!

Each species has its own manner, and each individual is endowed from birth with all the instincts required in order to adopt the appropriate behaviour for love when the time comes. The exact programme to be followed is written into the nerve cell wiring circuits by the genotype (genetic heritage) with the same precision as for the determination of the body's form and physiology.

Animal behaviour in this field provides us with practically unadulterated forms of the four instincts of love: sexual desire, choice of mate, protection of offspring and the instinct of fidelity.

Professor Jerome Lejeune, Professor of Fundamental Genetics of the Faculty of Medicine of Paris, Member of the Pontifical Academy of Sciences (Laboratoire de Génétique Fondamentale, 149 rue de Sevres, 75015, PARIS).

SEXUAL DESIRE

Controlled by hormones and regulated by the seasons, it is sexual desire which sets the male in search of a female and leads to her acceptance to mate. The mere mention of springtime and its implications is sufficient to illustrate that the mating season exists for us as well, even though its extension over the entire year gives rise to many questions.

All sorts of signals come into play in the search for a partner. From the female fire-fly's little lantern to the song of the enamored nightingale, all the senses are called upon. Sometimes a single one of them is enough, as is the case for certain butterflies whose antennae are so sharply sensitive to the female scent that they can detect the presence of a single molecule of it. The male will travel for miles to court the emitting party, even if it is only a phial containing a bit of the alluring fragrance!

With man, nothing is left out either, from the charms of dress and ornamentation to the intoxication of perfumes, not to forget music and dance and all the other arts brought together.

CHOICE OF MATE

The attraction between the two sexes is the absolute rule as an instinct can only be passed on if it is propitious to propagation. This explains why everyday language describes all homosexual practices as "unnatural". Homosexuality is practically non-existent with animals at liberty, but can be observed with those in captivity. For humans, with the exception of some extremely rare cases of constitutional defects and poorly defined genital organs (genetic or chromosomic anomalies), it seems that homosexuality can be more accurately described as a captivity of behaviour rather than a pathological deviation.

There are essentially two possible explanations for this erroneous course, both of which certainly include part of the truth.

Cerebral sexuality – It is known that the network of filaments which interconnect nerve cells, or the cerebral wiring circuit, is not exactly identical in the male and in the female. With birds, a glance at a cross section of the brain enables one to identify a singer, i.e. a male. This cerebral dimorphism is now well known and recognized for various members of the mammal species from the rat up to man.

Although the genetic sex is defined as soon as fertilization has taken place, this cerebral wiring is only gradually established. The injection of female hormones into a newborn male rat can reverse his behaviours and his cerebral wiring circuit takes on the female pattern without causing any change to the sexual organs.

The reciprocal inversion can be obtained with a newborn female rat (by injecting male hormones).

Practically nothing is known about this type of effect insofar as our own species is concerned. But it is possible that the maturation of our brain and nervous cell system occurs later on in development than it does with rats. The emotional and intellectual upset observed at puberty allows us to assume that the circuits are perfected and definitively established once this critical period is passed.

Following this line of reasoning, it is possible that a hormone disturbance could lead to imperfections, hesitations or even an inversion in the wiring network.

Similarly, it is not known what effect might be produced by the introduction of an excess of female hormones in girls and of male hormones in boys.

No doctor would apparently dare to undertake an experiment of this nature. And yet thousands of young girls at or close to puberty are offered chemical contraception in all legality. The "pill" does not contain natural substances, but synthetic molecules with certain properties which imitate the action of female hormones.

What will be the result of this pseudo-hormonal impregnation on the development of their cerebral wiring circuits? How will their behaviour be affected: more feminine or more feminist? more motherly love or more egocentricity? or no effect at all? Absolutely no one knows, but we will be in a position to make observations ten or twenty years from now.

Learning sexual identity – in addition to the role played by hormones, initiation and apprenticeship shape our habits and thereby modify the structure of the cerebral system. A well-known example is the story of the crow fed and tamed by Lorentz. Having known also his adoptive parent to the exclusion of any crows, the poor bird ended up behaving as though crows were men and men crows.

A child is certainly even much more sensitive to moulding than a bird and one can imagine the degree to which the family atmosphere, upbringing and the example of parental behaviour can influence the harmonious development of sexual identity. It seems obvious that it is only fair to our children to raise the boys as boys and the girls as girls, in spite of theories as to the merits of a unisex education, which does not exist anyway.

PROTECTION OF OFFSPRING

The marvels of the maternal instinct and the protection of his offspring on the part of the male are so deeply inscribed in nature that there is practically no need to mention them. A female defending her babies, a male bird sitting on the eggs or feeding the little ones or a bristling primate covering the retreat of his horde under attack are images of life itself.

But instincts as powerful and as highly integrated in an effective behaviour system as these are sometimes set off by very simple signals. The hen, for example, who represents the attentive mother if there ever was one, hurries towards her desperately chirping little one, but remains quite blind to the chick if a plate of glass prevents his call from reaching her.

Anyone who has heard a newborn baby's first cry can testify to the profoundly irresistible calling force it represents. If certain legislative authorities allow abortion, could this not simply be because the parental instinct is not set off when the rejected little one is not strong enough to cry out?

THE INSTINCT OF FIDELITY

Raising babies and providing them with their basic upbringing demands the persistence of their regular protectors, which is the reason for monogamy, whether seasonal or definitive. The longer the offspring require assistance, the longer monogamy is assured.

Within the monogamic species, so frequently encountered among birds and numerous higher mammals, the discretion of the finances followed by the stability of the couples formed would seem to be fairy tales if they were not facts directly observed in nature. The crows' engagement ceremony and indissoluble union, or the surprising folly which overcomes the female gray goose subsequent to an adultery illustrate that the old-fashioned colloquial French expression "une petite oie blanche" (a little white goose = an innocent young girl) was originally not at all derisive, but quite a natural comparison.

When fidelity extends through all generations and all members of a clan, we can see the cohesion and resistance that this instinct confers on the group as a whole. Our ignorance of the mechanisms responsible for this instinct of fidelity to the family in the broad sense of the term is a possible explanation for the periodic reappearance of proposals of euthanasia for defective young ones or the "over-aged", proposals which are invariably rejected each time but always crop up again.

Sexological theories

Human instincts are every bit as powerful as those of animals, the difference being that once we are aware of them, it is up to us to control them by using our reasoning capacities.

Two possibilities exist. One is to adopt what is thought to be the most reasonable line of conduct; this is the common sense way discussed later on. The other consists of trying to rationalize whatever the chosen line of conduct; this is the problem with theoreticians.

Similar to the way in which modern geometricians generalize a system, modern sexologists decide to abandon some obvious fact or other in order to adopt some other one which has received their intentional preference.

Several examples easily illustrate the results of this method.

To start with, sexual desire can be presented as an absolute principle, thereby underrating or even doing away with the other three tendencies entirely (choice of mate, protection of offspring and instinct of fidelity).

The consequences of this choice are direct.

In its simplest form, where sexual desire is the unique factor, solitary pleasure is channeled into a dead end, i.e. inveterate onanism.

If the choice of mate is still accepted as having a role to play but without the love of offspring, the result is egotism of the couple.

If the fidelity factor is played down, promiscuity becomes the rule and the family disappears.

Putting aside the choice of mate denies the very existence of the sexes and respect for ones fellow human beings totally disappears.

The extreme limit would be to imagine that pleasure alone remains. The relationships in a society based on this principle would be limited to a series of voluptuous performances as intense as possible, repeated ad infinitum.

Pleasure and procreation could also be separated entirely (by means of voluntary sterility) and equality of the sexes would be accomplished at long last (because all females would work). This is a much praised vision for the future by some people.

In fact, this society already exists and is even older than ours. It dates from the Tertiary Era and was invented by the so-called social insects.

The females, who are emancipated thanks to infernal work cadences (ants practically never stop working), are free from any concerns about procreation (worker ants are sterile). Only one female remains a slave to reproduction: the Queen.

However, the infertile females have permanent access to the keenest sensual pleasure. By means of unceasing mutual tickling of their antennae which provokes the supreme enjoyment of regurgitation, they compose a kind of immense social equivalent of a partial oesophageal ectasis that we call their society!

Balancing the love instincts

The most reasonable line of conduct still remains to be chosen. There are two possible solutions which provide a balance for the instincts guiding our behaviour. One consists of avoiding their stimulation: this is the case of chaste celibacy. The other consists of stimulating and satisfying the four instincts simultaneously; this is the state of matrimony.

In the case of celibate chastity, the instincts of sexual desire, choice of mate and protection of offspring do not receive any direct solicitation. Fidelity is the only one which can find an outlet (parents and relatives).

In order to balance the other three which remain unsatisfied, the instinct of fidelity must be elevated, magnified, extended to the reaches of love itself. Only dedication to the other, greatest, most perfect, most powerful and who, mysteriously, presents himself under the aspect of the poorest, weak and deprived can bring the unsatisfied tendencies into line. In short, the love of one's fellow beings becomes a necessity. Celibacy can only be accomplished within a context of total charity. This is as much a fact of nature as it is a theological precept.

On the other hand, marriage stimulates and satisfies all the instincts of love, although unequally in time and/or place. The potential fecundity of a healthy couple represents ten or fifteen children, largely exceeding modern day requirements. This is where family planning comes in.

A woman's fecundity is intermittent, dependent on the ovarian cycle. Therefore, it is evident that precise knowledge of the fertile periods provides a natural means of control.

Without any modification of physiology, as occurs when chemical methods are used, or disturbance of the act of love itself, as occurs when physical methods are used, periodic abstinence gives parents the means of procreating according to their own freely made decision.

The price of this freedom is the temporary but often repeated curbing of sexual desire. This conscious repression of one of the instincts of love is nevertheless accomplished to the obvious benefit of the three others as it is in order to obtain improved conditions for their development that satisfaction of sexual desire is postponed from time to time.

It is apparent here as well that total harmony can only be established through an increase in fidelity, in respect for the child, respect for the husband or wife and respect for fellow human beings in general.

To use the laws of procreation in moderation is implicitly to acknowledge that we are creatures and, from this recognition, to be prepared to rediscover within each of us the image and likeness of our Creator.

A FEW REMINDERS ABOUT THE MENSTRUAL CYCLE

Michele Guy, M.D.

To understand the human fertility mechanisms and the principles for their control, a few anatomical and physiological references are necessary.

A woman's genital system basically includes the following (See figure):

- Two sexual glands or gonads, the *OVARIES* (O) containing numerous little pouches, the *Follicles* (f); an *Ovum* (ov) develops in each of the latter.
- The *UTERUS* (U) or womb, a hollow muscular organ. The internal walls of the uterus are covered with a mucous lining called the *Endometrium* (end.).
- The *VAGINA* (V), a cylindrical muscular corridor leading from the *Vulva* (Vu) to the entrance of the Uterus, the *Cervix* (c), which is furrowed with cavities or *cervical crypts* (cc).
- The *Fallopian Tubes* (t), canals linking the upper end of the Uterus to the Ovaries.

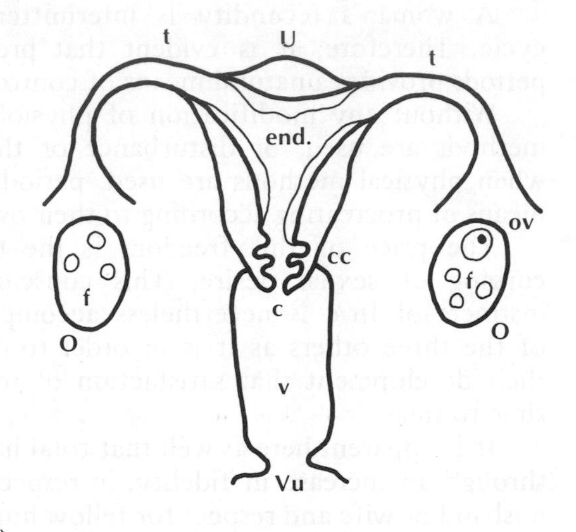

WHAT IS THE OVARIAN CYCLE? – or the menstrual cycle, or the feminine cycle?

It is a dynamic process, repeated regularly in most women between the age of 13 and about 45-50. This process takes place in the ovaries

Michele Guy, M.D., is Technical Assistant (with her husband) of "Action Familiale" in Mauritius (1964-1966); Assistant in the Maternity ward of the General Hospital of Grenoble (France), Family Planning and Family Education Centre of University Hospital of Grenoble.

and uterus, and its essential goal is the transmission of life.

This process has a triple effect:

1. It allows the *ovary* to liberate an *ovum* (or female gamete): this is *ovulation.* The ovum contains half of the future child's inherited traits, the half supplied by the mother.
2. It facilitates the meeting between this ovum and a spermatozoon (or male gamete), which supplies the paternal part of the future child's inherited traits. This is *fertilization,* in which a new human begins life.
3. It facilitates the implantation of the latter in the maternal nutritive area, the lining of the uterus, prepared for this purpose. This is the *nidation,* or *implantation.*

The cycle's aim is therefore *pregnancy* and a *child.* If this aim is not achieved, all the changes are interrupted: the shedding of the prepared endometrium results in a bleeding, the menstrual period (or menses) underlining the uselessness of the fertility process started at the beginning of a particular cycle.

Thus, a cycle, in the broad sense of the word, can last from the first day of the menses:

- until delivery, when the process is completed;
- until the first day of the following menses, when the process is incomplete.

FIRST OBJECTIVE: Allow the ovary to release an ovum: this is the first part of the ovarian cycle.

A few days after the beginning of menses (and this part of the cycle is *variable* in length) the ovary receives from an area in the brain (the hypothalamus), through a hormone secreted by the *pituitary,* the order to mature a follicle and its contents, i.e., the ovum. In fact, the pituitary sends a double order to the ovary: it consists of pituitarian *gonadotrophins,* FSH and LH.

Responding to this double stimulation (FSH and LH), the follicle matures, develops, and manufactures a hormone, *estrogen,* which is poured into the blood. The level of estrogen regularly increases up to maximum, the estrogen peak. The peak of FSH and LH reacts to the estrogen peak and causes the follicle to explode. The mature ovum is projected into the tube.

The follicle's maturation takes about eight days; the location of ovulation after the beginning of the cycle depends on when the maturation itself started.

The ovum survives 24 hours, at most, after ovulation.

It is important to remember that the day of ovulation represents the end of the first part of the cycle, and that this part is variable in length.

SECOND OBJECTIVE: Facilitate the meeting between the ovum and the spermatozoon.

It is clear that this meeting is possible during a limited period of time, the length of the ovum's life, i.e., about 24 hours.

But the fertile phase lasts longer than that, since nature makes it possible for the spermatozoa to be ready in advance.

About a week before ovulation, under the influence of the estrogen increasingly secreted by the follicle, the cervix softens and opens up, and its crypts start to secrete cervical mucus.

Cervical mucus, similar in appearance to raw eggwhite, becomes more and more clear, stretchy, stringy, and lubricative as the days go by, flowing into the vagina down to the vulva. This mucus will serve the eventual spermatozoa as a guide.

Assisted by cervical mucus, the spermatozoa deposited in the vagina during intercourse ascend to the cervix, where some will be stored, protected, stimulated in the cervical crypts. During the hours and days following intercourse, they leave in small groups for the inside of the uterus, and then the tubes, where an ovum may be waiting.

Thus, extended survival of the spermatozoa is a function of the continuing availability of a favorable cervical mucus.

THIRD OBJECTIVE: Facilitate the implantation of a new child in the maternal uterus: this is the second part of the ovarian cycle.

When the ovum leaves the ovary to enter the tube, a small temporary gland called the *corpus luteum* develops in its place in the follicle.

The corpus luteum (or yellow body), which we can compare to a gardener employed at each ovulation to prepare the garden (or uterus), pours into the blood the second female sexual hormone (or *progesterone*), intended first for the uterus but also for the brain. Progesterone joins the estrogen that the walls of the follicle are still producing.

Progesterone produced by the corpus luteum has four effects:

1. A life-supporting action, by the transformation of the endometrium, which becomes soft and spongy after having thickened under the influence of estrogen during the first part of the cycle. One can compare it at this stage to a ploughed garden ready for planting.
2. The closing of the uterus, by contraction of the muscular fibers of the cervix, which closes and becomes firmer, and by the transformation of cervical mucus into a gelatinous plug (the garden gate is closed).
3. The signal to the hypothalamus to stop all orders destined for the pituitary, which therefore stops its own stimulation of the ovary: neither follicle maturation nor ovulation can now take

place (the gardener prevents the production of new seeds).

4. The basal body temperature rises, 2 to 4 tenths of a degree Centigrade. This rise is useful for the future embryo's development (the gardener watches over the heat in the garden, as in a greenhouse).

These four progesterone actions start as soon as the corpus luteum is in place, i.e., at ovulation.

Subsequently one of the following two processes takes place:

a) If there is fertilization, on ovulation day: the tiny embryo enters the uterus after traveling down the tube 5 or 6 days. It immediately takes roots in the endometrium and, through its roots, which will become the placenta, sends a chemical message (human chorionic gonadotrophine or HCG) into the mother's blood, ordering the corpus luteum to continue its four actions: hormonal stimulation of the endometrium, closing of the cervix, inhibition of pituitary stimulation and therefore of all ovulation, raising of the temperature. One can look for the child's HCG in the mother's urine for pregnancy.

b) In the absence of fertilization, the ovum dies within 24 hours after ovulation. But the corpus luteum is not informed: each cycle, it systematically "bets" on pregnancy and prepares the endometrium for implantation. When this implantation does not occur, the corpus luteum does not receive any stimulation from the HCG and ceases its activity about two weeks (a maximum of 16 days) after ovulation. This leads to discontinuation of the corpus luteum's four effects:
   - The endometrium, no longer nourished, is shed in menstruation.
   - The cervical gelatinous plug becomes a liquid; the cervix opens and allows the menstrual bleeding to flow out.
   - The hypothalamus can once more stimulate the pituitary and therefore the ovary.
   - The temperature returns to its former low level.

CONCLUSION

1. The *first part of the cycle* is oriented, on the one hand, to ovulation and, on the other hand, to the male seed's reception, protection, and meeting with the ovum.
   The *second part of the cycle* is oriented to the child's reception and protection by the maternal environment.
   We all descend from these two successful processes of reception. Menstruation is only, as we have seen above, the sign of the failure of the fertility process.
2. The first part of the cycle is *variable* in length and is *fertile* around

the time of ovulation. The second part of the cycle is of relatively constant duration (on the average, nine months or two weeks) and it is a sterile period, which means that no meeting between a spermatozoon and an ovum is possible at this stage. The cervix is closed and the ovaries inhibited. Thus, if the woman is pregnant, she cannot start a second pregnancy during these nine months; if she is not pregnant, she must wait until the end of the two weeks and for the fertile phase of the following cycle to undertake a pregnancy.

3. Every woman who is correctly informed can observe the signs of her cycle, i.e., notice the modifications of the cervical mucus, shift of the temperature, and changes in the consistency of the opening and of the position of the cervix.

   At the same time, she can understand the mechanisms and the meaning of these transformations.

   These three different ovulation tests will be explained in the following chapters of this book.

References:

1. J.J. Billings. *Natural Family Planning: The Ovulation Method* (Melbourne).
2. J.J. Billings. *Methode Billings: La Regulation Naturelle des Naissances* (Edit. Paulines, Montreal, 1977).
3. J. Brown. *Scientific Basis of the Ovulation Method* (Melbourne).
4. S. Geller. *Temperature Guide for Woman* (Julliard).
5. F.M. Guy. *Les Methodes d'Auto-observation* (IREC, 1979).
6. E. Keefe. *Self-observation of the Cervix to Distinguish Days of Possible Fertility* (Dec. 1962).
7. E. Keefe. *Cephalad Shift of the Cervix Uteri: Sign of the Fertile Time in Women* (*Int. Rev. of NFP.* Collegeville, MN, Vol. 1, No. 1, 1977).
8. Nakamura (in *Reader in NFP.* Tokyo 1978, p. 149).
9. Serena Canada. *Precis de la Methode Sympto Thermique* (1977).
10. Serena Canada. *Planning Your Family the S-T Way* (1975).
11. WHO Colloquium. Geneva 1972. *Cervical Mucus in Human Reproduction.*

THE SYMPTO-THERMAL METHODS

Suzanne Parenteau-Carreau, M.D.

This title refers to family planning methods that are based on the sympto-thermal test, that is, on the study of the woman's morning temperature and on signs and symptoms at the time of ovulation that serve to delineate the fertile period as well as the infertile periods of the menstrual cycle.

The Sympto-Thermal Test

Temperature

The temperature of the human body is influenced by the organism's activity and by the time of day. Moreover, in the woman, it is influenced by progesterone, the postovulatory ovarian hormone. In order to bring out this latter influence, the temperature is taken daily under comparable conditions, that is, upon awakening at about the same time, using the same route (rectal, vaginal, or oral). Changes in schedule or sleep, strong emotions, infections, and medication are noted on the relevant dates in case the temperature should be affected. If the thermometer and the graph have a broad scale, the temperature will be easier to read and interpret.

If the temperature is taken every morning under comparable and normal conditions, the curve will reveal a first level that is rather low following menstruation, then a short rising segment called shift, and finally a higher premenstrual plateau. It is recognized that the higher or upper temperature plateau is a sign of progesterone activity. One deduces then that *ovulation occurred during the preceding days.* The temperature, therefore, is used to obtain a retrospective confirmation of ovulation; it does not indicate the day of ovulation, nor does it predict its approach.

Signs and Symptoms

Cervical Mucus at the Vulva

There are many details on observing and interpreting this symptom. In short, the woman is invited to denote each day as: 1) day of bleeding; 2) day without mucus; 3) day with transitional or "less-fertile" mucus; or 4) day of "maximum-fertility" mucus. When a menstrual period ends, whether there have been mucus-free days or not, any manifestation of mucus should be considered the result of estrogen activity, a sign of possible fertility, and a forerunner of ovulation sooner or later. Once the mucus has acquired and lost its maximum-fertility characteristics (mainly a sensation of lubrification), the woman enters and remains in the infertile phase until the next menstruation (or exceptionally, until a new mucus episode).

The sympto-thermal methods ask that the woman note her mucus observations either using her own words (NOFZIGER, 1979), or in the form of a chart (FALLACE, 1976), or using a code (PHARAND-LAPOINTE, 1980; LEBLANC, 1977; ROETZER, 1978; KIPPLEY, 1979; GUY, 1979).

Changes in the Cervix

In 1962 KEEFE showed that daily self-palpation of the cervix reveals changes corresponding to the phases of the cycle. In the phase following menstruation, the cervix rises more and more and is soft, open, straight; mucus flows from it. These changes are slow and gradual; they show fertility. They quickly reverse, within two or three days, indicating infertility until the end of the cycle. Initially some will be reluctant to make this examination. There is no doubt, however, that it is very useful, once the learning phase has passed.

Various Symptoms

Abdominal pain, bleeding, or breast sensitivity occurs in some women between the beginning of the mucus and the confirmation of the upper-temperature plateau. None of these signs reveal the day of ovulation, but they do show that it is close. Other women notice periodic changes in mood, sexual desire, skin, eyes, appetite, headaches, allergies, or other cycle-related problems.

Sympto-Thermal Interpretation

The total lack of mucus after menstruation is a sign of infertility for the experienced and careful woman.

The appearance of any mucus reveals the beginning of the fertile phase, culminating at the time of wetness/lubrication sensation. If the woman examines her cervix, she will find that it is high, soft, open, and straight. The temperature is still low, and abdominal pain or bloody discharge may occur.

Soon lubrification at the vulva will disappear; the mucus dries up while the temperature is rising and settling at a higher level. If the woman examines her cervix, she will find it is low, closed, firm, and dry. This all confirms the onset of the infertile phase, which will last until the return of menstruation some ten or twelve days later. This is the normal sequence of events in cycles.

There are situations, however, where estrogenic surges are not always followed by ovulation. Thus, there may be mucus episodes with or without the cervix rising, opening, and becoming soft; these will appear and disappear repeatedly during very long cycles, at the time of premenopause or in the postpartum phase, eventually alternating with nonmenstrual bleedings. The fact that the temperature stays at a low level indicates that these were not ovulatory episodes and that the reappearance of mucus should be watched for.

THE SYMPTO-THERMAL METHODS

A sympto-thermal method of family planning is one in which the knowledge of symptoms and temperature guides the planning of the couple's intercourse, either to help them conceive or to prevent conception.

THE SYMPTO-THERMAL METHOD TO FACILITATE CONCEPTION

Chances of conceiving are best when the mucus has maximum lubrification and fluidity. If this mucus is ovulatory, a temperature shift will soon confirm it. One can conclude that conception has occurred if the temperature stays high for at least 20 days. The couple may increase their chances of conceiving by abstaining for a few days before impregnating intercourse.

THE SYMPTO-THERMAL METHOD TO AVOID CONCEPTION

When a couple are not ready to welcome a child, they may abstain from intercourse during the fertile phase of the cycle. The sympto-thermal chart enables them to recognize the two infertile phases where infertile intercourse is possible. There are variations of detail around the world, but the essential points are held in common.

The Early Infertile Period

At the beginning of the cycle, a certain amount of time is required for the follicle and the ovum to develop before ovulation is possible. There is an infertile phase if the bleeding is really a menstruation, i.e., if ovulation occurred in the preceding cycle. The length of this infertile phase depends on the earliness of the next ovulation and on sperm survival for this particular couple.

From the very first sign of mucus, this infertile phase is over, practically speaking. Many groups add a mathematical rule that may terminate infertility at an earlier date, either a set number of days, or a calculation related to the shortest cycle.

The Postovulatory or Premenstrual Infertile Period

As regards the temperature component for the beginning of premenstrual infertility, there is general agreement that a minimum of three consecutive days of high temperature under normal conditions is required. There are variations in the way these high temperatures are set out: coverline (PHARAND-LAPOINTE, 1980; McCARTHY, 1977); temperature mean (VOLLMAN, 1977); or minimum upper shift (MARSHALL, 1978; KIPPLEY, 1979; NOFZIGER, 1979).

The symptom component for the beginning of premenstrual infertility refers mainly to the mucus, blood-spotting, or changes in the cervix. The mucus needs to dry up before hyperthermia is confirmed (PHARAND-LAPOINTE, 1980; ROETZER, 1978; MARSHALL, 1978; McCARTHY, 1977; KIPPLEY, 1979).

EFFECTIVENESS OF THE SYMPTO-THERMAL METHODS

The effectiveness of the sympto-thermal methods depends first and foremost on the precision of the sympto-thermal test. There should be regular observations through plotting, use of a thermometer and a chart, and teaching that is competent and progressive. Moreover, the couple should be able to consult with a teacher or counselor if they have a problem or a question, to prevent their making a mistake or becoming discouraged so that intercourse occurs at the fertile time even though they do not wish a pregnancy.

Effectiveness depends also on how the couple adapt to modifying their intercourse in terms of their objective (facilitate or prevent conception). The spouses' psychosexual adjustment will influence the effectiveness of the method; there is a strong chance they will tend to break the rules if they have not arrived together at their decision, or if they deny their problems.

Statistically it is very difficult to measure the effectiveness of natural methods as methods of conception avoidance. A multitude of subtle attitudes and behaviors have to be fitted into right concepts, whereas the assumption with natural methods is that of being open to the child. However, Table 1 shows the results of statistical studies on the effectiveness of the sympto-thermal method, calculated according to the classic Pearl technique (rate of unplanned pregnancies per 100 woman years).

In RICE (1777), couples who did not wish to have children (birth limitation) had better results than those wishing only to space births; this difference shows the effect of motivation. JOHNSTON (1978) differentiated, for users of the infertile period at the beginning of the cycle, between those who stopped on a set day determined by a modified Ogino calculation and those who stopped at the onset of mucus.

SYMPTO-THERMAL METHOD ACCEPTABILITY

The attention and care necessary to observe and make charts require an effort, but this effort can be compensated for by the fact that the method is effective and harmless. Moreover, it is very valuable for a woman to learn that she can detect and interpret changes in her body that formerly escaped her notice, and to understand what is happening if her cycle length is more irregular than usual.

Some people prefer the sympto-thermal methods, where they have to observe many cyclic signs; others choose natural methods based on a single parameter: temperature alone or mucus alone. In a multi-parameter method there is more to teach, more to observe, and more to chart: this may be viewed either as a burden or as the benefit of having more areas of awareness to grasp the changes from one phase to another. In those rare cases of non-correlation among the various signs, the discrepancy may be viewed either as a source of confusion or as a warning that extra care is needed.

Psychosexual adjustment to periodic abstinence will be influenced by the length of possibly fertile periods, previous experience in family planning, the stage of marital adjustment, and the teacher's attitudes toward natural methods and toward couples. Finally, it will depend on the couple's ability to feel and express love, tenderness, and caring without coitus as well as through coitus. Periodic abstinence calls for

Table 1 Sympto-Thermal Method Effectiveness

Authors Date		No. Couples	Months or Cycles	Unplanned Pregnancy Rate (Pearl)/100 Woman-Years	
				Overall	Method Failure
Roetzer 1978		491	17,026 c.	0.8	0
Rice, Lanctot 1978	Total sample	1022	21,736 c. 20,573 m.	7.5	0.9
Rice Lanctot Garcia-Devesa 1977	Spacers only	369	6,556 m.	14.8	
	Limiters only	637	13,653 m.	4.1	
Johnston, Roberts, Spencer 1978	Calculations for early infertile period	192 episodes	3,198 c.	8.6	1.9
	Early dry period	268 episodes	4,595 c.	15.9	3.7
	Post-ovulatory use only	121 episodes	1,402 c.	3.4	

the couple's communication because it implies repeated joint decisions. That is why it is important to encourage the participation of the man from the very beginning.

References:

1. Fallace, C. and J., 1976. *Family Planning Guide.* Smithtown, New York. The Natural Family Planning Association of Long Island.
2. Guy, F. and M., 1979. *Les Methodes d'Auto-observation.* Grenoble. Institut de Recherche sur l'Enfant et le Couple.
3. Johnston, J.A.; Roberts, D.B.; and Spencer, R.B., 1978. NFP Services and Methods in Australia: A Survey Evaluation. *International Review of Natural Family Planning* 2:143-154, 203-224, 328-353, and 3:20-53.
4. Keefe, E.F., 1962. Self Observation of the Cervix to Distinguish Days of Possible Fertility. *Bull. Sloane Hosp. for Women* 8:129.
5. Kippley, J. and S., 1979. *The Art of Natural Family Planning.* Cincinnati, Ohio. The Couple to Couple League.
6. Leblanc and Harel, 1977. *L'Action Familiale.* Ile Maurice.
7. Marshall, J., 1978. *Natural Family Planning.* London. Catholic Marriage Advisory Council.
8. McCarthy, J.J.; Martin, M.C.; and Gildenhorn, M., 1977. *The Sympto-Thermal Method.* Washington, D.C., The Human Life Foundation of America and the Natural Family Planning Federation of America.
9. Nofziger, M., 1979. *A Cooperative Method of Natural Birth Control,* 3d edition, Summertown, Tennessee, The Book Publishing Co.
10. Pharand-Lapointe, M.; Kavanagh-Jazrawy, F.; Plante-Charron, C.; Parenteau-Carreau, S.; and Doyle, R., 1980. *Planning your Family, the S.T. Way.* Ottawa, Serena-Canada.
11. Rice, J., and Lanctot, C.A., 1978. Results of a Recent Study of the Sympto-Thermal Method of Natural Family Planning. *Linacre Quarterly* 45:388.
12. Rice, F.J.; Lanctot, C.A.; and Garcia-Devesa, 1977. The Effectiveness of the Sympto-Thermal Method of Natural Family Planning. Communication at First International Congress of IFFLP in Cali, Columbia, June 1977.
13. Roetzer, J., 1978. The Sympto-Thermal Method: Ten Years of Change. *The Linacre Quarterly* 45:358.
14. Thyma, P., 1978. *The Double-Check Method of Natural Family Planning.* South Deerfield, Mass., Marriage Life Information.
15. Vollman, R.F., 1977. *The Menstrual Cycle.* Philadelphia/London/Toronto. Saunders.

THE OVULATION METHOD

Evelyn L. Billings and John J. Billings

The Ovulation Method is an individual method of fertility regulation in which days of infertility, possible fertility and maximum fertility are defined by self-observation of the cervical mucus pattern. These observations include the *feelings* produced at the vulva by the absence or presence of mucus and its physical characteristics, and the *appearance* of any mucus present in sufficient quantity to be seen. The technique involves the interpretation of symptoms with which the healthy, fertile woman is already familiar, and which she observes in the course of her normal activities; internal examination of the vagina is advised against.

There have been many references in the gynaecological literature to the importance of the cervical factor in human fertility. In 1855 Smith[1] pointed out that conception is most likely to occur at that time in the menstrual cycle when the mucus content of the cervix is "in its most fluid condition." In 1868 Sims[2] described what is now called the Sims-Hühner post-coital test for spermatozoa and emphasized that the test is most likely to show healthy, motile spermatozoa when "the cervical mucus becomes clear and translucent, and about the consistence of the white of egg." A lively interest in the cyclical changes in activity of the cervix in humans and various animals developed from 1940 onwards, when it came to be recognized that close to ovulation the cervical mucus exhibits a fern-like crystallization pattern, exhibits the formation of channels, has an increased content of glucose, sodium chloride and water and a decreased viscosity and cell content. It gradually came to be realized that infertility could result from a deficiency of the normal secretion and that the normal responsiveness of the cells of the cervical crypts to high circulating levels of oestrogen diminishes about the time of menopause.

Our studies began in the 1950's when almost all emphasis had been applied to laboratory studies of mucus aspirated from the cervix at different stages of the menstrual cycle, with only occasional reference to the occurrence of a *mucus symptom*, a truly remarkable situation.

The instruction is begun by inviting the woman to acknowledge that at some time between her menstrual periods she notices a vaginal loss of another kind. It is then explained that this "mucus" is an indication of the fertile time within the cycle. It is requested that she keep a daily record for a month during which time physical sexual activity and genital arousal are avoided. One is careful to avoid detailed description of an average mucus pattern, because there are individual variations. It is pointed out that the feelings evident at the vulva are more important than visual observation, and a few key words are suggested, such as "dry", "slippery", "sticky", "opaque" and "stringy". The record is made at the end of the day's activities, using a colour and a brief written description, or in the case of illiterate women merely the colour or a symbol.

More detailed instruction is given after this first month, when from her own record the woman is taught two fundamental concepts, that of the Basic Infertile Pattern of mucus and that of the Peak symptom. The Basic Infertile Pattern is the reflection of ovarian inactivity, so far as follicular development is concerned, and exists in the pre-ovulatory phase of the cycle, corresponding with a low circulating level of oestrogens. Ordinarily the "dry days" constitute the Basic Infertile Pattern. In other cases the woman may experience continuous mucus, when the Basic Infertile Pattern is that mucus which does not alter in any of its characteristics day after day.

The Peak symptom results from the hormonal events which occur at the time of ovulation. The high levels of oestrogen produce a slippery, lubricative mucus which alters abruptly as the progesterone level rises at ovulation, so that the mucus becomes sticky and opaque, or ceases altogether.

Our scientific studies undertaken in Melbourne in collaboration with J.B. Brown and H.G. Burger[3] have shown that ovulation occurs in a close time-relationship to the Peak symptom, usually immediately afterwards. Allowing time for ovulation to occur and the ovum to die, we can define post-ovulatory infertility from the beginning of the 4th day past the Peak symptom of the mucus – the Peak Rule. The hormonal verification of the definition of the fertile phase by reference to the cervical mucus pattern has been abundantly confirmed.[4,5,6,7] It has also been demonstrated that the woman's observations accurately reflect what is happening at the cervix.[8]

During the pre-ovulatory phase of the cycle, the days of the Basic Infertile Pattern are infertile. The rules for the avoidance of pregnancy (Early Day Rules) are simple to understand. There is avoidance of coitus during menstruation, in case the mucus warning of an early ovulation is obscured. Coitus is confined to the end of the day, so that the Basic Infertile Pattern has been identified. Coitus is avoided on successive days lest the seminal fluid and vaginal transudates following coitus obscure the commencement of the fertile phase. Any change from the Basic Infertile Pattern, that is, from dry days to mucus, or from mucus to a different kind of mucus, or the appearance of bleeding, are an indication for abstinence, allowing sufficient time after the return of the Basic Infertile Pattern for the woman to be sure of what is happening. In an average cycle, once there is a change from the Basic Infertile Pattern the woman proceeds to ovulation, after which the Peak Rule is applied. There is no need for coitus to be confined to the end of the day in the post-ovulatory phase of the cycle.

The cervical mucus is not merely an indicator of the time of ovulation, it actually determines the presence of fertility, it is the fertility factor. Conception requires a good ovum, a good sperm cell and a satisfactory secretion of a particular kind of cervical mucus in the absence of which coitus remains infertile. The secretion of two kinds of mucus is stimulated by a high level of oestrogens, as Odeblad[9] has shown, one forming strings and channels (Es mucus) which preserves and nourishes the sperm cells and promotes their migration, and another type which can be seen as small opaque lumps (El mucus) which appears to act as a filter whereby abnormal spermatozoa are prevented from reaching the uterine cavity. With a rise in the level of circulating progesterone a dense, sticky mucus (G mucus) is formed, and provides a complete barrier to sperm migration. The cervical mucus acts therefore as a biological valve, and determines the time for which sperm cells may survive, with the ability to fertilize the ovum, within the female genital tract.

Experience in many differing cultures and social conditions has demonstrated that even illiterate women living in poverty can understand the Ovulation Method, and this understanding is not prevented by the presence of abnormal vaginal discharges. Competent teaching is essential and it is important that the teacher concentrate on the essential simplicity of the observations. It has been our constant experience both in Australia and in other countries that attempts to teach the Ovulation Method are always unsuccessful if the teachers are also employed in offering a variety of contraceptive techniques. Additionally, there is to be noted that the biological features of the Ovulation Method exclude the concurrent use of barrier methods of contraception. The biological principles of the Ovulation Method make it incompatible also with cervical palpation. Once there has been a change from the Basic Infertile Pattern, as an indication that follicular development has commenced, the woman must observe the changing characteristics of the mucus from day to day until after ovulation, without the confusion created by genital arousal, internal examination or physical sexual activity.

Knowledge of the natural manifestations of her phases of fertility and infertility is knowledge which every woman should be given. It promotes the development of self-respect, recognition of the wonders of the human reproductive physiology and a deeper respect for life. Our own programmes have expanded to include this teaching of fertility and infertility awareness within the schools.

In communicating the fundamental principles on which the rules of the Ovulation Method are based, the teachers make it clear that the husband and wife are completely free in their exercise of the option to apply the rules for the achievement of pregnancy or the rules for the avoidance of pregnancy.

Many people have used the Ovulation Method in an effort to determine the sex of the child before conception, with variable success. It is suggested that the Y-chromosome sperm cell is shorter lived but more motile than the X-chromosome sperm cell; according to this theory, an act of coitus on the day of the Peak symptom is more likely to produce a boy child, whereas if there is coitus a day or two before the expected time of the Peak symptom, and then abstinence until the time of post-ovulatory infertility the child is more likely to be a girl.

Current research in Melbourne and other parts of the world is directed to the production of a "do-it-yourself kit" to define the fertile phase by testing an overnight specimen of urine for its oestrogen and progesterone (Pregnanediol) content. It should not be assumed that such a kit would be a new "method" but rather a *teaching-aid* to help women to learn the Ovulation Method well, particularly those women who lack confidence in their own observations or perhaps have a pathological condition disturbing the normal mucus pattern.

By defining the fertile phase from its beginning, the Ovulation Method brings the husband and wife into confrontation with their fertility, and this has been repeatedly observed to promote sentiments of respect for human life. By learning to identify the Peak symptom, which may be absent in many cycles, the method can help many apparently infertile couples to have children. By teaching the woman to recognize infertility it provides a natural technique for the confident management of fertility regulation during breast-feeding and that permanent infertility which occurs at menopause. The husband and wife can be assured that if they have a serious need to avoid pregnancy, observance of the rules for the avoidance of pregnancy will give them a security that is not surpassed by any contraceptive technique,[10,11] that they have avoided the ill-effects which complicate contraception and that they remain free to employ the method for the achievement of pregnancy at any time in the future.

References:

1. Smith, W.T. The Pathology and Treatment of Leukorrhoea, Churchill, London, 1855.
2. Sims, J.M. Brit. Med. J., 1868. 2:465,492.
3. Billings, E.L. et alii. Lancet. 1972, 1,282.
4. Flynn, A.M. and Lynch, S.S. Brit. J. Obstet. Gynaec., 1976, 83,656.
5. Casey, J.H. Human Love and Human Life. Published by Polding Press, Melbourne 1978, 68.

6. Hilgers, T.W. et alii. Obstet. Gynec., 1978. 52,5,575.
7. Cortesi, S. Primo Corso Nazionale sul Metodo della Ovulazione Billings, Universita Cattolica del Sacro Cuore, Roma, 10-15 Dicembre, 1978.
8. Hilgers, T.W. and Prebil, Ann M. Obstet. Gynec. 1979. 53,1,12.
9. Odeblad, E. Cont. Gynec. Obstetr. 1978, 4:132.
10. Weissman, C. et alii. Lancet. 1972, 2:813.
11. A Prospective Multicentre Trial of the Ovulation Method of Natural Family Planning. *World Health Organization Task Force on the Determination of the Fertile Period:* Special Programme of Research, Development and Research Training in Human Reproduction. (To be published).

Dr. John Billings graduated in Medicine from the University of Melbourne in 1941. He is a Fellow of the Royal College of Physicians of London and a Fellow of the Royal Australasian College of Physicians. He is Head of the Department of Neurology at St. Vincent's Hospital, Melbourne, Dean of the Clinical School and Associate Dean (Clinical) in the Faculty of Medicine of the University of Melbourne, Physician to the Royal Victorian Eye and Ear Hospital and Consultant Neurologist to the Cancer Institute. He is President of the World Organization of the Ovulation Method (Billings).

Dr. Lyn Billings graduated in Medicine from the University of Melbourne (1942), and subsequently took the Diploma of Child Health in London. She is Senior Demonstrator in Histology and Embryology in the Department of Anatomy of the University of Melbourne. She is a mother of nine children and is Assistant Physician at the Family Planning Clinic in the Department of Community Medicine at St. Vincent's Hospital, Melbourne.

THE FIRST TEACHER OF THE SYMPTO-THERMIC METHOD OF NATURAL FAMILY PLANNING

Rudolf F. Vollman, M.D.

On April 20, 1938 Father Hillebrand wrote the following letter to H. Knaus. "In short succession, I have observed three pregnancies in couples who had received careful instructions from me in your teaching and rules on natural family planning. These pregnancies resulted from intercourse BEFORE the fertile days according to your rules, but which fit exactly into the days of rare conceptions according to Ogino, viz. days 20 to 24 prior to menstruation. These cases shocked me and forced me to study and search for a simple but reliable means to identify the time of ovulation, first for these women and then for all other women."

"Then I suddenly remembered that I read, some time ago, in Van de Velde's 'Perfect Marriage' a chapter entitled Periodic Functions in the Female Organism in which he stated that the hormone of the corpus luteum exerts, amongst others, a characteristic influence on the body temperature of women. This caused me to determine, in as many women as possible, their monthly temperature cycles with the aid of a clinical thermometer. In the short period from August to December 1935, 21 women, married and single, had been investigated. They had recorded BBT curves for 76 menstrual cycles."

"I soon found in a woman that she showed a deviation from your norm, viz. ovulation on the 15th day before the onset of menstruation. She seemed to ovulate at the 19th day before menstruation. This greatly upset me, and I reproached her with not having kept sufficiently accurate measurements. However the impression made by her as a person and the way she put her case were overwhelming. A further case finally convinced me . . . . "

"Sofar, I do not doubt that you have discovered the physiological and normal time of ovulation in women. However, I have found that deviations from your norm occur, both at the beginning and at the end. Therefore one cannot accept your rules blindly. Fortunately the estima-

Rudolf F. Vollman, M.D. Hiltbrunnerweg, CH-8713-Uerikon, Switzerland. After medical school he specialized in Obstetrics, Gynecology and Biostatistics Stages in Veterinary Pathology; Research Associate with the Department of Embryology Carnegie Institution; Medical Officer of the NIH Primate Colony, San Juan; Head of the Department of Obstetrics, NIH; Consultant to the Section on Human Reproduction, WHO.

tion of the time of ovulation by the basal body temperature curve resolved the uncertainty and thus gave birth to natural family planning."

With a letter written on November 30, 1949 Father Hillebrand explained to me how he got involved with Natural Family Planning. "Let me first introduce myself. I am a catholic parish priest but (!) the son and brother of physicians. When I first heard, in 1933, that there is a so-called natural method of family planning, I studied the subject with the intention to get an estimate of its reliability."

"I first got the impression that the method seemed to be effective, but I was shaken when I observed, simultaneously, as many as three failures though the couples, had faithfully followed the rules. This was in 1935. Of the three couples two conceived in the first cycle and the other couple after a few cycles but after I had suggested to them that they may use the "infertile" days of the postmenstrual phase, too."

"The first failure immediately enticed me to find the cause of the fiasco. I remembered that I once read in Van de Velde's 'Perfect Marriage' that a woman's temperature rises shortly after ovulation and that in the case of pregnancy the temperature remains elevated. I decided to test Van de Velde's observation. First of all I checked the correctness of the common clinical thermometers and I experimented with the different techniques of taking the temperatures . . . ."

"To sum it up, from that time on to this day I have used the basal body temperature, more and more successfully, in the service of natural family planning."

"Through Dr. Doering I have heard about you and I have read your publications. This has caused me to write to you, and send you my compliments. I should like to hear from you. You know now my motives which forced me into this new and remarkable occupation. How did you get pinned?"

How did Father Hillebrand operate as a family planning adviser? "I have concentrated my efforts on the methodology how couples may be best and safely introduced to natural family planning. This is not possible through popular or scientific publications of any kind though they may be helpful. This must be done by a kind and competent person who takes the pains and time to introduce the couples not in general but individually for so long until they have become capable to master the method."

In summary Father Hillebrand wrote (1949):

1. "First of all, the present status of natural family planning must be fully documented. Only then can a further discussion of physiologic, medical, psychologic, moral and pastoral issues be fertile."
2. "To serve the cause and progress of natural family planning the available data must be collected and systematically analyzed . . . . The facts will then decide on future plans but not the so-called authority

of a name."

3. "That natural family planning may occupy the position in human society which it deserves, requires that the political and clerical authorities give their full support . . . ."

(Summary of a paper published in the Winter 1979/1980 issue of the International Review of Natural Family Planning, with the permission of the publisher, Father Paul Marx.)

References:

1. Hansen, T.B.: Ueber praemenstruelle Temperatursteigerungen. Beitr. Klin. Tuberk., 27: 291-310, 1913.
2. Hillebrand, H.: (brother of Father Hillebrand) Zwischen aerztlicher und seelsorglicher Ehehilfe. Mainz, Matthias Gruenewald Verlag, 1962.
3. Knaus, H.: Die Physiologie der Zeugung des Menschen. Wien, Verlag W. Maudrich, 3rd ed., 1950.
4. Ober, K.G.: Dr. med. H.C. Wilhelm Hillebrand. Geburtsh. Frauenheilk., 20: 188-192, 1960.
5. Ogino, K.: Conception Period of Women. Harrisburg, Penn., Medical Arts Publishing Company, 1934.
6. Smulders, J.N.J.: Periodische Enthaltung in der Ehe. Regensburg, G.J. Manz, A.G., 1931.
7. Vollman, R.F.: The Menstrual Cycle. Philadelphia, Penn., W.B. Saunders, 1977.

TEACHING NFP IN WINNIPEG

Paul and Louise Adams, M.D.

Winnipeg is a city in central Canada with a population of about half a million. In our area, there are a large number of Catholics of French and Irish descent and the largest concentration of Ukranians in Canada. In 1962, when Doctor Adams was finishing his studies in Obstetrics and Gynecology in eastern United States and returning to Winnipeg, there was no centre for the teaching of natural family planning in that city. As a Catholic couple, we felt it was imperative that this teaching be made available. This was before the encyclical *Humanae Vitae* of Paul VI and just at the time that the contraceptive pill was rapidly becoming the most widely used method of birth regulation around the world.

We sought the support of the Catholic Physicians of Manitoba and began under their sponsorship. Thus originated the Family Planning Centre (natural methods) of Manitoba. At first, we instructed in Calendar Rhythm based on a system established at St. Vincent's Hospital in New York. We taught once a month at the Misericordia General Hospital and the women were invited to mail their dates of menstruation each month. The days of probable infertility were calculated immediately and were sent by return mail. Women with very irregular cycles were encouraged to take their temperatures. Considering the much improved teaching today, the results were amazingly good. Some women, scattered across the country, were still corresponding with us after ten years although we encouraged them to used the more refined, newer methods of natural family planning which we had adopted.

In 1972 we were invited to St. John's University in Minnesota by Father Paul Marx to hear Dr. John Billings describe the Ovulation Method. We were much impressed and decided to start teaching after we had tested the method to our satisfaction in our own married life. Later that year we taught seven couples in our home. All the women were patients who had irregular periods for whom the temperature method required long periods of abstinence and who were having children in rapid succession. The Ovulation Method was effective for these couples and subsequently several of them became active teachers at our centre. On the basis of this experience, we transformed our centre into a centre for the teaching of the Ovulation Method.

In 1973 we were invited to join Serena Canada, an organization which was founded in 1955 and which is expert in the Sympto-Thermal Method and a leader in the field of research. Serena accepted us as a centre with similar views in natural family planning although our approach was different. Serena hoped to gain insights into the reliability of mucus as an indication of fertility and into the effectiveness of the Ovulation Method. It did not take long for us in Winnipeg to realize that although the Ovulation Method was very effective for a large number of couples, it was not suitable for about a quarter of those who sought our services. We found that some couples required the more objective evaluation provided to them by the Sympto-Thermal Method.

In 1975, Serena Manitoba became a centre for the teaching of all parameters of natural family planning. Each month, the couples who register are encouraged to attend three sessions. The first session is devoted to the philosophy of N.F.P., to reproductive anatomy and physiology and to the Ovulation Method. The second session is devoted to the Sympto-Thermal Method and to the self-examination of the cervix. At the last session, the couples are seen individually and with our assistance, they choose those parameters of N.F.P. which seem most appropriate for them.

Now we are in charge of teacher training and we have several teacher couples working in Winnipeg and others who teach in different parts of Manitoba. Serena Manitoba is also involved in marriage preparation courses and in the teaching of fertility in some private Catholic high schools. We feel strongly that the strengthening of the institution of marriage and the providing of an understanding of the beauty of married love are of prime importance.

Our biggest problem now is to cope with the demand for our services and the accompanying financial exigencies. Providing good teachers is a problem here as it is everywhere. However, we are very much gratified by the enthusiasm and dedication of our young couples and the knowledge and expertise which they have acquired over the years.

EACH NATURAL METHOD HAS ITS OWN CONDITIONS OF APPLICATION

Gabriele Bonomi, M.D.

After about twenty years of study and experience in the field of natural methods, I can draw the following conclusions.

I believe that valid and effective family planning by means of the natural methods alone is always possible, provided that one is able to use, in certain particular situations, different natural methods in combination.[1]

In fact, each method has its own features in showing, through the interpretation and use of a specific biological phenomenon (such as the menstrual flow, a rise in the BBT, or the cervical mucus), the presence of physiological factors of fertility and sterility.

These features are, at the same time, the specific character and the limit of each method.

Then, only by recognizing the limits or the conditions of application of each method, it becomes possible to use them always according to their maximum degree of effectiveness. It goes without saying that for each method there is always the possibility of a satisfactory solution of natural family planning, even though limited to favorable circumstances.

The same is true for the cervical mucus method. As for my personal experience with this particular method, I can say that it cannot be considered as a rule that every woman in every situation can apply.

Any absolute approach to this subject or generalization decreases the possibilities of recognizing in the biological phenomenon of the cervical mucus a valid clinical test indicating the presence of possible fertility in the woman.

As the structure and biological function of the cervical mucus become more definite,[2] it appears clear that this mucus secretion can-

Curriculum Vitae:

Gabriele Bonomi, born in 1927, a degree in medicine, specialist in Constitutional Medicine and Endocrinology, married, with three children. He has been studying for 18 years the problems of natural family planning. He founded and runs a Center of Studies of Sexology in Pavia (Italy) with a bimonthly review, La Coppia. In particular he studies and verifies the cervical mucus in its practical application to family planning in a different light than the Billings ovulation method.

not be seen as a sign or a symptom indicating ovulation, but rather as a factor in possible fertility or in sperm penetration.

In this perspective, more scientific and more in conformity with the real nature and function of cervical mucus, the definition of the conditions of application or use of the cervical mucus as a method of natural family planning acquires a considerable significance.

The cervical mucus, verified as leucorrhoea as it appears when it comes out at the vulva, can be used as a unique and natural family planning method only if the following conditions are fulfilled:

- That the cervical mucus appears only once within a menstrual cycle.
- That the mucus secretion lasts at least eight or nine days.
- That the mucus secretion follows this typical course: beginning with a gradual increase till it reaches the peak, and then a decrease till it disappears.
- That the mucus begins to appear at least four days before it reaches its peak days, which can last more than two days.
- That the typical cervical mucus secretion verified does not disappear before the end of the ovulatory period, measured following the rise in the BMT or following Ogino retrospective calculation.

Beyond the above-mentioned conditions of application of this method, the cervical mucus always remains a valid clinical sign, but it has to be associated with other clinical tests and signs of fertility.

Notes:

1. "*I metodi naturali: Ii punti di verifica*" [The natural methods: The points of verification], ed. Centro Studi Pavese di Sessuologia. Pavia, 1978.
2. See "La Coppia," bimonthly review of married-life sexology, No. 68, 1980, ed. Centro Studi Pavese di Sessuologia.

SELF-OBSERVED CERVICAL SIGNS:GUIDES TO CONTROL OF CONCEPTION BY SELECTIVE SEXUAL ABSTINENCE

Edward F. Keefe, M.D.

Controlling their fertility by selective abstinence, a couple ask the question, in short, "Is it safe – today?" The answer, depending on the signs, will be "Yes", "No", or "Maybe". "Yes" days are those when it is certain ovulation will not occur before deposited sperm will have lost their fertility. "No" days are those when ovulation seems soon to occur. "Maybe" days are those when it is uncertain whether ovulation is soon to occur or may have just occurred; in retrospect they will often have been "Yes" days.

The cervix is a built-in *bioassay* for estrogen and progesterone to answer the question stated above of the relative likelihood of a given day being fertile. A domestic *chemical assay* "to predict ovulation", moreover, is a futile dream because experience of 20 years with self-examination of the cervix has shown that the daily progression toward ovulation is often erratic and varies from cycle to cycle and from woman to woman.

To reach her cervix, the woman passes two fingers through the vagina and presses down on the body of the uterus through the abdominal wall with her other hand if necessary. She observes the status of the cervix and collects a sample of the current secretion in the os between her fingers. She interprets her findings according to Table I.

"Yes" days follow an ovulation up to the sixth day after the onset of menstruation, and even longer depending on the signs. On "Maybe" days, whether the couple allow coitus is determined by: (1) length of the fertilizing life of the sperm in a favorable cervical environment (as yet unknown), (2) need to avoid a pregnancy, (3) sexual drive of the marital partners, (4) skill in examination and interpretation of the signs, (5) variability of signs from cycle to cycle, (6) confidence of the couple in the method.

Keefe, E.F.: *Cephalad shift of the cervix uteri: sign of the fertile time in women. International Review of Natural Family Planning 1: 55, 1977.*

Dr. Edward F. Keefe M.D. has promoted control of fertility by selective abstinence since 1948 when he developed an open-scale thermometer for women and began to teach the role of cervical mucus as a guide to fertile time. Since 1958 he has taught the changes in the cervix itself and direct collection of mucus from the cervix.

One can not measure "effectiveness" of cervical examination statistically because it is used not in isolation but with temperatures and consideration of previous "cycle-patterns"; moreover the couple is permitted to apply abstinence with variable care on "Maybe" days. However the examination is gaining popularity, especially in the "special conditions", postpartum, lactation, and the climacteric.

Most women when they realize the usefulness of self-examination overcome their fastidiousness about it. The attitude of a teacher influences its acceptance. Sometimes the husband makes the examination and the couple share responsibility for interpreting the signs.

Table 1: Practical interpretation of typical self-observed cervical signs

SIGNS	INFERTILE	FERTILE	INTERMEDIATE
CERVIX:			
accessibility	easy, "right there"	"out of reach" needs supra-pubic pressure	slight effort to reach
level	lowest	very high	moderately high
texture	firm like cartilage	soft like sponge	slightly soft
surface	gritty	slippery	slippery
patency of os	tightly closed	wide open	partly open
CERVICAL SECRETION:			
volume	scanty, absent	abundant	moderate
collection	difficult	easy	slightly difficult
viscosity	semi-solid	watery, runny	tacky
clarity	opaque	transparent, clear	hazy
filability	no test possible	forms threads up to 5 in. long	forms short, thick strands
TEMPERATURES:	high	low	low
"IS IT SAFE?"	"Yes"	"No"	"Maybe"

SYMPTO-THERMAL METHODS OF NATURAL FAMILY PLANNING

Josef Roetzer, M.D.

"Sympto-thermal" methods involve charting symptoms of the fertile time, as well as waking temperature, and allow couples to seek or avoid conception (conception regulation). Changes in cervical mucus secretion are the most important fertile time symptom. Since 1951 I have made evaluation of the temperature rise dependent on cessation of cervical mucus flow; my handbook (1965)[1,2] and a later study (1968)[3] presented the first authentic sympto thermal methodology—"sympto thermal" methods then current merely noted symptoms and interpreted the temperature independently of them.

The woman must learn to recognize at the vaginal entrance (vulva) the various forms of cervical mucus; she gradually develops a nuanced appreciation of the mucus symptom if she receives repeated instruction or herself studies a suitable handbook. With today's improved pedagogical techniques almost 100% of fertile women can successfully recognize both the increased fertile time cervical mucus secretion and its various forms ("more fertile type" and "less fertile type").

I consider only those elevated temperature readings significant for defining infertility which lie after cessation of that form of cervical mucus secretion which indicates the woman's particularly fertile time. A very simple rule ("after cessation of this cervical mucus flow watch for 3 'higher' temperature readings which are higher than the preceding 6 lower readings") identifies onset of a period of absolute infertility continuing into the beginning of the following cycle—the Pearl Index is "zero" (no pregnancies per 100 couples per year of use).[4]

A combined approach is used to determine early cycle infertility. The beginner may assume Days 1-6 infertile (Day 1 = the first day of "true menstruation"); the experienced woman may consider additional days infertile by attending to fine points of mucus observation or self-examination of the external cervical os. The probability of pregnancy from intercourse on or before Day 6 is less than 1 to 6,000 – Pearl Index 0.2 (better than the Pill). Use of both pre-and post-menstrual infertile

Josef Roetzer, M.D. former lecturer in Pastoral Medicine at the Universities of Innsbruck (Austria) and Regensburg (Germany) and at the Philosophical-Theological Universities of Linz and St. Poelten (Austria). Director of Marriage Advisory Service, A 4840 Voecklabruck (Austria), Vorstadt 6.

days by 491 women in 17,026 cycles[4] yielded in practice an overall Pearl Index of 0.8 (as reliable as the Pill, but without its harmful and sometimes even lethal side effects[5]).

Footnote: These results were obtained from couples of differing socio-economic backgrounds, some of them with only primary school education. In contrast with clients of some other studies, these couples were not canvassed by a researcher but came of their own accord to my advisory service to learn NFP. The motivation was already there. Perhaps the teaching method enhanced motivation. This will help explain why among these clients we have an unplanned pregnancy rate of only 0.8 per 100 women years, whereas in some of the funded studies the rate may be as high as 20 or more. Another reason for differences in results among various studies of NFP is that even within what is called "the sympto-thermal method" there are in fact *several* approaches, of varying effectiveness. The principal differences concern the interpretation of the rise in temperature, and the determination of the post-menstrual infertile period.

References:

1. Roetzer, J. "Kinderzahl und Liebesehe, Ein Leitfaden zur Regelung der Empfaengnis" (Family Size and Married Love: a guide to conception regulation). Herder: Vienna-Freiburg-Basel, 1st ed., 1965; 9th ed., 1978. Italian version "La regolazione delle nascite secondo natura", Aldo Martello-Giunti 1975. Now out of print in German (replaced by Nr. 2).
2. Roetzer, J. *Natuerliche Geburtenregelung, Der partnerschaftliche Weg.* Herder: Vienna-Freiburg-Basel, 1979. Japanese version, Tokyo 1979; English manuscript ("Natural Birth Control: partnership in family planning") recently completed; Dutch and Spanish versions in preparation.
3. Roetzer, J. "Erweiterte Basaltemperaturmessung und Empfaengnisregelung" (Supplemented Basal Body Temperature and Regulation of Conception), *Archiv fuer Gynaekologie* 206 (1968), 195-214. English version to appear in the *International Review of Natural Family Planning* (1980).
4. Roetzer, J. "Fine Points of the Sympto-Thermic Method of Natural Family Planning", Nos. 1 and 2 (Human Life Center, 1977). – "Further Evolution of the Sympto-Thermal Methods", *International Review of Natural Family Planning*, Vol. 1, No. 2, Summer 1977, 139-150, The Human Life Center, St. John's University, Collegeville, MN 56321, USA. – "The Sympto-Thermal Method: Ten Years of Change", *Linacre Quarterly,* Vol. 45, November 1978, 358-374 (850 Elm Grove Road, Elm Grove, WI 53122, USA).

5. Mortality Among Oral-Contraceptive Users. Royal College of General Practitioners. (8 October 1977) Lancet ii, 727-731. – Vessey, M.P., et al., Mortality Among Women Participating in the Oxford/Family Planning Association Contraceptive Study. (8 October 1977) Lancet ii, 731-733.

SOME PRACTICAL OBSERVATIONS ON THE NATURAL FAMILY PLANNING PROGRAMS IN LATINAMERICA

Armando Cifuentes, M.D.

1. Comparison of results

The need to count with results comparable to those of other programs, including the anti-birth programs, has led to the adoption of similar biostatistical methodology.

However the NFP Programs incorporate some characteristics that must be taken into account when analyzing the numerical data, and failure to do so would alter the meaning of the results.

For example the NFP programs include an educational component inherent to its design which has to be accounted for in the interpretation of acceptance and coverage data. This is due to the fact that a rather extensive period of time is required for training and motivating people on this approach before a stable change in attitudes and behaviour takes place.

For this reason the NFP programs show slow development in the initial stages. An evaluation of the quantitative results covering the first few years generally shows a limited or moderate number of participants. However, its educational aspect makes the program more likely to become permanent and to expand spontaneously and without cost once it has become established in a given community, because a core of couples knows and practices the natural methods without further help from outside the community, and practically at no cost.

A long range evaluation shows that the number of couples that have been influenced by the program is higher than the one expected.

2. Is it an NFP research program or a service program?

When the program is a research program it is generally complex in design and it has stricter norms.

Many couples can not be admitted to the research because they do not meet the needed requirements, for example due to the duration of the menstrual cycles or age; other couples leave the research program for reasons such as the wish to change from one NFP method to another, which is not allowed if there has been a random assignation of couples.

It is easier for couples to enter and remain in a service program than in a research program. That is the reason why the conclusions reached in a research program regarding the acceptation and length of stay of the couples can not be extrapolated to service programs without due considerations.

3. Public opinion and the Natural Family Planning Programs

There are large sectors of the population who favor contraception in Latin America today. The people have been under the impact of some 20 years of intense neo-malthusian propagandistic action through all the media (radio, TV, newspapers, etc.).

In spite of that they mistrust sterilization and reject the legalization of abortion which a small group of anti-birth radicals are trying to impose. Even people recurring to abortion are conscious that killing the embryo is something evil in itself.

But said propaganda makes the initial acceptance of natural methods of fertility regulation difficult for a larger number of people.

On the other side there is a growing number of people looking for alternatives to contraception because of the unwanted or dangerous side effects which those methods have caused.

Other people are also looking for alternatives for cultural reasons or for their own criteria.

4. Influence of special groups on NFP

In the health sector it can be said that doctors, nurses and pharmacists are quite unaware of the natural methods of fertility regulation. As a result they almost always recommend contraceptives and surgical sterilization. And some of them, in spite of that ignorance, take a negative stand on natural methods because of personal prejudices.

Within the ecclesiastic sector we found that priests and members of religious orders know little about natural methods; several still believe that such methods are the Ogino calculation of probabilities.

It is imperative that schools of medicine, nursing, seminars, post graduate courses offer ample information on the human physiology area on which natural methods are based.

Moreover seminarians and priests must get a deeper understanding in Church doctrine in this respect because the differences of opinion confuse many couples.

5. Machismo and NFP

In Latin America today many men and women believe that any limitation in sexual relations may lead to upsets of the widest variety. And we know that natural methods require periodic abstinence.

Our experience has taught us that when a couple decides on using natural methods based on sound information and motivation they have a solid and sustained opportunity to better their reciprocal understanding and to overcome the machista culture pattern of dominance and subservience and to intensify their love.

In this new style of married life the sexual relations retain their wonderful meaning but are not the only way to express love.

There is a great need for deeper research on the psycho-sexual aspects of the couple.

RESEARCH IN NATURAL FAMILY PLANNING

J.M. Spieler, Scientist

Task Force on Methods for Determination of the Fertile Period
Special Programme of Research in Human Reproduction
WHO. Geneva (Switzerland)

The Special Programme of Research, Development and Research Training in Human Reproduction, World Health Organization, was started eight years ago in response to the increasing demands placed on the health sector to provide family planning care. The directions and priorities of the Programme are determined by the WHO member states in accordance with their own needs and requirements. The Programme addresses itself to research on the safety and effectiveness of current methods of family planning; the improvement of these methods and the development of a variety of new techniques; research on the psycho-social aspects and the delivery of family planning care; research on the diagnosis and treatment of infertility; and to the strengthening of resources for research in this field in the developing countries.

Research on the natural methods of family planning and on the development of new methods for the determination of the fertile period represents one of the priority areas of the Special Programme. In family planning, more than in most areas of therapeutics, the preferences of the individual woman, man and couple play a vital role. Such preferences are determined by a number of factors, including cultural, moral, geographical and medical; whether one wants temporary or permanent protection; the cost, and the availability and ease of obtaining the method desired.

There are basic problems associated with the delivery and use of all methods of fertility regulation. Those unique to NFP include the accurate identification of the fertile days of the menstrual cycle, the number of days of abstinence required and the implementation of abstinence if pregnancy is not desired, and the need for daily continued motivation and cooperation of both partners. These problems, especially the requirement of abstinence, are certainly considered as overwhelming by many people and need careful consideration before NFP is sug-

This paper is taken, in part, from an address made on behalf of WHO at an International Seminar on Natural Methods of Family Planning, DUBLIN, 8 October 1979.

gested or adopted.

Natural Family Planning as it is presently being practised is a relatively new development that has had only token research support compared with the vast amount of money which has been spent over the last two decades on the development and testing of contraceptives. With the exception of WHO and the USA Department of Health, Education and Welfare, the international and national research councils and agencies supporting research on family planning are devoting very little attention to NFP.

The first multicentred, cross-cultural evaluation of the ovulation method was set up by the WHO three years ago, and the results of this study are now becoming available. The only other international study on NFP was the Fairfield project on the sympto-thermal method. Both of these studies have surfaced areas that are in urgent need of further research.

There are a number of challenges facing NFP that require research. I will mention a few of them:

1. The development of uniform data collection tools, e.g. clinical records, follow-up questionnaires and forms, discontinuation and pregnancy report forms, which will enable both service delivery programmes and research projects to evaluate and compare their results in a standardized manner.
2. The identification of the psychosocial and psychosexual factors that affect the demand, choice and use of NFP, including the effects of NFP on conjugal stability; the perceptions and effects of abstinence inherent in the practice of NFP and the role of NFP instructors in presenting this aspect of NFP; and the characteristics of the couple as a psychosocial dyad, and of each of the partners individually, that are significantly related to the success or failure of NFP.
3. The exploration of modes of presenting NFP to the public which would increase its acceptance and stimulate demand, and how the education, training and monitoring of couples choosing NFP should be designed in order to maximize compliance.
4. The definition of the conditions under which NFP can be applied, e.g. in situations of irregular ovulation such as occurs during lactation, prior to the menopause, and immediately following the discontinuation of hormonal contraceptives.
5. The definition of the actual duration of the fertile period, which requires, in particular, increased knowledge about the duration of the fertilizing capacity of sperm.
6. The development of NFP modalities which will reduce the length of abstinence to the days of the actual fertile period.

All of these important issues require the interest and commitment of much more scientific manpower than is now involved, including disciplines such as gynaecology, reproductive biology, endocrinology, bioengineering, anthropology, psychology, sociology, as well as, of course, educational specialists and experts in Natural Family Planning.

One of the challenges facing NFP advocates during the 1980s is to strengthen the basis of NFP methods through good scientific research and to obtain the financial support required to do so.

J.M. Spieler has been working for the World Health Organization since 1972, and engaged in research in Natural Family Planning since 1974. Before joining WHO he was a Research Biologist in a contraceptive development group at Lederle Laboratories, New York. Mr. Spieler has a Bachelor of Science degree in Zoology (University of Florida) and a Masters of Science degree in Reproductive Endocrinology (Rutgers University).

MY EXPERIENCE WITH THE TEMPERATURE METHOD OF REGULATING BIRTHS

Gerhard K. Doering, M.D.

About thirty years ago I became interested in the basal body temperature changes during a woman's menstrual cycle. Before long I came into contact with Father Wilhelm Hillebrand (later Dr. med. h.c.), who was the first person to develop a rhythm system of Natural Family Planning that used the temperature cycle. In 1954 I wrote a guidebook providing general instructions on the temperature method of regulating births. Part of the time I advised and regularly cared for several hundreds of patients who were planning their families with the temperature method.

In 1967 a report of the experiences during 1946-1965 could be published, including 59,566 cycles of 996 women. The longest observation of a patient was nineteen years; the average was four years and ten months. The average age was twenty-eight years and nine months. The results depended upon whether couples used the strict form or the combined form of the temperature method.

The combined form of the temperature method

Eighty percent of the couples followed this form of the method, in which days both before and after menstruation are used for intercourse. A total of 48,214 cycles of 689 women were evaluated. The number of unplanned pregnancies observed was 125, for a failure rate of 3.1 by the Pearl Index.

The strict form of the temperature method

This method was used by 307 women in 11,352 cycles. According to this strict form of the temperature method, the "infertility time" lasts only from the third day of the hyperthermic (high-temperature) phase until the next menstruation. The number of unplanned pregnancies observed was 8, for a failure rate of 0.8 by the Pearl Index.

In every case after an unplanned pregnancy was reported, the patient

Dr. Gerhard K. Doering was born at Schleiz in 1920. He studied medicine at Gottingen. He was assistant at the Institute of Physiology of Gottingen and at the Institutes of Gynecology of Gottingen, Muenster, Tuebigen and Munich. He served as Professor at Munich in 1959. Since 1965 he has been director of the Department of Gynecology and Obstetrics of Munich.

was immediately questioned extensively in order to learn the reason for the failure. The most frequent reasons for failures were: genital contact during the fertile days, an incomplete measurement of the temperature, and a mistaken interpretation of the temperature rise. In accordance with the methodology of biostatistics, all patient errors were counted as "failures."

There is a marked variation in the number of failures of the temperature methods reported in the literature. In our study the highest failure rate was in users of a "combined method," in which the postmenstrual infertile phase was reckoned by a calendar method. The lowest failure rate was among followers of the "strict method."

Literature:

1. Doering, G.K.: Ueber die Bestimmung des Ovulationstermines mit Hilfe der rhythmischen Schwankungen von Atmung und Koerpertemperatur. *Klin. Wschr.* 27 (1949): 309.
2. Doering, G.K.: Die Temperaturmethode zur Emphaengnisverhuetung. *Thieme,* Stuttgart, 1. Aufl. 1954, 7. Aufl. 1968.
3. Doering, G.K.: Ueber die Zuverlaessligkeit der Temperatursmethode zur Empfaengnisverhuetung. *Dtsch. med. Wschr.* 92 (1967): 1055.
4. Doering, G.K.: Detection of Ovulation by the Basal Body Temperature Methods. In Uricchio, W.A., and Williams, M.K., *Natural Family Planning* (Proc. of a Res. Conf.), The Human Life Foundation, Washington, D.C., 1973.

USE-EFFECTIVENESS OF THE OVULATION METHOD INITIATED AFTER CHILDBIRTH, PRELIMINARY REPORT

Alfredo Perez-Sanchez, M.D.

During the period following childbirth couples request very frequently some family planning method. Therefore, any family planning method must be effective during the postpartum period. Some natural family planning methods have not been designed to be used during the postpartum and nursing period.

The Ovulation Method (OM) has been reported (Billings E.L. et al., 1977) to be suitable for being learned and used during the postpartum and nursing period. Nevertheless, no report has been published about the use-effectiveness of the OM initiated during the postpartum.

Our programme, the first on the OM in Chile, began in May 1978 sponsored by the World Health Organization, after the author of this preliminary report had made a training visit to Australia and New Zealand to learn the OM. During the first year we personally trained the programme's teachers.

In April 1979 we started the postpartum programme; couples who requested NFP were trained in the OM soon after childbirth. Couples were trained according to the technique proposed in the Atlas of the Ovulation Method (Billings E.L. et al., 1977). This preliminary report covers the ten month period from April 1979 to February 1980.

During this period, 44 couples were accepted for the study. All of them were white and belonged to the middle-class. All women were delivered in the Maternity Ward of the Universidad Catolica de Chile – University Hospital. Their age range was 18 to 39 years, with a mean of 28.4 years.

Parity was from 1 to 8 live children with a mean of 2.7. Couples entered into the study between the 5th and 12th postpartum weeks. At the beginning of training 28 women were in full nursing (breastfeeding exclusively); 12 were in partial nursing (breastfeeding plus supplemental feeding); and 4 had already finished the nursing period.

Five out of 44 couples knew the Method previously; 39 learned it for the first time during this programme. 32 have already presented their first postpartum ovulation during the ten month programme; 31 of them recognized the mucus pattern of the first postpartum fertile period.

Obstetrics, Gynecology and Perinatology Department, School of Medicine, Universidad Catolica de Chile, Santiago, Chile.

Table 1 shows woman months of use. During the ten month period 44 couples already completed 258 months of use. There was one pregnancy; this occurred in a woman in full nursing, during her fourth month on the Method and during her sixth postpartum month. This woman failed to recognize her first postpartum fertile period. We consider this pregnancy as a method failure.

Only one couple abandoned the programme, changing the Method, because the woman had extremely long fertile periods.

The Pearl Index of this 258 months of use with one pregnancy is 4.6. Nevertheless, if we subtract the postpartum amenorrhea months (41) and only consider the woman months of use after the reinitiation of menstrual periods (217) The Pearl Index is 5.5.

We consider the OM easy to use and to learn during the postpartum period, especially by full nursing mothers, since they have at least an annovulatory period of 70 days. (Perez, A., 1977). This allows them to recognize their infertile pattern; afterwards they will easily appreciate the changes toward fertility.

References:

1. Billings, E.L., Billings, J.J., and Catarinich, M. Atlas of the Ovulation Method. Advocate Press Pty. Ltd. Third Edition, May 1977. Melbourne, Australia.
2. Perez, A., Lactational amenorrhea and natural family planning. In "Human Ovulation", edited by E.S.E. Hafez, Elsevier/North Holland Biomedical Press 1979, pp. 501.

Table 1. Ovulation Method – Women Months of Use
April 1979 – February 1980

ORDINAL MONTHS	WOMAN/ MONTHS OF USE	USERS OF THE METHOD	PREG-NANCIES	CHANGE OF METHOD	LOST TO FOLLOW UP
1	44	4			
2	40	5			
3	35	5			
4	30	3	1		
5	26	1		1	
6	24	2			
7	22	5			
8	17	5			
9	12	4			
10	8	8			
	258	42	1	1	0

Pearl Index: $\frac{1.200 \times 1}{258} = 4.6$

THE PSYCHOLOGY AND PSYCHOPATHOLOGY OF FERTILITY

Wanda Poltawska, M.D.
Psychiatrist
Cracow, Poland

I. The Normal Situation

A. *The normal development of love.* A young couple become aware of their love; they decide to marry; they prepare themselves to receive the sacrament of matrimony.

B. *After marriage* they take up their sexual relations with joy and spontaneity.

C. *The child is announced;* the parents joyfully await his birth. A man who really loves his wife will accept without objection the periodic abstinence that may be necessary during the final weeks of pregnancy and in the immediate postpartum.

D. *After the birth of the first child* the situation changes. New parental tasks arise, and it is often difficult for the young mother to continue being a "wife"; she is inclined to be more a mother than a sexual partner. Her husband, on the other hand, must learn to be a father, although he prefers the role of husband. Fertility should now be brought under control, because the next child should come at a favorable time, a moment chosen by both spouses.

E. *Regulation of conception.* Parental responsibility now requires that they become acquainted with the biological methods and choose the right times for their sexual intercourse. The woman's fertile time becomes a time of abstinence, when intercourse is postponed. This way of living is sometimes difficult, but family planning by periodic abstinence, without use of artificial methods, is the only way worthy of man, especially of a Christian. In a dialogue of love, they decide how many children they can afford to take care of under their actual living conditions. They act in accordance with their own program, respecting the natural law (which is also God's law).

II. The Real Situation

A. Some young people *begin their genital life* before marriage. This situation may cause the neurotic reaction of fear of having a child and consequently the contraceptive mentality, with all its harmful implications and complications.

B. If the woman becomes pregnant in spite of having used a contraceptive, three solutions are possible:

1. The best of the three is that they wake up to their responsibili-

ties and *decide to marry.* They can go to confession and begin a new life under the sacramental bond of marriage. But difficulties may be carried over; after the child is born they may live in constant fear of a new conception, and this fear may incite them to resume a contraceptive attitude. Because that first child was neither expected nor wanted, fertility appears to dominate them. They multiply contraceptive means, and in case of a "mishap" they often sentence the next child to death.

2. If there are obstacles to marriage, the woman may decide to bear the child and to *remain alone.* The single mother may resent and distrust all men. Sometimes she marries another man. Experience shows that a man who marries a woman with a child is kind-hearted, and the marriage may well be happy.

3. The unexpected pregnancy leads to a *decision for abortion.* Such a decision is like a heavy weight burdening the couple's relationship. Some women break off their liaison with the man immediately and do not even want to see him any more. Others continue the relationship for some time, but mostly in an atmosphere of disputes leading to eventual separation. Sometimes the end is an unhappy marriage. The woman cannot forget what happened; she loses all her trust in the man and often remains unbalanced the rest of her life.

C. *The couple marry*, but their living conditions do not favor their having a child immediately. In this case, everything depends on their attitude; if they know and accept the natural methods and conform themselves willingly to periodic abstinence, then all is well. The time will come when they will be able to accept a child.

III. The Influence of a Contraceptive Attitude

A. Sexual intercourse with contraception takes place in the climate of fear of a child – *a kind of neurotic reaction.* The couple's fear is inappropriate; the child, who is so very tiny at the moment of conception, cannot reasonably be treated as a dangerous enemy.

B. The woman, who is biologically more involved in parenthood than the man, is also the more paralyzed by this fear and cannot surrender herself entirely during the sexual act. In an ambivalent situation of affection the union does not bring her joy, nor even orgasm, but very often a neurotic reaction of aversion. At first she directs this aversion toward those parts of the man's body from which the "danger" of pregnancy originates. It is very strange that many women show aversion to their husband's genital organs, being unwilling to touch or even look at them.

With time, this aversion extends to sexual relations, as the effect of ambivalence. But since the husband does not want to abandon intercourse, he forces her to comply. Now there is more at stake than aversion to her husband's body and the sexual relationship; the woman begins to hold a grudge against her husband; she doubts his love and treats the marital intimacy as an "inescapable evil" – which she nevertheless tries to escape at any cost. Thus begins an open conflict that often ends in divorce.

C. At first the man is not aware of the crisis that is already beginning. Sometimes he takes his wife to a sexologist to have her treated for frigidity; he does not attribute the problem to his own actions. Sometimes he suspects her of not loving him any longer, or even of having another lover. If the woman continues to refuse intercourse, he forces her at first; later he looks for other consolations, such as drink and other women.

D. The situation goes from bad to worse when a pregnancy occurs despite contraceptive efforts. Abortion often provokes the woman's ill-feeling or even hatred for the man.

E. Since very many persons use coitus interruptus, this situation requires a more thorough explanation. At first thought, it may seem that this method would be used only by men who are selfish and primitive, but that is not always true. Men about whom women say, "He is kind; he takes care of me," use this method, too. It appears that they choose it because it gives them the illusion of being responsible for fertility. Moreover, they have the feeling of being in control of the situation and of being its master, and that gives them some satisfaction. At the same time the man is persuaded that he is harming neither his wife nor her fertility. A man often considers this method to be "natural," harmless, morally blameless.

During coitus interruptus the woman is passive, in accordance with her psychical structure. She prefers to leave the whole responsibility to the man. The men's disposition to be responsible and to play the active role has its merits. But one must explain to them that the proper way to act is not to use coitus interruptus but to choose the proper times for normal sexual relations. The man's task is to observe periodic abstinence as indicated by knowledge of the physiological functions of the woman's organism. The woman should teach him that and explain her intimate self. Then he may take all the responsibility and control the situation. The passive woman may then – just as she desires – give herself in all confidence into the care of the man she loves.

IV. Natural Methods of Family Planning as a Means of Curing Marital Neurosis

When a couple really understand human fertility, contraception becomes unnecessary for them, since conception is possible only at a given time in each menstrual cycle. Contemporary man can consciously control his fertility; one might say that human fertility has become truly human only today, when it can be placed under the control of his intellect and will. But one must keep in mind the dangers inherent in hedonism, for without making efforts one cannot solve this problem. The man must – in the name of love – adapt himself to the woman's biological rhythm. The woman must give up her easy passivity in order to teach her husband chastity and tenderness. However, it is not the method but the couple's attitude that solves the problem.

There are two tendencies in the contemporary world: one favoring the child, the other opposing him. Sometimes, when parental responsibility requires the limitation of births, periodic abstinence is the only proper course of action. But many people do not understand the true significance of periodic abstinence; they consider it "too difficult," "against nature," and so forth.

In reality, *all* couples practice abstinence for various reasons. The man's organism is not always disposed to perform the sexual act; every man has his own rhythm, depending on age, temperament, health, and other conditions. The woman's organism also needs some times of sexual silence. Most couples abandon intercourse during menstruation. Every somatic illness of the partners is an obstacle to intercourse. The child is just another factor that spouses must take into account. Thus, Catholic teaching presents nothing extraordinary, but is simply an orientation toward the child. There is no foundation for the claim that its requirement is too difficult.

Testimonies given by couples show that acceptance of periodic continence does not lead to neurosis, since it does not create ambivalence or fear. The partners are happy and peaceful in their intercourse, and during the phase of abstinence they are attentive to each other and show mutual tenderness. Abstinence does not destroy their harmony but strengthens their spousal and parental love.

When couples with conflicts freely decide to use periodic abstinence, after a while their marital neurosis disappears.

NATURAL FAMILY PLANNING PROGRAMS DEVELOPMENT AND EVALUATION

Claude A. Lanctot, M.D., MPH
Executive Director of IFFLP

INTRODUCTION

Several distinctive aspects of Natural Family Planning (NFP) differentiate it from other family planning techniques. Although these have been generally spoken of in the past, it is only recently that a significant theoretical contribution has been made by Thomasina Borkman, Ph.D.[1] to better conceptualize this distinctiveness. Before a discussion of NFP programs it seems appropriate to review her key concepts. Dr. Borkman defines Natural Family Planning from a sociological perspective as "a value oriented inter-personal behavioral innovation", and then analyzes some of its key characteristics. Four areas are thus underlined, namely:

1) That NFP is *innovative* in that it is not viewed narrowly as a method to limit or space births but more broadly as a user-controlled approach to fertility acceptance and family planning that lets couples choose to limit, space, or plan births. NFP is *knowledge* and *not technology* dependent, and therefore users can truly aspire to a relative independence or fertility *autonomy.* It also emphasizes knowledge and working with one's or a couple's fertility (fertility awareness) rather than relying on multiple technologies (contraception) which interfere with fertility or destroy it (sterilization).
2) NFP is *interpersonal* in its focus in that its major active principle, besides self-knowledge of fertility, is sexual behavior modification which requires cooperative interpersonal behavior by the couple. This aspect can be an initial deterrent or a long term reinforcer depending on how it is presented or approached and integrated by each couple.
3) Its *value orientation* is explicit both in its fertility objectives and in affecting the complex interpersonal sexual behavior in different cultural contexts. One can also observe how to a greater or lesser extent some major ideas and values linked with contemporary trends in ecology, preventive health, holistic and self-help groups and women's health movements are incorporated in numerous NFP value clusters. The primary NFP value cluster emphasizes the shared responsibility of the couple, the innocuity of NFP with no impingement on the physiological processes, the personal awareness of sexual and fertility processes, the self-sufficiency leading from professional and technological dependence to true autonomy, and

finally the integration of sexual behavior modification or periodic abstinence, viewed as a positive element, and not just a deprivation, opening the way to possible changes in communication and role relationships often referred to as a *way of life*.

4) NFP is also primarily experiential in its learning principles. Knowledge and competence grow more through experience (doing and practicing) than by theoretical knowledge. The emotional aspects of NFP are especially facilitated through peer influence. Therefore it has many similarities with other self-help groups such as breast feeding, natural childbirth, alcoholics anonymous, or others.

Although the many facets of Natural Family Planning are viewed in the preceding chapters of the first two sections of this book, special insights into the development of NFP as a movement and its perception by various user-couples from their personal experience are expertly described in recent American reviews by Shivanadan[2] and Aguilar.[3]

In view of the above it is not surprising to meet a variety of concepts and forms of NFP programs. NFP is perceived either as a movement or a social service program developed essentially with goals of fertility regulation or even with a population control emphasis. It can be integrated as one aspect of a comprehensive family life promotion program (more often than not within a religious context or diocesan structure) or, again, it can be part of a maternal and child health, a nutritional or community development program.

Some of the key factors which significantly influence NFP program development can be summarized as follows:

1. The existing unmet needs and the presence of satisfied NFP users;
2. The development of appropriate and clearly stated program goals and policies;
3. Good NFP program organization (good leadership);
4. Adequate support with appropriate funding;
5. Competent NFP instructors (teachers);
6. The existence of additional good program elements such as continued supervision, evaluation, follow-up, teaching aids, record-keeping, etc.

The importance and value of program planning and evaluation need to be stressed both from a developmental point of view within each program and from the crucial aspects of accountability both to members of the organization and to outsiders such as the funding supporters. It is important to stress that evaluation is an essential aspect of the planning process not only in justifying project expenditures but especially to determine and evaluate special needs and problems, and to determine the most appropriate future course of action. In the field of

Natural Family Planning, evaluation efforts are still very much in their infancy. These have primarily concentrated on the biomedical evaluation of NFP as a family planning method in terms of use-effectiveness but very little, if at all, on the evaluation of NFP programs.

THE STATE OF THE ART

NFP Program Development: Overview Discussion

The growth of NFP programs and their expansion is of recent origin and can be traced for more than 10 or 15 years in only a few isolated instances. To better understand the many factors involved it is appropriate to discuss some aspects of NFP program development:

Stages of Development: Most programs are still in their pioneer phases or that of initial implantation with very few programs having reached the second or third phase of maturation and expansion at the national level. The fact also that some programs are primarily movements and resist or hesitate in the evolution toward services or fear the loss of some of the experiential learning principles that the movement fosters is an important consideration.

Knowledge about NFP: Competent research in NFP is still very limited having few competent, motivated, and adequately funded scientists since most population research resources are currently involved primarily in contraceptives, sterilization, or abortifacient technology development or program implementation. Although some of the major biomedical parameters of the fertile period have been established, their variations in special circumstances (post-partum, post-pill, premenopause) remain to be established or better defined. The renewed emphasis on sexual behavior modification or periodic abstinence and the determinant role it plays in initial acceptance, continuity, and variation in use-effectiveness has just begun. Applied research in teaching technology, program characteristics concerning organization, records, follow-up, has hardly been initiated.

Rivalry in NFP Methodology: The existing rivalry between the fertility determination approaches such as the emphasis on a single index by the Ovulation Method or cervical mucus ovulation parameter only, and on the other hand, the insistence that multiple indices of fertility such as cervical mucus with cervical changes and BBT (Basal Body Temperature) should be taught to all NFP teachers in order to then make it available to all users for their choice, continues to plague the field and divide some programs, workers, and leaders. This is especially wasteful of human and other resources at program, national and international levels.

Religious Auspices: The fact that at this point the majority of programs are under specific Catholic or diocesan structure may impair and probably limits in some cases the access of NFP to potentially interested persons of other religious persuasion. In several countries this is perceived as a necessity at least initially to provide both legitimation, resources and manpower. In several countries it has not prevented NFP users to be over half non-Catholics. A progressively increasing number of non-Catholics are interested in NFP and NFP program development.

Relationships to Governments: This is often closely tied to that of private national or international Family Planning Associations who have dominated the recent governmental involvement in family planning services both nationally and abroad. The situation varies greatly in each country based on a host of factors. It is especially important in the United States which finances more than half of all foreign aid in family planning and where many scientific and development programs originate.

Funding: This issue is very closely tied to governmental influence. The fact that in the last 20 years (from the 1979 *Sri Lanka UN Population Conference*) the annual international population assistance increased from $\$2 \times 10^6$ (US) in 1960 to approximately $\$400 \times 10^6$ (US) in 1979 might give one an idea of the financial drive in family planning and population programs. One of the priorities, no doubt is to insure a more equitable distribution of these resources to NFP programs, which are currently supported primarily by private non-governmental organizations (a large number are Catholic development organizations). Progressively, in addition to some governmental support to national NFP programs as in France, Canada, Australia, New Zealand, United States, England, Kenya, Liberia, and Sierra Leone, a few governments have begun to support the international development efforts in NFP programs. This includes those from Canada, Germany, England, USA, and France. Quality NFP programs become an increasing priority to ensure accountability not only to the funding agencies but also to the NFP users themselves.

NFP Program Development: Initiatives

NFP program development efforts can be considered under the following three categories: (1) information sharing; (2) applied research; (3) special development programs.

Information Sharing – This has been the major form of program development of the last 20 years whereby consultants from earlier programs visited interested groups and countries or vice-versa, and shared their expertise with colleagues and other countries. During the last ten years these have been formalized through NFP training congresses or seminars such as those held by the Human Life Center in Collegeville, Minnesota (USA); those by CLER (Centre de Liaison des Equipes de Recherches) at Poissy near Paris (France); the Ovulation

Method Institute now regularly held in Los Angeles, California. A large number of the more developed national programs also hold regular annual meetings with or without scientific meetings and publish their own newsletters and teaching materials. In the last five or six years various governments and even the World Health Organization have facilitated and supported these and even instituted assistance such as exchange and training scholarships.

In 1974 and 1977 respectively two international NFP Associations were created:

- The *International Federation for Family Life Promotion* (IFFLP), with members in 70 countries and some 50 structured national organizations in 40 countries. Its primary interest is to help to develop national organizations interested in family life promotion in general and Natural Family Planning in particular;
- The *World Organization of the Ovulation Method – Billings* (WOOMB) whose main goal is the certification of teachers in the Billings Ovulation Method and monitoring the standards of teaching in those areas of the world where the Billings method has been introduced.

These two organizations have contributed significantly to the increased sharing of NFP program information and the rapid growth of NFP expertise.

Applied Research – Major applied research efforts can be outlined under the following:

Biomedical Research, towards the improvement of our knowledge of NFP, whether through effectiveness studies or major refinements in ovulation parameters. These for the most part are described in the earlier research section and date back only 10 or 15 years.

Programmatic Research, in addition to special individual program efforts producing their teaching aids and developing training tools, special mention of two general categories of research efforts should be described:

a) *Curriculum Development* – most organized programs have had sooner or later to formalize their teaching component by developing their own teacher training programs. This has also been standardized at national and international levels to insure better quality control; and

b) *NFP Program Guidelines* – this area of research is still in its infancy with most programs undertaking their own development.

Special Development Programs – Most NFP programs have grown through informal NFP knowledge sharing meetings and exchange of visits described earlier. During the last few years two major new categories of organized NFP program development efforts have taken place either from a strong financial support of national expansion efforts or from broad implantation efforts at a continental level. A few words of description on each category are indicated as follows:

a) *Major National Expansion Efforts* — of the significant national expansion efforts currently underway in several developing countries, a couple are worthy of comments, such as:
   - The *Family Life Promotion Program* (Carvajal-Misereor), is under the sponsorship of both the Fundacion Carvajal and the National Episcopal Conference of Colombia, S.A. Initiated in 1975 this program focuses specifically on responsible parenthood, and the training of NFP teachers and development of services as key objectives. Its program evaluation should be forthcoming sometime in 1980-1981;
   - The *All-India NFP Program*, sponsored by the Commission for the Family of the Catholic Bishops Conference of India (CBCI), this is a two year substantial NFP expansion financed by Misereor, to be administered nationally by IGSSS (Indo German Social Service Society) and implemented by the local diocesan delegate agencies. This NFP service expansion program has been operational since 1978 with a growth from eight programs in January 1978 to over 59 programs by early 1980.

b) *Multinational NFP Development Efforts* — The "African Life and NFP Instructor Training Project" is a major on-going NFP development program administered by the International Federation for Family Life Promotion and financed by various development agencies and governments. The process is essentially one of accelerated NFP program development by the use of initial site visits, by IFFLP consultants, followed by NFP and Family Life Education Training Workshops where interest is present and this will be followed by a major Trainers' Workshop scheduled for the fall of 1981 to train NFP program leaders. More than 20 African countries are involved.

NFP PROGRAM EVALUATION

Although this is the last aspect to be discussed, it is no doubt among the most important, and one that will strongly influence the future of the NFP movement. This discussion is complex by the fact that in many countries NFP still is considered more of a movement than a service, rendering its evaluation and accountability far more difficult. However, with the progressive increase in resources available for NFP services, increased needs for accountability, program planning and evaluation are becoming more evident. It appears important to elaborate here on three pertinent areas, namely:

Programmatic Knowledge – In order to better develop or plan NFP programs or to evaluate on-going ones, special understanding of program administration or evaluation principles should be integrated. The basic structure, organization and policies of programs should be considered along with measurements and/or estimates, efforts and costs of efforts for the three basic components of any program –

Resources	Clients	Fiscal
Staff, Services, Time, etc.	Data-Intake, Follow-up	Income, Expenses

The evaluation must extend beyond efforts and costs (activity report) to whether the actual program accomplishments or client outcomes match with initial program objectives. Such efforts at accountability require a minimal management information system on these three components.[4]

In the last 10 years two or three academic centers in the USA have concentrated in adapting such program administration principles to family planning and population programs and their evaluation manuals should be on the book shelf of any serious NFP program administrator or evaluator.[5,6]

NFP Program Evaluation Initiatives – It is important that family planning program evaluation principles be appropriately adapted and applied to NFP programs, with a full understanding of the distinctive aspects of the latter as specified by Thomasina Borkman. In addition to the major Australian NFP survey (Johnston et al[7]) which concentrated primarily on NFP method comparison rather than program elements, a few program evaluation projects are now under way or about to begin. The recent report from Dr. Kathleen Dorairaj of the Indian Social Institute, in New Delhi, as one of the four regional commissioned evaluations brings such an insight to the large All-India program supported by Misereor.[8] Similarly in 1980 and 1981 the evaluation reports on the two national NFP programs of Colombia and Mauritius are expected to be available.

New NFP Program Guidelines – In addition to the existing informal NFP program guidelines it is pertinent to refer here to recent efforts of the Human Life and Natural Family Planning Foundation in producing a "Handbook of Operating Procedures for NFP Programs" which it is hoped shall soon be published and available to the public by the US Government[9]. New initiatives in this area are urgently needed.

Efforts should be undertaken not only to better adapt NFP program criteria to the international scene and the variety of NFP programs but also to incorporate some of the distinctive aspects of NFP which

Borkman underlines, such as self-knowledge, interpersonal communication between spouses, fertility management or autonomy, and areas of family functioning in general.

CONCLUSION

This section presents a summary of the State of the Art in NFP program development. Only an overview and initial insight are provided here as most of the developing program experience remains buried in the field.

With an increase in both private and public funding of NFP programs and the increasing demand for accountability, program planning, and evaluation are beginning to surface as crucial issues, and this will surely influence the future development of NFP programs.

Bibliography

1. Borkman, T.: "A Social-Science Perspective of Research Issues for Natural Family Planning", *International Review of NFP*, Vol. III, No. 4, pp 331-355, Winter 1979.
2. Shivanadan, M.: NATURAL SEX, published by Rawson, Wade, New York City, N.Y., and Hamlyn Group Astronaut House, Middlesex (England). 275 pages, March 1979.
3. Aguilar, N.: NO PILL, NO RISK BIRTH CONTROL, published by Rawson, Wade, New York 1980.
4. Broskowski, A.: "Management Information Systems for Planning and Evaluation in Human Services", in *Program Evaluation in the Health Fields*, Vol. II; edited by H.C. Schulberg/F. Baker, Behavioral Publications, New York 1976.
5. University of Chicago, Community and Family Study Center, *RFFPI (Rapid Feedback for Family Planning Improvement) Family Planning Evaluation Manuals* (1970-1975, series of 15 manuals); available from the Community and Family Study Center, Publications Secretary, University of Chicago, 1411 E 60th Street, Chicago, Illinois 60637.
6. Columbia University "Manual for Evaluation of Family Planning and Population Programs" (10 numbers in series) 1970-1975; available from International Institute for the Study of Human Reproduction, 6 Haven Ave., New York 10032.
7. Johnston, J.A., Roberts, D.B., and Spencer, S.: "NFP Services and Methods in Australia: A Survey Evaluation", in *International Review of NFP,* Vol. II, No. 2, pp 143-154, Summer 1978; Vol. II, No. 3, pp 203-223, Fall 1978, Vol. II, No. 4, pp 328-358, Winter 1978, Vol. III, No. 1, pp 20-35, Spring 1979, published by the Human Life Center, Collegeville, Minnesota.
8. Dorairaj, K.: "Fertility Control in India: NFP as an Alternative

Strategy", Report of the Sample Study and Evaluation of the NFP program in India, submitted to Misereor via the Indo-German Social Service Society. (Personal communication to IFFLP) November 1979.
9. Office for Family Planning HHS (Health/Human Services) "Operational Guidelines and Procedures for Natural Family Planning Programs"; developed by Dr. M.C. Martin of the Human Life/NFP Foundation, under U.S. Government contract to provide guidance to NFP programs. Can be obtained directly from: Office of Family Planning (US Government), 5600 Fishers Lane Rm. 749, Rockville, MD 20857 (USA).

THEOLOGY

THEOLOGICAL SECTION: SPOUSES AS MINISTERS OF GOD'S DESIGN

D. Tettamanzi, Editor, Part 3

In Search of God's Design

What is *the meaning of "theological" reflection* on the problem of the regulation of birth?

The answer can be found in these words of the Council: "The People of God believes that it is led by the Spirit of the Lord who fills the whole world. Moved by that faith it tries to discern in the events, the needs, and the longings which it shares with other men of our time, what may be genuine signs of the presence or of the purpose of God. For faith throws a new light on all things and makes known the full ideal which God has set for man, thus guiding the mind towards solutions that are fully human" (GS, 11).

Among the current problems of mankind, often so difficult and acute, are those concerning the regulation of birth. Now, the proper role of theology is to search for "God's design," to discover "God's intentions" *with regard to man* and his problems. This design is "impressed" *in man* himself, who has been created in God's image in his basic structure and in his inmost dynamics; a design that is "expressed," that is, revealed by the light of faith and of human reason. Thus the "discernment" of the divine design and intentions for man takes place "in the light of the Gospel and of human experience" (GS, 46).

Theological reflection makes reference, then, to the "new light" of Christian faith, that is, to the written Word of God, transmitted and authentically interpreted by the "living teaching office of the Church alone" (DV, 10). It thus arrives at the "ultimate truth" on man and his problems. In fact, "the most perfect answer to these questionings is to be found in God alone, who created man in His own image and redeemed him from sin; and this answer is given in the revelation of Christ His Son who became man. Whoever follows Christ the perfect man becomes himself more a man" (GS, 41).

In this sense theological reflection can and must remain "human" reflection. Hence, a second reference essential to theology is to the light of human experience, namely, to the discernment of human values and exigencies by right reason and by wisdom.

On this level theology, even when dealing with the particular problem of the regulation of birth, must be attentive to the *witness of married life* as experienced by so many married couples who, with all sincerity and honesty of purpose, are trying to interpret and to practice responsible fruitful love. No one can deny that there do exist numerous couples who believe in the Christian teaching on sexuality and who embody it in their daily lives. Such couples have a profound insight into the singular service which the encyclical *Humanae Vitae* of Paul VI has rendered and continues to render in promoting the human authenticity and perfection of their conjugal love.

Paul VI manifested the feeling of hope which accompanied him in the "laborious redaction" of the encyclical, in particular the hope he placed in Christian spouses: ". . . and finally the hope that Christian spouses will be the ones to understand how Our words, however severe and difficult they may sound, are meant to interpret the authenticity of their love, a love which is called to transform itself in imitation of Christ's love for His mystical spouse, the Church" (Allocution, July 31, 1968).

As time goes on, hope produces its fruit. Many couples, in reading the deep exigencies rooted in their mutual and total giving, "admit" that their "real" will does not seek "contraception," but rather tends to "follow" the logic of "nature." Other couples "perceive by intuition" that conjugal love, when sought in all the richness of its meanings, cannot express itself in diverse and contrasting forms of sexual behavior. Does not the genuineness of love become falsified by actions that rob it of some of its essential meanings? There are still other spouses who are more than ever convinced that man's control over the world of things and over his very body must have "limits," unless he chooses to suffer the counterblow of antiecological situations, even in the area of artificial contraception. And so there are spouses, sensitive to the social dimension of problems, who have by now become "detoxified" of the neurotic fear of an unrestrainable population growth and are consequently coming to rediscover the value of a large family. There is, too, the increasing awareness that opening the door to contraception means, speaking realistically, opening the door to other no less serious moral disorders: the connection between contraception and abortion cannot be overlooked or in any way underestimated.

Over and beyond the reasons just mentioned, this growing trend on the part of many couples towards natural family planning can also be explained by the increasing parallel developments of science converging on this problem. Now, even *the data of science* cannot but attract the interest of theological reflection, not only because the human sciences can in their own way uncover some lineaments of God's design for man, but also because by their results they can testify, as the Church points out, that "there can be no conflict between the divine laws governing the transmission of life and the fostering of authentic married love" (GS, 51; HV, 24). It is in this latter sense that Paul VI declared on the tenth anniversary of the encyclical *Humanae Vitae:* "It seems to us that the decade that has already passed since its promulgation is long enough to evaluate better, after the confirmations received from the most rigorous science, the import of the decisions we made at that time 'coram Domino'. . ." (Allocution to Cardinals, June 23, 1978).

But theological reflection shows its originality by going to the root of human problems. The role of theology is to throw light on the "mystery of man" and of his most high calling beginning with and in relation to the "mystery of the Word Incarnate" (cf. GS, 22). This holds true for every human problem, even for the specific problem of conjugal love and responsible fecundity. The conciliar statement, placed at the conclusion of the discourse on responsible fruitful love, reveals the problem in its deepest meaning: "Let all be convinced that human life and its transmission are realities whose meaning is not limited by the horizons of this life only: their true evaluation and full meaning can only be understood in reference to man's eternal destiny" (GS, 51).

The Magisterium as authoritative service for the faith of the People of God

An essential element of theological reflection is its reference to the Church Magisterium. This applies also to the problem of the regulation of birth, concerning which the Church, as we know, has a "constant and firm" doctrine, which was recently expressed not only in the Second Vatican Council, but also in a more complete and organic form and "with a more accurate formulation," in the encyclical *Humanae Vitae* of July 25, 1968.

For the Catholic there is no doubt about the legitimacy of the Magisterium's intervention in this area: "No believer will wish to deny that the teaching authority of the Church is competent to interpret even the natural moral law. It is, in fact, indisputable, as our predecessors have many times declared, that Jesus Christ, when communicating to Peter and to the Apostles His authority and sending them to teach all nations His commandments, constituted them as guardians and authentic interpreters of all the moral law, not only, that is, of the law of the Gospel, but also of the natural law, which is also an expression of the will of God, the faithful fulfillment of which is equally necessary for salvation" (HV, 4).

One who wishes to grasp *the profound meaning of the Church Magisterium* must interpret it in a specifically "theological" key. This is the only key which, while placing in a clear light the unmistakable originality of the Magisterium in comparison with other human forms of teaching and authority, makes it possible to overcome diluted and/or distorted interpretations of sociological, juristic or psychological coinage. In fact, only within the "mystery of the Church," sharing in the Spirit of the "prophetic" mission of Jesus Christ, can the proper nature of the Magisterium be understood as authoritative service for the faith of the

People of God.

The Magisterium is a service in the sense of a *ministry* with which the Spirit endows the Church. It expresses itself in the responsibility of announcing the saving Gospel to all, and hence of spreading and defending the faith, and of *serving Jesus Christ and, in Him, man himself* by enlightening him in his vocation and guiding him in the accomplishment of his mission. This service, however, is not some sort of general service for the faith of the Church; its distinctive trait is that of being *ex auctoritate Christi:* it actuates itself "in the name of the Lord," that is, it shares in a particular way in the authority and mission of Jesus, the great Prophet (Lk 7, 6).

The magisterium is an authoritative service for the faith; to be more precise, for the faith considered in all its dynamic unfolding: "faith which expresses itself through love" (Gal 5, 6), "faith which is destined to inform thinking and direct conduct" (LG 25). In this sense there is not only a dogmatic magisterium; there is also in the Church *a specifically moral magisterium,* one that is ordained to enable the faithful to live according to "the law of the spirit in Christ Jesus" (Rom 8, 2), even by the proposal of norms concerning the various areas of life, including also the area of marriage and its values and obligations.

In its "moral" aspect the Church Magisterium more explicitly stresses its twofold and inseparable service for the good of man and for his growth in Christ: namely, *the service of truth* announced in its purity and integrity, and *the service of the person* – in this case the spouses – to help them live according to truth. In this sense Paul VI writes: "Our words would not be an adequate expression of the thought and solicitude of the Church, Mother and Teacher of all peoples, if, after having recalled men to the observance and respect of the divine law regarding matrimony, we did not strengthen them in the path of honest regulation of birth, even amid the difficult conditions which today afflict families and peoples. The Church, in fact, cannot have a different conduct towards men than that of the Redeemer: She knows their weaknesses, has compassion on the crowd, receives sinners; but she cannot renounce the teaching of the law which is, in reality, that law proper to a human life restored to its original truth and conducted by the Spirit of God" (HV 19).

The two roles just mentioned are *co-essential* to the intervention of the Church. They belong, in fact, to the Church – as possibility and responsibility – by reason of her constitutive bond with Jesus Christ, who "was indeed intransigent with evil, but merciful towards individuals" (HV 29). Furthermore, just as truth constitutes the supreme good to which the person is called, so does the person find the very meaning of its value by walking towards the truth.

In the specific case of the regulation of birth the encyclical *Humanae*

Vitae was followed, in the spirit of "collegiality" and at the explicit request of Paul VI, by a series of statements, notes, and comments addressed by the various Conferences of Bishops throughout the world to their respective Churches. As a result many questions and spirited discussions arose concerning the interpretation of the episcopal documents both in themselves and in relation to one another (with regard to their magisterial value and their precise content) and to the encyclical. Also discussed was the "theological" qualification of the doctrine of *Humanae Vitae* (see the article by M. Zalba).

What cannot honestly be called into doubt is, on the one hand, the feeling expressed by Paul VI: "Never have We felt the burden of Our office more keenly than at this juncture . . . We have noticed the inadequacy of Our poor person to the formidable apostolic obligation of making a pronouncement on this matter . . . and We have had no doubt about Our duty to formulate Our judgment in the terms expressed in the present encyclical . . . We have endeavored to study it (the theme of the encyclical) and to expound it with the truth and charity that this theme demanded of Our teaching office and Our ministry . . ." (Allocution, July 31, 1968). On the other hand, there can be no doubt about the grave moral duty incumbent on all, both pastors and the faithful, of giving "the example of loyal internal and external obedience to the teaching authority of the Church," obedience which "obliges not only because of the reasons adduced, but rather because of the light of the Holy Spirit, which is given in a particular way to the pastors of the Church, in order that they may illustrate the truth" (HV 28; cf. LG 25).

In the service of "homo humanus"

The Church's position is well known – or ought to be – on conjugal morality in general and on the regulation of fertility in particular: "In the light of the Gospel and of human experience," the Magisterium teaches that "every conjugal act must remain open to the transmission of life" (HV 11). Consequently, the Magisterium condemns "contraception" as moral disorder and declares that "it is licit to take into account the natural rhythms immanent in the generative functions for the use of marriage in the infecund periods only" (HV 16).

The Church is convinced that she is thus placing herself *at the service of man:* "In defending conjugal morals in their integral wholeness, the Church knows that she contributes towards the establishment of a truly human civilization" (HV 18). This conviction arises and develops by reason of the very close bond which the Church perceives between sexuality and the human person. Here we are touching on a decisive point: only in the context of an exact and profound concept of man can we understand the moral position of the Church on responsible fruitful love. *Anthropology commands ethics* if the latter translates into terms of personal "responsibility" the objective "meanings" impressed in man's very being.

This is the crucial point from which the Church makes and continues to make its moves. Paul VI begins the presentation of the "doctrinal principles" of conjugal ethics with the following words: "The problem of birth, like every other problem regarding human life, is to be considered, beyond partial perspectives – whether of the biological or psychological, demographic or sociological orders – in the light of an integral vision of man and of his vocation, not only his natural and earthly, but also his supernatural and eternal vocation" (HV 7).

When read attentively, this dense and comprehensive text of the encyclical reveals in particular three fundamental dimensions of the anthropology professed by the Church and which we can qualify as *integral, vocational, and existential.* This anthropology provides the coordinates which justify and call for the Christian moral response to the problem of the regulation of birth in the terms expressed by the encyclical.

The Church professes, above all, an *integral* anthropology, whereby man – in his constitutive structure – is a unitarian whole, a *unitotality* of body and spirit. One would include here the theme of the sexual corporality of man: precisely because *it belongs to man,* sexuality not only is not reducible to the body (physical genitality), but, even when it involves the body, it involves it as a *human body,* that is, as the *person itself in its giving of itself.* In this way, "human" sexuality is by no means an "object" or a "thing" for man to "use" or "manipulate"; it is instead man himself as a "subject" who can and must accept and live his sexuality with a sense of responsibility.

We can now grasp the criterion that distinguishes and sets in opposition, on an objective level, artificial birth control and natural regulation of birth: the dilemma exists between the "thing" concept and the "personalist" concept of the human body, that is, between the body as object (in the first case) and the body as subject (in the second case).

In integral anthropology there emerges a first connotation of the sexual conjugal experience: the *opus conjugale* is not merely an *opus naturale* in terms of a merely biophysiological act, but rather an *opus personale,* that is, an expression and actualization of man in his unitotality of body and spirit (see article by C. Caffarra). But what is the "meaning" of the *opus personale*? The answer is given by another fundamental dimension of anthropology: the *vocational dimension,* whereby man, in his radical meaning, is *called by God* and enabled and obligated to *respond to Him.* In truth, "God's design" does not reach man from the outside, but is impressed in a living way in man's very being, it is stamped in his structure, it is enmeshed in his dynamics: these are the "meanings" with which the Creator enriches the work of His hands. But insofar as it reaches man, an intelligent and free being, this design takes the shape of a "vocation," as a call addressed to man to accept this design in a conscious and responsible manner. The "meanings" become the "tasks" entrusted to man to be conscientiously and responsibly carried out by him, as one who with respect to God becomes a "minister" enabled and obligated to make God's design "his own." This truth achieves extraordinary depth and richness of expression in the "identity" of man as *imago Dei* (cf. Gn 1, 27).

Vocational anthropology has an immediate impact on conjugal ethics. In fact, the fundamental "meaning" of the sexuality of man and woman is love; more precisely, love which finds in God its source and goal and, by that very fact, its norm: Since the love of God is inseparably connected with the gift of life, human sexuality also is destined to be in service of love which makes the two "one flesh" (cf. Gn 2, 24) and disposes them for the gift of new life. "God has willed to make spouses sharers in His love: in the personal love which He has for each one of us and by which He calls them to help each other and to give themselves to each other in order to achieve the fullness of their personal lives; sharers also in the love which He bears for mankind and for all His children and by which He desires to multiply the children of men in order to make them sharers in His life and in His eternal happiness. Born of the creative and paternal love of God, marriage finds in human love, corresponding to the design and will of God, the fundamental law of its moral value" (Paul VI, Allocution to the Congress of Italian Women, February 12, 1966).

One can now perceive the ultimate meaning of the conjugal act: it is specifically an *opus personale* inasmuch as it is an *opus procreationis,* or, if we may so express it, an *opus con-creationis,* in which and by which the spouses co-operate "with the love of the Creator and Saviour, who through them will increase and enrich His family from day to day" (GS, 50).

This intrinsic meaning of the conjugal act calls for spouses to be "dependent" on God, to "measure up" to His design, to "interpret it faithfully." Such dependence is exercised by "respect" for God's creation, that is, for the structure and dynamics of human sexuality. In other words, such dependence is exercised when man and woman fulfill themselves as "images of God," which means that they love themselves mutually, give life to other persons, and *do not arbitrarily separate love and the gift of life, since God is love giving life, a life that is never given without love.*

Once again there emerges the essential diversity, indeed the opposition, between artificial birth control and the natural regulation of fecundity: in the first case man sets himself up as "lord" of creation by separating the two inseparable meanings of the conjugal act – the unitive and the procreative meanings — and destroying the capacity for transmitting life; in the second case man acknowledges himself to be the "servant" of creation by respecting it in its meanings (see the article by G. Martelet). Vocational anthropology explains why "an act of mutual love which is detrimental to the faculty of propagating life which God the Creator has implanted in it according to special laws, is in contradiction to both the divine plan, according to whose norm matrimony has been instituted, and the will of the Author of human life." It also explains why "to use this divine gift destroying, even if partially, its meaning and its purpose is to contradict the nature both of man and of woman and of their most intimate relationship, and therefore it is to contradict also the plan of God and His will. On the other hand, to make use of the gift of conjugal love while respecting the laws of the generative process means to acknowledge oneself not to be the arbiter of the sources of human life, but rather the minister of the design established by the Creator" (HV 13).

In referring to Paul VI speaking of man's "not only natural and earthly, but also supernatural and eternal vocation," we are emphasizing also the *existential* dimension of the anthropology professed by the Church. In other words, we mean to refer to man precisely as he is *situated in history,* in a history that unfolds according to the threefold phase of the "good" creation on the part of God, the condition of conflict linked with man's sin, and salvation bestowed by Jesus Christ and His Spirit. Even sexuality, like the other values and the other tasks of the person, is deeply "involved" in this history of creation, sin, and grace. Thus are explained the original and indestructible goodness of the sexuality of man and woman, the ambiguity of the "gift of love" threatened by egoism and "hardness of heart," and the "newness" bestowed on human sexuality by salvation in Christ.

It is this that gives rise to the "realism" and "hope" with which the Church proclaims sexual morality. Concretely and in relation to conjugal morality the following words of Paul VI addressed to spouses now take on meaning: "The Church, while teaching imprescriptible demands of the divine law, announces the tidings of salvation, and by means of the sacraments opens up the paths of grace, which makes man a new creature, capable of corresponding with love and true freedom to the design of his Creator and Saviour, and of finding the yoke of Christ to be sweet" (HV 25).

From what has been said, there follows the effect that anthropology has on the problems of conjugal morality, not only in its fundamental values of love and fecundity, but also in the particular area of "how" to regulate birth, in the area, that is, of methods and means of regulating birth (see article by D. Tettamanzi). Thus we see justified the qualification of "intrinsic disorder" attached to contraception, a qualification of something that is "unworthy of the human person" (HV 14) and that is "in opposition to the true good of man"(HV 18). This is the necessary corollary of the concept the Church has of sexuality and of its essential relation to the human person.

A journey towards freedom

It has already been pointed out that the Church has not only the task of proclaiming the ideal and proposing the norm of moral life, but she must also help man concretely to achieve the ideal and to observe the norm.

And so we enter into the subjective area of existence of couples at grips with actuating the normative ideal of responsible fruitful love. In this area also we stress the "pedagogy of the Church" in its originality, its characteristic traits being indicated in the words of Paul VI to priests: "To diminish in no way the saving teaching of Christ constitutes an eminent form of charity for souls. But this must ever be accompanied by patience and goodness, such as the Lord Himself gave example of in dealing with men. Having come not to condemn but to save, He was indeed intransigent with evil, but merciful towards individuals. In their difficulties, may married couples always find, in the words and in the heart of a priest, the echo of the voice and the love of the Redeemer" (HV 29).

The first basic pedagogical rule of the Church is that the spouses "*walk in truth*" (1 Jn 1, 7). This means that they should have the humility and the courage to call things by their name: order order, disorder disorder! Only on this condition does one become a servant of the truth that sets free, not its master. This means that the first step in moral honesty to be taken by spouses consists in admitting that, on the objective level, contraception is "moral disorder" and is not, nor can be, at the service of true and full conjugal love. This is precisely the meaning of the encyclical of Paul VI viewed in its historical moment: "Since contraception was presented in the Church as a real right of love, or at least as behavior indifferent in itself, the encyclical had to deny the soundness of such thinking" (G. Martelet).

It is, then, with the light of this truth that conscience must be enlightened. It is certain that in his conscience man "finds himself alone with God" (GS 16), with a responsibility that is so personal that it can never be imposed by others or delegated to others; but it is a responsibility that cannot shrink from seeking and clinging to Truth by listening to the Word of God, in communion with brothers in the faith, in docility to the teaching office of the Church. Authentic "autonomy" of conscience is based on and sustained by "theonomy" (see article by B. Honings).

But the truth which the couples commit themselves to serve is a truth *to be realized:* the commitment to call things by their real name becomes genuine only if and to the extent that the spouses *keep on their journey.* Man is an existential being who becomes and develops day by day by a multiplicity of aims and efforts. Conjugal life too is a journey, marked by rhythms of growth. On this journey the spouses must not reduce the normative ideal to the measure of their own will, but they must lift themselves up to the goal set for them. We can apply to the moral norm of responsible fruitful love what John Paul II said to families on marriage in general: "If Christian marriage can be compared to a very high mountain that places the spouses in immediate proximity to God, one must admit that climbing it requires much time and much effort. But is this a reason for removing or lowering that summit?" (Kinshasa, May 3, 1980). It is a question of always starting over again, in an ongoing process of conversion and liberation: "Who does not know this? It is only little by little that the human being succeeds in ordering and integrating his multiple tendencies to the point where he can arrange them harmoniously in that virtue of conjugal chastity where the couple find their total human and Christian fulfillment . . . . The realization that one has not yet achieved interior freedom and is still subject to the impulses of passion, the discovery that one is almost incapable of respecting at the moment the moral law in so fundamental an area — all this naturally moves one to a reaction of sadness; yet that is the decisive moment when the Christian in his disorder, instead of abandoning himself to sterile and destructive revolt, proceeds in humility to the opening up of man before God, a sinner before the love of Christ the Saviour . . . . In the midst of the great Church this small Church then recognizes itself for what it truly is: a weak community, at times sinful and penitent but forgiven, on the march towards holiness, 'in the peace of God that surpasses all understanding (Phil 4, 7)' " (Paul VI to the Equipes Notre-Dame, May 4, 1970).

To keep on the journey, the couple must possess *certain conditions:* no flower can germinate and sprout except in favorable soil. This holds true also for the moral life of spouses. Among these conditions must be mentioned in particular *the virtue of conjugal chastity.* The Council authoritatively affirms this when, after saying that spouses must "respect the total meaning of mutual self-giving and human procreation in the context of true love," it concludes: "All this is possible only if the virtue of married chastity is seriously practiced" (GS 51). This is not only continence, it is also a guarantee and progress of authentic love (see the article by E. Hamel). Among the conditions, or rather, among the motivating principles of the moral life of spouses, one must always remember *the grace of the sacrament of marriage:* it is the "gift" of the Spirit of Christ, bestowed in the sacramental celebration, and it becomes the "commandment" of life for the spouses. And it is a "new" commandment, because it gives interior strength for the filial fulfillment of the will of the Father, sharing in the loving obedience of Christ. "The sacrament of marriage, by pouring out the gift of the Spirit which transforms betrothed love, becomes the new law of the Christian couple . . . . In this way Christian conjugal morality does not remain an external imposition, but it becomes an exigency of the life of grace, a fruit of the Spirit acting in the hearts of the spouses and guiding them to the freedom of the children of God" (Conference of Italian Bishops: Evangelization and the Sacrament of Marriage, June 20, 1975, 49). Thus, conjugal sexual morality finds its source in the sacramental gift of Christ and His Spirit: this is the reason for its "newness" and "originality."

The ministry of love and life

We have discussed spouses as ministers of God's design: this is a key idea of the entire encyclical *Humanae Vitae,* an idea which finds its most graphic and explicit declaration in the words addressed by Paul VI to spouses: "Christian married couples, docile to the voice of God, must remember that their Christian vocation, which began at baptism, is further specified and reinforced by the sacrament of matrimony. By it husband and wife are strengthened and as it were consecrated for the faithful accomplishment of their proper duties, for the carrying out of their proper vocation even to perfection, and the Christian witness which is proper to them before the whole world" (HV 25).

It is in this light that one can perceive in depth the meaning of conjugal sexual morality proposed by the Church in the service of man. The passage just quoted recalls fundamental realities, interwoven with one another: the "ministry" of the spouses (their "duty," their "responsibility," their "task"), the "mystery" of Christian spouses (the "grace" given them by the sacrament), the "witness" they must give to the world. It is a manifold and diversified witness. But in a social and cultural context where sexuality tends to be lived as a "consumer item" in the service of a so-called love "disjoined" from the value of life, the task pointed out to spouses by Paul VI takes on the character of extreme actuality and urgency: "To them the Lord entrusts the task of making visible to men the holiness and sweetness of the law which unites the mutual love of husband and wife with their co-operation with the love of God the author of human life" (HV 25).

In a certain sense, the real encyclical on the right regulation of birth is not the one which Paul VI presented to the Church and mankind on July 25, 1968, but that which the spouses continue to "write" day by day and to "proclaim" by the life they lead: a life that becomes "prophecy," a life that "accuses the world of sin and enlightens those who search for truth" (LG 35). It is the life made new by the gift of the

Spirit. In this perspective the Church can repeat to the faithful and to the men of our day what the Apostle wrote to the Corinthians: "You are our letter, known and read by all men, written on your hearts. Clearly you are a letter written not with ink but by the Spirit of the living God, not on tablets of stone but on tablets of flesh in the heart" (2 Cor 3, 2-3).

Translated by Fr. Paul Pavese, OSJ

A PROPHETIC TEXT UNDER CHALLENGE: THE MASSAGE OF *HUMANAE VITAE*

G. Martelet, S.J.

The Contestation

Rarely has any intervention of the apostolic magisterium of Peter and his successors been more challenged than that of Paul VI in *Humanae Vitae.* By some, this encyclical was deplored as an "intellectual catastrophe," to some it was a cause for rejoicing. With the pontifical magisterium thus discredited, its claim to infallibility would obviously have been contradicted and the Christian conscience left to itself. In certain countries *Humanae Vitae* is blamed for the serious and massive disaffection for the authority of the Church. Nearly everywhere, indeed, many families thought that the Pope did not understand them. He keeps himself, they said, short of the "Council;" he is bringing us back to that detestable world of legalism and sexual guilt. In short, the encyclical was received with so many reservations that its teaching, some say, is outdated in itself and will be declared so before long in high places.

Nevertheless, without ever adding to its meaning, the apostolic authority of Rome and of the bishops has not disavowed that encyclical. Could this be the stubbornness of an institution that one should force to yield? Or is it not rather that, properly understood, the encyclical can in no way be disavowed? For my part, I have suggested since 1968: "If the captain of the Titanic had been able to see the iceberg in time, would he not have cried out to the engine-room crew 'Full speed astern!' That might have frightened the crew but it would have saved his ship. The encyclical *Humanae Vitae* is such a cry."

It is what *Rerum Novarum* was in its time in another domain. Though of different eras and subjects, these two documents present a didactic aspect which might cause one to miss their true import. Both are indeed texts to alert, not to say alarm. Addressed to Christians, and through them to the world, they deal with subjects which are vital but as yet misunderstood by many of those for whom they are destined. The Church, like the prophets, does not have the habit or the mission before the world to heave arcane sighs. However, in her case, the reasons that she alleges may not have immediately the same depth as the intuitions which guide her. Paul VI said so in just so many words in *Humanae Vitae*, a point often overlooked.

Without listing here what made the way in which the Church expresses herself on sexual matters age two thousand years in a few decades, we may aver that certain foundations, particularly the philosophical ones, on which the ordinary teaching of the Church leans in this domain, risk henceforth to compromise its relevance and solidity. I am thinking especially of that only too famous "natural law" which one finds usually playing the role of sentinel in documents emanating from Rome. It stands guard at the frontiers of the sexual realm as it used to at the frontiers of the social order. Useful in its own way, it surely needs more explanations than it brings to light in the first place. People must constantly be reminded that nature or the natural law, of which the Roman magisterium willingly speaks, has nothing to do with a more or less stoic vision of the world, wherein all planes merge and where, especially, the will of God which must guide man could be read in nature as in the lines of the hand. No doubt, a direct and naked appeal such as the present Pope seems to want to make to the rights and duties of the human person would be more justified, better understood, more directly capable of integration into the Christian mystery than an obstinate referring to this bare nature, which most present-day minds interpret in a naturalistic and therefore infra-human manner. Undoubtedly they are wrong, but why not take into account this erroneous interpretation, since it is so widespread?

When one rereads the succession of papal texts on the social question, from *Rerum Novarum* in 1891 to the Letter of Paul VI to Cardinal Roy in 1971, one discovers, along with a permanence of intuition, a development which is not merely a matter of how things are expressed. Why should the same thing not hold for questions of conjugal ethics? In fact, we have no guarantee that for such very delicate problems just the right language will be hit upon, nor even that the kind of thinking or so-called 'referents' employed by the Roman magisterium are the most adapted to the Christian intuitions which give worth to the intended message. In this domain, as in so many others, the Christian meaning outstrips the cultural expression through which it is disseminated. Thus, *Humanae Vitae* does not represent, in its category, the *ne plus ultra* of the Christian message on love; it only expresses, so to speak, its *ne unquam contra*, namely, the profound vocation with regard to which the Church cannot change course. But all this could be deepened, put in a better context, so that the same doctrine would emerge renewed, though not unrecognizable.

It would be a very serious error to reduce to mere questions of expression the resistance encountered by *Humanae Vitae*. The various forms of resistance deal with the underlying realities involved and with their resulting concrete practice. The underlying realities relate to anthropology. Are there or are there not "laws inscribed in the very being of man and woman" as claimed by *Humanae Vitae*, laws which rule the true identity or "nature" of the sexes, as the encyclical states?

Or, in the language of the Council in *Gaudium et Spes,* similar on this point to that of the encyclical: are there or are there not objective criteria "drawn from the nature of the human person and human action, criteria which respect the total meaning of mutual self-giving and human procreation in the context of true love?" The problem of the underlying reality is there, truly and uniquely there.

From a practical point of view in Christian circles, it seems that the Church, ordinarily patient even to excess with human weakness, would suddenly show itself inflexible with regard to a quite excusable frailty. What is to be done, people ask, if the only means deemed licit for avoiding a contraindicated pregnancy are not practicable, and the spouses feel that the full conjugal expression of their love is irreplaceable? The encyclical, it would seem, makes no provision for borderline cases. Everything seems to be regulated in advance by a law which conscience can only endorse completely or completely violate; conscience thus becomes gravely sinful because it cannot be heroically holy. In reality, borderline cases are legion, but since the law seems to leave them out of account they become the occasion for the conscience to declare itself objectively guilty, contrary to all internal evidence. Certainly, every conscience is at bottom sinful, but is it so in a mechanical fashion through a negative punching at the time-clock of the law? Is the conscience not judge of the circumstances in which it is involved and which could drastically change the judgment which conscience does – indeed must – bring to bear upon its morality? In the view of Christians whose complaint I am trying to relate, to accept the encyclical is to suppress completely the life of conscience, since this encyclical, they say, recognizes only the law and seems to neglect the role of conscience, except when it comes to repenting for having broken the law.

Having judged Church authority guilty of ignoring the rights and duties of conscience, they see no alternative to revolt. Open or underground, the revolt provokes or presupposes a disaffection, clamorous or suppressed, toward a Church whose inhumanity is considered scandalous. Since the disaffection appears to increase as conscience seems more honest, is this not a sign that there is a misapprehension of the meaning of the message supposedly understood?

I. AN ERRONEOUS INTERPRETATION

It has been said that the encyclical intended to domineer over each conjugal act in the life of the spouses and to reduce this act to procreation. This is false. No doubt the encyclical does speak generally of the "conjugal act," whose meaning it wishes to make clear in its totality. But in doing this it cannot nor does it wish to supplant the spouses, who are in their soul and in their conscience the only ones responsible before

God for the conduct of their love. It is, therefore, to consciences that the encyclical addresses itself, not to supplant or abolish them, but to enlighten and help them in their very freedom. In this light, the central affirmation of the Roman document can have all its meaning.

After noting that acts of conjugal union "do not cease to be legitimate if, for causes independent of the will of husband and wife, they are foreseen to be infertile," since they remain "ordained to expressing and strengthening their union" – and let us not forget this essential point – the encyclical recalls nevertheless the Church's "constant teaching" according to which "each and every marriage act must remain open to the transmission of human life." Then the text continues: "This teaching, set forth by the Magisterium on numerous occasions, is founded upon the inseparable connection, willed by God, and which man may not break on his own initiative, between the two-fold significance of the conjugal act: the unitive significance and the procreative significance. Indeed, by its intimate structure, the conjugal act, while closely uniting husband and wife, makes them apt for the generation of new lives, according to laws inscribed in the very being of man and woman. By safeguarding both these essential aspects, the unitive and the procreative, the conjugal act preserves in its fullness the sense of true mutual love and its ordination to man's most high vocation to parenthood." And Paul VI adds to this: "We think that men of our day are particularly capable of confirming the deeply reasonable and human character of this fundamental principle."

The encyclical does not say: every use of marriage must be controlled by the transmission of life. That would plainly be an error, since the encyclical itself recognizes "as experience bears witness, not every act of marital intercourse is followed by a new life," and since the encyclical ascribes not to the randomness of nature but to the wisdom of God the existence of "natural laws and rhythms of fertility, which already of themselves bring about a separation in the succession of births." How could the encyclical then pretend that "each use of marriage" is or ought to be "of its very nature" bound up with human procreation, when the connection of the two is, periodically, impossible? But that is not what the document says. In declaring "that each and every marriage act must remain open to the transmission of life," it is not asking that "every marriage act" be under the command of procreation in a *positive* way, but it is asking that it remain open to it, that is to say, that the power to generate, which of itself is interior to the union, not be altered. It does not thereby identify union and procreation; it even declares them quite distinct at various moments; but it asks that their unity not be contradicted once it is given. This is the refusal to accept contraception, which alters the power of generating given in the union.[1]

Such a refusal remains incomprehensible as long as it is not seen – and it is not ordinarily seen nowadays – that the power to generate which is at the disposal of the couple has not been left entirely to their discretion. For man and woman, this power, in effect, belongs to the mystery of God passing through their love to bring human beings into existence: the mystery of God who furthermore commands the truth of man. Human procreation does not involve merely the physiological processes of reproduction, as if man were only a natural product of the evolution of life and of the sexual functions proper to humans. If that were the case, the begetting of man could be treated, in the borderline case, as any natural phenomenon, subjected only to the demands of reproduction, since human conception would in the final analysis be merely biological. Everything rises up against such a view of human generation which a technological approach to genetics would perhaps not disavow. But there is far more to human generation than that. Indeed, it surpasses even the spousal love which is one of its essentials. It brings into play, in a way which is beyond explanation, the creative love of God, his fatherhood, which makes each human individual the beneficiary of a personal divine love to which he owes his own identity.

Although of such importance, this relationship of the couple to the creative mystery of God is not ordinarily conscious, nor does it have to be so. To wish that it would be so could sometimes remove its naturalness from the conjugal relationship. So it is not at first an idea which can express in this case the deference of the couple to the creative power of God. The same situation prevails already in the use of the world: to respect God while using the world, it is not enough that one should have in mind that God created it; one must avoid misusing for oneself and others the things thus created. Recognition of God does not consist merely in bearing in mind that God has created; it consists in not opposing in our actions the meaning which God gave the world when he made it *for us.* That is why an unjust appropriation and a shameless squandering of the riches of the world which, obtaining the so-called happiness of some brings about the misery of others is not only an *iniquity* from the social point of view; it is also an *insult* to God. God did not create the world that such aberrations should be perpetrated. That is why the justice of our behavior in our free use of the world is our way of recognizing the creative mystery. The confessing of God takes shape in the quality of our action, not in the pronouncing of formulas; it is spoken in deeds, not in words; it is lived, rather than portrayed: it is found in our actual existence, rather than in our words. This is also why a man will be judged by his actions more than by what he professes. And this is so when it is a matter of recognizing that the injunction to procreate can only be understood within the creative paternity of God which it must serve and with which it must collaborate.

Just as God, in entrusting the world to our freedom, did not abdicate his own creative power, so also, in entrusting to the love of the spouses the task of procreating human life, he did not cancel his paternal role, without which no human can *really* be begotten. Just as we show our recognition of the creative power of God by forbidding ourselves the misuse of the world he gave us, so also the spouses show their recognition of the elusive but essential role of divine parenthood at the heart of their union, by not undertaking anything in conflict with their power to generate. It is through this power, enclosed in the expression of their love, that passes the creative paternity of God who has command over the basic identity of man. One sees immediately the reason why the encyclical speaks to us of meanings.

II. DUALITY OF MEANINGS: INDISSOLUBLE, IN WHAT SENSE?

The rejection of contraception, whose true and often hidden basis we are approaching here, does not imply a material respect for some kind of mechanics of procreation. It is directed essentially toward the mystery implied in this generation of man which God entrusts to the love of the spouses. Here again, the role of the spouses does not abolish the role of God. Since his role is truly sovereign and alone creative, in the most rigorous sense of the term, that is to say, capable of conferring on man his absolute value as an individual loved in himself by God, the couple should be able to recognize its creative dependence in the very act wherein it can be procreative. The couple expresses such dependence, not by words but by the respect it has for its own power to generate. God, who communicates to conjugal love such a power, does not do so by cancelling his own power to create. He does not give himself over, then, to the arbitrariness of the couple, but to their freedom. But this freedom includes within it a deference toward Him who can give to men such a power. The spouses cannot, therefore, treat this power to generate which their love receives as if it depended only on them, when it depends, throughout their love, on the very gift of God. Not, once again, that they must have the intention or the certitude of being able to generate in order to be united: to be united is to be united! But to be united in the fullest sense, when one realizes the true grandeur of the sexuality which permits this to be done, means not to impose any violence, by oneself or through the other, on this more-than-human power of procreation that one has.

The inseparability of meanings in "every marriage act" does not, then, rest primarily on a biological structure which in fact separates them; on the contrary, it rests on a decision: that of maintaining in the conjugal act its "sense of mutual and true love," no less than its "ordination to the exalted vocation of man to parenthood." Thus, everything takes place in depth at the spiritual level of meanings, themselves found at the heart of a vocation which qualifies the love. Besides, the term inseparable connection, used here, carries the same import.

Actually, nothing is really inseparable in the world of nature, where everything changes and everything passes. Indissolubility is a matter of persons; it only really appears in Revelation, when there is a question of alliance. Without the word inseparable having to be spoken, what it represents is signified with the coming of man and woman. "What God has joined together, let no man put asunder." God is the first one to be faithful in love, and never reneges on his Covenant. What explains then the indissolubility of marriage, the case typical of all inseparability, is not just some structure of the flesh, since so many marriages break up after being consummated, but rather that the freedom of the partners commits itself in an irrevocable fashion, relying on the fidelity and grace of God, without which, as Scripture says, "the flesh profits nothing." Because they did not yet properly understand, the chosen people of God themselves tolerated a bill of divorce which Christ abolished. Christ did not return marriage to its primordial indissolubility in virtue of a power which might come from the flesh; he did so by fidelity to the design of God, revealing in his incarnate Son a manner of loving which renders possible and necessary the inseparable union of the spouses.

If, then, the encyclical, to characterize the connection of meanings in the conjugal act, calls them inseparable, it is not because they are so by reason of the flesh or by the biological facts; they are such because the spiritual truth of the conjugal act demands that love do no violence to fecundity in the performance of the act. The indissolubility of meanings does not then imply that the union is always tied to generation or that it ought to be; it simply means that one cannot dissociate them when they are united, by attacking directly the immanent procreative power in oneself or in the other. The dissociation of the two by the positive suppression of the second term is the disorder of contraception. How can one fail to see that this disorder, which thus attacks the deep truth of love, is sinful since it places the spouses in real disagreement with the God who has called them to be, through their love, his images and his servants? To be sure, it is not the gravest of sins. To dissociate in love the heart and the flesh, to dissociate oneself from one's own partner, is quite another thing from dissociating, often through weakness, union and generation. But it is true nevertheless that, considered in its profundity (much of which escapes people today), contraception, as the Church understands it, puts conjugal love in real opposition to the creative mystery of God, whence the procreative responsibilities of the spouses originate.

The disorder of which we have been speaking shows up clearly only in the light of Revelation. Since the duality of meanings in the conjugal act depends on the mystery of God, in which love is never in opposition to life and by which life is never given without love, the inseparability of the two meanings is rooted in the same mystery. The full truth of the conjugal love directly excludes the possibility that one could voluntarily sacrifice either of the two meanings which together give the conjugal act its depth, at once divine and human. And it is just as certain that the indissolubility of meanings which the encyclical mentions is not primarily a natural given or a fact of nature, but a truly spiritual task wholly incumbent upon the freedom of the spouses, just as incumbent upon them as is the indissolubility of their love itself.

Doubtless there was a time when procreation seemed to sum up the entire meaning of marriage. At least, procreation was given as the primary element in marriage, and the unitive meaning was called secondary. This was underestimating the full truth of conjugal love, since God himself, who is the pre-eminent model for the spouses in this matter, is never the Creator except by being so through love. Assuredly, procreation is a fundamental value in the couple and for humanity; what would become of humanity if it no longer handed on existence, or if it no longer transmitted it by love? Still, essential though it be, the procreative meaning should not obscure the unparalleled value of the union.

Certainly, the spiritual analysis of the conjugal act requires that one keep in mind, as does the encyclical, that the expression of conjugal love depends on the organs of generation. Never, though, does the encyclical say that procreation, however linked with the union, must always produce its effect in the conjugal act for the latter to possess its full truth: the union of love is authentic even when it is incapable of generating. And yet, the full truth of the union implies, on the part of the spouses, that they do not destroy in themselves the astonishing power they have of conceiving a new human being. But such a respect for meanings is a value for the spouses only if they realize that this respect conditions and governs the total truth of the act in which their love is expressed. Truly, so difficult a realization is this, so disputed in our day, that Paul VI, in the name of the entire Church, perceived the duty and the right to reiterate its spiritual sources and its humanizing import for the spouses and for love.

Who can deny that such a spiritual vision has, and ought to have, direct repercussions for the conduct of marriage? But the encyclical can only have its envisioned spiritual effect through free agents, discovering the harmony of meanings implied in their act. Paul VI seemed persuaded that this discovery only stands to reason and that it is enough to express its content for "the deeply reasonable and human character of this fundamental principle" to be recognized by "men of our day." Sadly, the reaction of western opinion seems to have convinced him of the opposite, and there has been no sign of improvement with the passage of time.

III. CONTRACEPTIVE MENTALITY AND THE MESSAGE OF THE CHURCH

The knowledge we have accumulated concerning biological mechanisms has actually fortified the assurance that the conception of life ought to come under technical control. Why should procreative matters be exempted from human mastery, when this is scientifically possible? Furthermore, all aspirations are permitted; we have even walked on the moon! Even though there still seems to be worries about the results of genetic manipulation, even though there is a general refusal to be smothered under the leaden cloak of progressively invasive "techno-nature," still contraception is constantly portrayed, even and especially by public authorities, as one of the greatest conquests of man and woman over the apparently inevitable character of fecundity.

How can one be surprised at such an opinion in a world where increasing secularism, based on a practical atheism, imposes itself everywhere, especially in the West? Contraception is looked upon as just another perfectly normal convenience. The problems which it still poses for certain consciences are to be classified as mental lags, meriting respect but lacking true significance, which a backward religious outlook imposes upon its victims, preventing their access to the benefits of modernity.

Thus there is developing, there has already developed, in western opinion at least, a mentality of which few are free. Should not one speak of a *contraceptive world*, in the same way that one could speak of a *concentration-camp world*? In any case the sway, which some call liberating, of the *contraceptive mentality* – and it is this, and this alone, which is here in question – is so great that it casts into the shadows its ever-increasing train of demonstrated abnormalities. These concern, in adults and in youth, "love," health, marriage and life. By an odd twist of values, for the contraceptive mentality the union, or rather (for divorce goes without saying) the pleasure of the union has become primary and self-sufficient, while generation, second if not altogether secondary, is to be carried out in a technical manner or even simply excluded. This is proven throughout the world by the already considerable number – eighty million according to the experts – of those throughout the world who have voluntarily mutilated their capacity to generate.

In this contraceptive civilization, Christians are not absentees. Sometimes it seems that all they need — at least those among them whom the mass media make stars — is to be faced by the sexually novel or unusual to discover in it a misunderstood facet of humanity. Behavior or ideas which thoroughly destroy the Christian truth of love easily become in their eyes "values" to be preserved. With regard to children, the family, marriage, love, being in favor of divorce, abortion, contraception (above all), pre-marital and extra-marital relations, masturbation and every sort of homosexuality, under the pretext of open-mindedness, respect for the opinion of others, of indulgence to others, or simply through fear of being singled out as Christians, the weeds have been sown open-handedly in the consciences of Christians, by Christians themselves. A far cry from the optimism of Paul VI, who was so sure of finding a friendly echo among Christians to his teaching on contraception.

In the face of this situation, the Church's mission is not merely to insist on the existence of law. It is also and especially to open hearts to the total meaning of love. To bring to light again the fact that a given disorder is objectively such, as *Humanae Vitae* did and had to do, is not enough. No matter how difficult it may be for the Church to find proper language for such subjects, a clumsy word is in this instance better than a seemingly prudent silence, which is only interpreted as approbation anyhow. In the moral realm, the Church's prophetic pronouncements often amount to protest. Maybe she will convince no one who was not convinced already. There may be smiles at the efficacy of an intervention by the Church. Yet something is gained: breaking the silence prevents prescription, that is giving consent by remaining silent. In publicly breaking with dominant opinion it judges seriously erroneous, the Church's apostolic authority gives consciences an objective landmark by which they can reorient themselves. Such a pronouncement of the Church is the Polestar which shows true north, the lighthouse which signals the reef, the buoy which averts shipwreck. Anyone who underestimates this service would show that he loses sight of — or pretends to be unaware of — the disarray of freedoms in a night of foundering values. Such a serious misunderstanding in the very domain with which the encyclical deals should be overcome at all costs.

The indissolubility of meanings in the conjugal act is being contested as publicly as the indissolubility of marriage itself. That inseparability, in the profound sense understood by the Church, is a spiritual program now become difficult to grasp and even more difficult to honor. The dominant opinion justifies the contraceptive mentality by pointing to the dilemmas of life, while this mentality, in its turn, creates further dilemmas; it paralyzes disapprovals too timid to be really efficacious but still too deep to be kept quiet, especially in the woman. Denied to the point where they seem to have disappeared, many of the hesitancies about a contraceptive world are simply neutralized. Only love, in whose name the contraceptive mentality wants them annulled, can bring them to the surface again and give them new voice. That is why to content oneself with recalling a norm of conjugal love, without increasing that very love which alone can recognize in this norm its own true law, would be a terrible error. Besides seeming to disregard tragic situations, the Church would let Christian morality risk being nailed to the pillory of terrorisms and of scorn for freedom.

Everyone must know and be able to know that in this domain as in all others, but *in this domain more than in any other,* the Church – I speak here of her authorized magisterium – seeks no moral domination over the private lives of the spouses, something which would be not only unjustifiable but also chimerical. Their conscience is their guide and their light. The role of the Church is to help them see more clearly within themselves, but their personal responsibility remains total; it is that of a love the Church helps, a love whose existence the Church always supposes and whose rectitude the Church wishes to support. In a word, from start to finish, it is for her a matter of the reality of Christ at the service of man.

The Church's Message and the Human Condition

Sent to all nations to announce till Christ's return that there is no other Name but Jesus whereby humanity may be really saved, the Church has a mission to reach and serve man himself. In the problem of contraception, so foreign in appearance to the mystery of Christ and involving, one might easily be led to believe, only humanly liberating techniques, we find that the identity of man and woman, the total truth of their love, are as a matter of fact incriminated. That is why, baffling as this may appear at first, the Church's teaching on contraception is not a sectarian opinion: it is addressed through Christians "to the men of our time," as Paul VI put it. Despite this claim to human universality, the light which enables the Church to penetrate such depths of love is not merely human.

Hence the need of a truly fundamental evangelization which recreates in hearts a genuine sense of God. This task is all the more difficult, but also all the more urgent, since we are in a time of atheism where the destruction of the sense of the living God is an accomplished fact for many consciences. It brings about an unconscious but deep and grave denaturation of conjugal love and its true responsibilities. That is why we are unable to integrate, as we must, the spiritual ethics of conjugal love's inseparable meanings into the mystery of Christ without restoring the sense of the true God in his relationship to everything human. We lay ourselves open to presenting Christ in his true depth. He will be evoked to meet the needs of a "cause" which, being without any fundamental relationship to the mystery of God in man, cannot have a real relationship either with the Person of Christ, who binds us in our entirety to God. Not that Christ is to be substituted for the reality of one and all, but his presence in us, his light and his grace for the total humanization of love, are those of one born of our humanity, not an intruder. On this ground, he takes hold of us profoundly to lead us back to ourselves, revealing to us the true depths of God. In this, Christ is not separated or separable from his entire Church.

Given the incorporation of God to man and man to God in Christ, how could the Church fail to have, despite impressions to the contrary, a sixth sense for all that concerns the grandeur of love and its relationship to the body? It is no chimera today that the human body risks being treated as an *object* of production or reproduction, of consumption or pleasure, and that men will forget that, although it is part of the world of things, it possesses, because *human,* a value which begins it anew in the world of *subjects.* Hence the purely scientific knowledge of the human body cannot be the only key to understanding, and still less can its transformation into a technological object be the only conduct, befitting our dignity. Beyond the simplistic views which still did not know things which biology now has revealed to us, we must surely rediscover a spiritual ethic for man through an enlightened respect for his body.

The world of life has, in fact, followed an amazing path of ever-increasing organization which made possible the spiritual awakening, more amazing still, of the human being himself. Man does not appear as something random or chaotic, but as a marvel of evolutionary accomplishment. His body constitutes, therefore, the culmination point of forms and functions, wherein integrated sets of structures are unified and regulated. Science discovers them, man benefits from them; he must respect them unless he destroy himself, but he must also appropriate them. The human ethic is situated therefore between two equally harmful extremes. The first would be that of an archaic prejudice which would only see abnormal meddling and destruction in a better mastery of human physiology, especially the sexual; the second, would see in the body, and even more in sex, only a "thing," over which it should have complete power. This is the extreme of unrestrained manipulation in the genetic and genital domain. Between these two reefs the Church should be able to give an open, balanced, and liberating interpretation of the total human being, body and sexuality included. The Church should recognize whatever is helpful, and give it full approbation, but it must remain sufficiently careful and lucid enough about the "natural" which it extols in its teaching and which modern man needs, so that the "natural" appears as a *vivifying* norm and not as a *taboo*.

What is more, how can we forget in the case of contraception the principle advanced by Saint Thomas himself, that a certain amount of well-being is necessary for the practice of virtue? There are thresholds beyond which human ethics become impracticable. This is not a reason for believing, as is believed today, that anything and everything is permitted to control the birthrate among the very poorest peoples. Certain powers, public and private, would eagerly recommend programs of contraception, sterilization, or abortion to which the Church is absolutely opposed; she does not agree that social misfortune should be accompanied by sexual or genital mutilations. However, subhuman living conditions dissuade from presenting the Church's teaching on contraception as an absolute priority. The Gospel can certainly inspire and sustain a spiritual promotion of love even in the worst of conditions, but it does not ask that the Church forget, in this case, its most pressing duty. This does not consist primarily in preaching about some aspect of conjugal morality; it consists in struggling so that human beings in altogether inhuman conditions may be rescued from their present lot. Moreover, what is true in this regard for a great part of the Third World, is also important even in the Western world for more individuals and families than one might at first imagine.

Christian Existence and the Prophetic Role

In this context of the total education of the humane sense under the light of Revelation the Christian can discover, or rediscover if he has lost it, the sense of the Church's message on conjugal love. The Christian, since he is inherently God's image and God's service, attains his spiritual fullness in Christ without any stunting of his humanity. Notably, the Christian must fit the Church's teaching on contraception into the set of questions which deal with the authenticity of love. To be a Christian in these domains does not mean either being obsessed with the problem of contraception or refusing to see in it a real problem, without ever forgetting that conscience is equally concerned with quite different problems as well. Obsession on this point is as harmful as levity. But since it is love alone which constitutes the problem here, then love alone, if it is true, can find the path to the real answers.

In the conflict of meanings which conjugal love can rarely avoid, the union of the spouses remains, concretely speaking, the root meaning of the couple, since all truly human generating depends on this union alone. To de-dramatize the conflicts which arise from the duality of meanings is an imperious duty of Christian conscience. This does not mean that one should imprudently deny that the channels of love, which touch so closely the depths of God, can escape the infiltrations of sin.

The inseparability of meanings which remains the spiritual norm of the conjugal act casts light so deep into love that conscience might prefer to shy away. A legitimate fear or an actual impossibility could then become a refusal of principle, which would distort the conscience and put it at odds with God. But even the discovery that one has truly sinned in shunning the deepest demands of love should never darken the heart with suspicions and new fears about itself, about the other, about the Church, about Christ, or about God. All should be lived in the light of the Gospel for which the sanctity of the morals of the Kingdom is never separable from the superabundance of pardons granted and promised.

Such a type of existence in no way destroys the ideal, though our common weakness may fall short of it. It soon becomes an existence of witness which sheds for others light by which it has itself been penetrated. This light, enriched by pardons, does not cast any shadow on the true grandeur of the message; on the contrary, it authenticates it. It dissipates only pharasaical self-complacency and inhumane harshness toward others. It bestows, on the contrary, the transparency which lets the Spirit shine through. It thus creates the conditions for a propheticism of sanctity which the world, often unbeknown to Christians, needs in affairs of love as in all other domains, although the same world rebels against it, ridicules it, or even denies it. Christians must not allow themselves to be demolished by foreseeable opposition; they must continue to enlighten themselves in order, with dauntless humility, the better to serve others and to serve love itself.

Footnote:

1. It is the use of a contraceptive method, and not the use of the sterile period given by the organism, which defines, in the Church's eyes, real contraception. In both cases, it is certainly the refusal of generation which governs the conduct of the spouses. But in the second case periodic infertility is used; in the first case however there is definite intervention to destroy or inhibit this fertility. It is this practice that the Church forbids and that she calls contraception. The other practice enters into the behavior she calls responsible parenthood or birth control: this formula entering into the subtitle of the encyclical.

GUSTAVE MARTELET was born at Lyon in 1916, has taught theology at the scholasticate of the Jesuits of Fourviere for twenty years, and since 1972 has taught at the Centre d'Etudes et de Recherches de Sevres at Paris. He was theologian for the Bishops of French Equatorial Africa during the Council, and is a past member of the International Theological Commission. Among his theological works we note the following:

— *Victoire sur la mort, èlèments d'anthropologie chrètienne, Chronique sociale, Lyon 1972;*
— *Saintetè de l'Eglise et vie religieuse, Toulouse 1974 (èpuisè);*
— *Les idèes maîtresses de Vatican II, Introduction à l'esprit du Concile, DDB 1966, ≪Foi vivante≫ n. 105;*
— *Rèsurrection, eucharistie et genèse de l'homme, chemis thèologiques d'un renouveau chrètien, Desclèe 1972;*
— *L'au delà retrouvè, Christologie des fins dernières, Desclèe 1975;*
— *Vivre aujourd'hui la foi de toujours, Relecture du Credo, le Cerf 1977;*
— *Oser croire en l'Eglise, le Cerf 1979.*

RESPONSIBLE PARENTHOOD AND THE MORALITY OF BIRTH CONTROL METHODS

Dionigi Tettamanzi

The image one has of birth regulation on the one hand, and of the meaning of human sexuality on the other, influences decisions about use of specific methods. We address ourselves specifically to the moral value of methods of birth control, to the aspect of their human value or lack of it, to their conformity or disconformity with man as man. We begin with a discussion of the concept of responsible parenthood as presented in the encyclical *HUMANAE VITAE.*

1. Responsible parenthood is a far-reaching concept

Early in the encyclical *HUMANAE VITAE* Pope Paul VI refers to two great realities of married life, namely love and fecundity, and he places them in juxtaposition to the concept of responsible parenthood: "Since, in the attempt to justify artificial methods of birth control, many have appealed to the demands both of conjugal love and of "responsible parenthood," it is good to state very precisely the true concept of these two great realities of married life . . ." (HV 7).

Ten years later the same Pope returned to the topic, this time locating the concept of responsible parenthood within the context of divine wisdom and the laws of nature which flow from it:

DIONIGI TETTAMANZI was born in Renate, province of Milan, Italy, in 1934. He teaches moral theology at the Seminary of Milan and at the Istituto Regionale Lombardo di Pastorale, in Milan. Among his works, in addition to numerous articles in theological and pastoral reviews, we note the following:

Humanae Vitae. Commento all'enciclica sulla regolazione delle nascite, Milano 1968.

La risposta dei vescovi alla Humanae Vitae, Milano 1969.

Temi di morale fondamentale, Milano 1975.

La comunita' cristiana e l'aborto, Bari 1975.

Il ministero conjugale, Roma 1978.

La Chiesa domestica. Per una pastorale familiare oggi, Napoli 1979.

Il matrimonio cristiano, Studio storico e teologico, Milano 1980.

The coordinator of the project of this book, Father Zimmerman, has adapted Fr. Tettamanzi's original Italian text to the needs of the English version; some parts have been omitted or shortened.

"It seems to us that the decade that has now passed since its promulgation [HV] . . . is an opportunity to confirm the important principles which, in the wake of the Council, not long concluded, we enunciated with the greatest care: the principle or respect for the laws of that nature which, to use Dante's expression "takes its course from the divine intellect and from its art"; the principle of conscious and morally responsible parenthood."[1]

With the passage of time in the postconciliar period, discussion about responsible parenthood has become more subdued and peaceful, but one wonders whether the full meaning of the concept is appreciated adequately. Some tend to restrict the concept to mere considerations of quantity and timing, that is, the number and spacing of births. Pope Paul VI teaches that spouses should rightly be aware of responsible parenthood in its truer meaning, which has various aspects:

"Conjugal love requires in husband and wife awareness of their mission of 'responsible parenthood', which today is rightly much insisted upon, and which also must be understood exactly. It is to be considered under different aspects which are legitimate and connected with one another" (HV 10).

Let us consider various aspects of the concept of responsible parenthood.

1) Conjugal love as source and norm of fruitfulness

The full truth about responsible parenthood can be understood only in the light of its internal and vivifying relation to the love of the spouses. Conjugal fecundity is not something outside of the love that constitutes the two in the reality of one flesh (Gn 2, 24), but it is that same love in one of its intrinsic and essential dimensions. Conjugal love, in other words, is the supreme donation of self to the point of bringing into being a new human life.

Fecundity is the *fruit* of the love of the spouses. The mutual and total giving of self, while it fully involves the spouses in their reality as couple, transcends them by constituting them into a new reality, a family. Their giving of self blossoms and bears fruit in the living gift of the child. As the fruit of conjugal love, fecundity constitutes its living sign, its permanent witness. The singular unity of the spouses broadens out and finds itself confirmed and perfected in the child. The child is the living and indissociable depository of the love of father and mother.

The connection between fecundity and conjugal love is basic and has moral significance for the spouses. As Pope Paul VI said on one occasion:

"Born of the creative and paternal love of God, marriage finds in human love, corresponding to the design and will of God, the fundamental law of its moral value: in the mutual love of the spouses, whereby each one endeavors with one's entire being to help the other be what God wants him to be; in the common desire of faithfully interpreting the love of God, creator and father, by bringing new lives into being."[2]

The bond which ties love to fecundity connects responsible love in the service of unity with responsible love in the service of life. Responsibility for the gift of the child originates from responsibility for the mutual giving of the spouses who love each other. The point was made by the then Cardinal Karol Wojtyla:

"The only spouses capable of responsible love in marriage are those who recognize their mutual responsibility for the gift itself of love. For love is above all a gift, and this is precisely what constitutes its essential content . . . . The responsibility for this gift of love is expressed in a constant awareness of being given and, at the same time, in a clear vision of the tasks which this gift entails . . . . Parenthood belongs to the nature of this specific love, which is conjugal love; that is, it constitutes its essential trait, it shapes it in its sphere of intentions, and in the end it imprints on it the seal of a particular accomplishment. Conjugal love fulfills itself through parenthood. Responsibility for this love is at the same time entirely, one might say, responsibility for parenthood. This means that one is part of the other and that one decides concerning the other."[3]

2) Elements which constitute the meaning of responsible parenthood

Elements mentioned in connection with responsible parenthood in the text of *HUMANAE VITAE* are a relation to the biological processes, to the tendencies of instinct or passion, to the physical, economic, psychological and social conditions, and finally to the objective moral order. If one is to avoid emptying the concept of responsible parenthood of its real meaning, and to desist from sundering its internal ties, one must view these elements in the context of their structural unity. We shall limit ourselves to a brief analysis of these aspects, interpreting them within the living context of a conjugal love that is at once *knowledge, freedom, discernment of the situation, and service to God.*

a) "In relation to the biological processes, responsible parenthood means knowledge and respect of their functions; the human intellect discovers in the power of giving life biological laws which are part of the human person" (HV 10).

Love is knowledge: *ubi amor, ibi oculus*, as the ancients said.[4] In reference to responsible parenthood, love stimulates, favors, and involves the spouses in the knowledge of themselves, of their corporeality, and of human sexuality in its fertility rhythm. The knowledge of oneself and of the partner, of the biological processes that are connected with the generative faculties, supplies an enrichment to the union. Biological realities are a part of the human person, even though they do not constitute its total reality. This knowledge enables the spouses to live their conjugal life more fully "in the truth." Biological awareness also assists the couple to accept knowingly and responsibly the design of God which is written into the structure of man as husband and of woman as wife.

b) "In relation to the tendencies of instinct and passion, responsible parenthood means the necessary dominion which reason and will must exercise over them" (HV 10).

Love is control of self, is freedom, is contributive to the meaning of being human. A free man is one who holds himself in hand, who controls his actions intelligently.[5] The fruitful love of spouses, if it is truly human, also operates in a manner proper to man, who is a thinker and a chooser. Such love is conscious and deliberate, not a blind operation of chance, not a dehumanized automatism of instinct. Indeed, if the humanity of an act can be measured by the extent to which the intellect and will are engaged, the conjugal act, by reason of its unique meaning, is also uniquely human. It is human activity with enlightened awareness carried out as a deliberate and responsible act of the will. Intellectual awareness is teamed up with heightened love.

c) "In relation to physical, economic, psychological and social conditions, responsible parenthood is exercised either by the deliberate and generous decision to raise a numerous family, or by the decision made for grave motives with due respect for the moral law, to avoid for the time being, or even for an indeterminate period, a new birth" (HV 10).

A love which is conscious and responsible bases its choices not on disembodied abstractions uprooted from reality, but on real life situations wherein the abstract principles are encountered in concrete and historical circumstances. Conjugal love discerns parental responsibilities in the actual family situation. Choosing to have a child – a unique choice in view of the lofty values involved – must come with discernment of the situation. The sign of God's plan is to be seen in the conditions in which the spouses find themselves, in which they are called to carry out their mission of fruitful love. The will of God, read in the concrete situation, can lead the spouses to a regulation of birth that does not always mean limitation; it may mean a "deliberate and generous" choice to have a "numerous family" (cf. HV 10).

d) "Responsible parenthood implies also and above all a more profound relationship to the objective moral order established by God, of which a right conscience is the faithful interpreter" (HV 10).

Love, ultimately, is conformity with the Uncreated Good expressed through various created goods. Responsible parenthood, like other created goods, is an expression of love of spouses, by which they conform themselves with the Supreme Good, with God and His holy will. Seen in this light, human love is a service of God; and responsible parenthood is service which a couple render to God; for that reason it must be practiced in a manner which respects its intrinsic soundness, which follows the pattern of the moral order established by God. Spouses, acting with a right conscience, are interpreters of God's design. They are co-creators of this design and make it emerge in their concrete pattern of life as husband and wife, as father and mother. They are collaborators with God who "through them continuously increases and enriches His family" (*GAUDIUM ET SPES*, 50).

3) Responsible parenthood in its execution: the problem of methods and means

Responsibility for fruitful love exists not only as a disembodied intention; it is action as well, love in a couple who exercise human sexuality in their spiritual and corporal totality. In this context the problem of the moral character of the various ways of limiting births arises.

One notes, in some quarters, a tendency to empty of its moral meaning the question of means of birth regulation. The tendency has developed on the basis of two opposite thrusts. The first stresses so strongly the role of intention (*finis operantis*) in moral acts that a morality of interiority results, one that prescinds from the contents *(finis operis)* in which the subjective intention is embodied. The second thrust stresses results, evaluating the moral act on the basis of consequences alone. What is effective is seen as being good. Both views have been publicized extensively and have found considerable acceptance. Attempts at theological reflection have also been made. Some call into question the existence of intrinsic evil (of an objective content which is universally and unchangeably valid). They presume to fabricate theologically (on the basis of results only) the moral norms of man's behavior with regard to himself and to others, while allowing for some exceptions. In the area of the regulation of births the two perspectives have merged into an identical conclusion: the negation or minimization of the specifically moral significance of methods and means.

Other aspects of birth regulation which receive attention are mentioned in this context. One is the *technical* advantage of this or that contraceptive in terms of safety and effectiveness. Another is the *medical* aspect, in terms of greater or less advantage or disadvantage to health, especially of the woman. Another is the *psychological* factor, in terms of acceptability by couples. In their own limited way, these aspects have also a moral significance. For example, when another pregnancy would be a major risk to health, the reliability of a method becomes a moral issue. The duty of the spouses to cultivate harmony implies efforts to come to agreement about the method to be used. These moral considerations are partial and derivative, being coincidental with the core moral imperative which requires that man may not use methods which do not conform to his basic existence as man.

2. The moral value cannot be detached from the act

Vatican II and the encyclical *HUMANAE VITAE* affirm explicitly that the means which are employed to regulate births have moral implications. Vatican II states:

"When it is a question of harmonizing married love with the responsible transmission of life, it is not enough to take only the good intention and evaluation of motives into account; the objective criteria must be used, criteria drawn from the nature of the human person and human action, criteria which respect the total meaning of mutual self-giving and human procreation in the context of true love" (GS, 51).

When making a moral evaluation of methods used for regulating births, therefore, the method of actualization of responsible parenthood must be considered as well as the intention. Objective criteria, those drawn from the nature of the human person and human action must be considered in addition to subjective criteria.[6] Objective criteria are drawn from the nature of true love, from the total meaning of mutual self-giving and human procreation. Authentic human sexuality is the measure of the moral norm. As Paul VI expressed it:

"In the task of transmitting life, therefore, they (the spouses) are not free to proceed completely at will, as if they could determine in a wholly autonomous way the honest path to follow; but they must conform their activity to the creative intention of God, expressed in the very nature of marriage and its acts and manifested by the constant teaching of the Church" (HV 10).[7]

There is, in fact, an intimate and necessary connection between the end and the means, between responsible parenthood and the concrete manner of its actualization. True, the means are a way to the end, but they can be a way which either respects the values and exegencies of man as man, or does not respect them. Beyond the subjective intention of regulating births, an intention which can be subjectively sincere and at the same time objectively erroneous, there are the objective elements. That is, there are means whose qualities are coherent, homogeneous, and compatible with the purpose of responsible parenthood as a truly human activity; and there are means which are non-coherent, non-homogeneous, and non-compatible with fruitful love as it should exist in man. Means are employed by a person who is using them to perform a human act. The action involves the person himself. Thus the problem of means is always a human problem. And if it is a human problem, it is always a moral problem.

In other words, if one were to maintain that methods and means of regulating births do not posit a moral problem, one would logically have to affirm that morality is solely and entirely determined by the *intention* of the person acting, prescinding from the *contents and modalities* of the action. If we were to admit this, how then could we safeguard the principle of *bonum ex integra causa* (unless it is totally good, it is not good)? If morality were reduced exclusively to the *why* of one's actions, without taking into account *what* is being accomplished and *how,* then the end justifies the means. That is, in fact, the facile and compelling temptation of a technical and pragmatic culture, where one applies the otherwise correct principle of man's legitimate intervention in natural processes to an area where the principle does not apply; namely to the area of specifically human values, such as that of fruitful and responsible love.

As everyone knows, among the many methods and means of birth control, there are two essential categories, artificial contraception and natural family planning.[8] We deal here with two forms so different that they are antithetical. The contrast arises from a number of objective factors. The one group interferes with biological processes, the other does not; one does not require periodic abstinence, the other does; one opposes the typical symbolism of sexual language, the other harmonizes with it.

Methods and means in the context of authentic responsible parenthood

A moral judgment on ways of regulating births can be formed by drawing a comparison between their dynamics and the responsibility of parenthood. Thus we discern their conformity with the human values of responsible fruitful love, or their opposition to them. A fundamental and decisive role is played by the concept of responsible fruitful love. If this concept is restricted or distorted, one makes mistakes, judging to be moral what is in reality immoral.

The core concept of responsible parenthood distinguishes artificial means from natural means without possibility of confusion. Artificial means are "monovalent" being designed to suppress actual and potential procreativity. Natural means are "bivalent" capable of serving to avoid procreation or to achieve it.

Beyond this core concept of procreativity we see other distinctions. Natural methods require and develop knowledge of and respect for the biological processes of the person; whereas artificial practices tend to leave such knowledge and respect in a state of under-development. Spouses lean on the methods, instead of on knowledge, to achieve their purpose. Again, natural methods presuppose and favor the dominion of intellect and will over the instinctive and psychic spheres of sexuality;

this dominion is conjugal, since it involves the couple as such, without undue unilateral burdens. Artificial ways, on the contrary, while requiring some form of control, essentially depend on employment of a means as such rather then on control.

The above aspects, while presenting some sort of moral value, still do not express the radical motivation which explains the objective moral incompatibility between artificial ways and natural ways. This motivation is seen properly only in the more profound and original aspect of responsible fruitful love, that is, in respect for God's design imprinted in human sexuality by way of its "meanings."

3. The connection between the meanings of human sexuality

The response of Paul VI to the moral problem of ways of regulating births refers explicitly, as to its radical motivation, to the "meanings" which God has inscribed in human sexuality:

"The Church, calling men back to the observance of the norms of the natural law, as interpreted by her constant doctrine, teaches that each and every marriage act must remain open to the transmission of life" *(quilibet matrimonii usus ad vitam humanam procreandam per se destinatus permaneat)* (HV 11).

Then he defines and explains:

"That teaching, often set forth by the magisterium, is founded upon the inseparable connection willed by God and unable to be broken by man on his own initiative, between the two meanings of the conjugal act: the unitive meaning and the procreative meaning" (HV 12).

Paul VI speaks of a connection "willed by God," and he therefore addresses himself to the design which the Creator has stamped on the biological structure itself of man and woman. The couple are at the service of this design by accepting and integrating the biological structure into the broader and deeper context of all personal values. The divine design is stamped on the "unitotal" reality of man, that is, on his interiority and corporality, which include human sexuality.

The psychological meaning of the conjugal act is not totally fulfilled and exhausted by the realization of procreation alone. On the other hand, the physical meaning of the act is not exhausted and totally fulfilled by the integration and unity of the spouses when procreation is excluded. A human aspect is missing when either the one or the other is excluded. In its totality, in its fully human essence, the conjugal act has a unitive meaning and a procreative meaning, a function of integrating the couple if the act remains open to life.

Man is a psychological unity, a compositive of body and spirit. The sexual experience is truly and fully human only if it reflects this psychological unity, and in the measure that the unity remains intact. The connection between the unitive meaning and the procreative meaning of the sexual act is unbreakable. The connection must be left intact, unless one wishes to distort the conjugal act, that is, deprive it of the meaning which is truly and fully human.

HUMANAE VITAE declares that this connection between the unitive meaning and the procreative meaning is off limits to man by the will of God; it is an area which man is not permitted to attack, not allowed to infringe upon:

"That teaching, often set forth by the magisterium, is founded upon the inseparable connection between the meaning of unity and the meaning of procreation, both of which exist in the conjugal act. The connection has been established by God. Man is not permitted to infringe upon this connection on his own initiative" (HV 12).

Hujiusmodi doctrina, quae ab Ecclesiae Magisterio saepe exposita est, in nexu indissolubili nititur, a Deo statuto, quem homini sua sponte infringere non licet, inter significationem unitatis et significationem procreationis, quae ambae in actu conjugali insunt.

The point is not that every conjugal act is supposed to be fruitful. The fact is, most conjugal acts do not result in new life, following biological processes which God has created in man. Nature frequently allows the procreative *effect* to be negated; the *effect* is therefore separated from the act by the natural processes. Man is allowed to engage in the sexual act during these periods of infertility, acting always with reason. When he does so, man enters into God's design without separating on his own initiative what happens to be already separated as to *effect.*

The practice of contraception, however, is different. On his own initiative, outside of and in opposition to the rhythmic cycle of fertility, man dissociates the two meanings, and willfully eliminates the procreative meaning. By thus eliminating the procreative meaning through a positive intervention, man also impairs the totality of the mutual self-giving, and offends against the unitotality of the persons who supposedly give themselves to each other in an act of intercourse. Intercourse is not a true and effective conjugal union in such a case, despite the psychological impression of the two, despite sincere subjective intentions. By interfering with the procreative meaning of the act, the couple also compromise the unitive meaning by unavoidable necessity. The two meanings are interdependent; one cannot exist essentially when the other is suppressed.

From this we understand why contraception is a disorderly act in its very nature *(quod ex propria natura moralem ordinem transgrediatur, HV 14).* It is "unworthy of man" *(ibid)* who must establish his actions in accordance with the directive ordering of Divine Wisdom. Contraception is already a disorder by reason of its inner unsoundness, without need of a declaration to this effect from the outside. The act of contraception falsifies the conjugal relationship, transforming it into a congress which is non-conjugal. The unitive and procreative meanings exist together in the conjugal act, and when one is destroyed, the other suffers with it.

Some may ask why it is not permitted to man to separate on his own initiative the two meanings of the conjugal act, especially since we know that natural processes routinely exclude the effect of fecundity. The question becomes more urgent because we already admit the perfect legitimacy of controlling the world of nature in so many areas. Are we not in danger of falling into an exasperating biologism when we make the good of the spouses, their personal and conjugal integrity, depend so unconditionally on non-interference with this biological process?

Paradoxical as it may seem, the very notion of conjugal sexuality indicates the imperative to respect the biological integrity of the act. If we keep the total concept of the act in mind, without uprooting the biological processes from their human context, we can understand the proper answer. The sexual act, when performed in its conjugal and human integrity, is not a thing by itself, nor a piece of a human being which may or must be sacrificed in favor of the whole organism. And sexuality is not so much a part of man, as a dimension of his personality. Man *has* other things, and he may rightfully exercise dominion over them. But a person's sexuality is on the level of *being, of this person in his sexual connotations.* Over this dimension of being a man does not have true and proper dominion. If a man were to attempt such dominion, he would no longer be acting in his personal identity and dignity; rather he would be an object of manipulation.

At issue, therefore, is the profound concept of human sexuality. Some may falsely interpret the concept, regarding sex as a thing, a purely biophysiological object. In line with such thinking they suppose that man may use sex for desired purposes. In truth, however, sexuality is a dimension of the person. Man may only *exercise* his sexual dimension, not *use* it by virtue of a supposed right of usurped dominion. He may assume it, and live it in accordance with its inner structure and dynamics, but not manipulate it as a thing.[9]

4. Demographic problems and the regulation of births

Up to this point our discussion has been limited to the morality of ways of birth regulation in their objective aspects. Our reference was to single couples, to their mission and vocation of responsible fertile love. There is another aspect of the problem of birth regulation, namely its social implications, and this is much discussed today. The phenomenon of demographic increases, especially in certain countries, has become a subject of great concern.

With good reason the question is asked whether the kind of birth regulation which Catholic moral teaching permits has real meaning and practical application in respect to a solution of a problem so vast and complex, and in some cases so pressing. Should the solution of Catholic moral teachings be a judgment in abstraction, proposing a kind of true and proper utopia?

We do not intend to enter into a scientific analysis of the real extent of the world demographic phenomenon nor judge about the correctness of forecasts, although, on the other hand, it is well known that during recent years, at least for certain countries, assertions have been modified which until yesterday were stated in absolutely certain terms. We will take into consideration those aspects of the problem which are of a moral nature, selecting from among them the more important ones.

1) The social dimensions of responsible parenthood

The first point which comes to mind when making a moral evaluation of the question is that, among other factors, responsible parenthood includes a social dimension. When deciding about their fecundity couples may and must take into consideration not only their own good and that of their children, but also the *common good*: that is to say, the good of the community, civil as well as ecclesiastical. It cannot be otherwise since man is a social being and the family is the first and most vital cell of society. It is along these lines that *Gaudium et Spes* requires of couples, in their fulfillment of the mission of responsible parenthood, to consider the good of "the community, of temporal society, and of the Church itself" (GS 50). The Encyclical *Humanae Vitae* confirms this stating that a responsible use of parenthood implies that "husband and wife recognize fully their duties toward God, toward themselves, toward the family and toward society, in a correct hierarchy of values" (HV 10).

In this sense Paul VI generally speaking—and thus referring to the community context too—has clearly emphasized that responsible parenthood is not unidirectional:

"In relation to physical, economic, psychological and social conditions, responsible parenthood is exercised either by the thoughtfully made and generous decision to raise a large family, or by the decision made for grave motives and with respect for the moral law, to avoid a new birth for the time being, or even for an indeterminate period" (HV 10).

As indicated, couples will be concerned also about the common good when deciding about their responsible fecundity: but it is a decision that must be made by the couples themselves, without an arbitrary intervention on part of the state and public authority in the sphere of the consciences of the couples:

"The government has, assuredly, in the matter of the population of its country, its own rights and duties, within limits of its proper competence. . . .

"Since there is widespread opinion that the population expansion of the world, or at least some particular countries, should be kept in check by all possible means and by every kind of intervention by public authority, the Council exhorts all men to beware of all solutions, whether uttered in public or in private or imposed at any time, which transgress the natural law. Because in virtue of man's inalienable rights to marriage and the procreation of children, the decision regarding the number of children depends on the judgment of the parents and is in no way to be left to the decrees of public authority" (GS 87).

Just as we have given attention to the morality of the means to be used in regard to fulfilling the requirements of responsible parenthood in reference to individuals and the family, so now the question before us is the morality of the means to be used in the context of its application to the question of the common good. The reason mentioned above about the connection between the natural regulation of births and human sexuality, respected and affirmed in its structure and its dynamisms, is a reason which is always valid because it is rooted in the nature of things. It is also valid, therefore, when confronting the gravity of the problems arising from demographic increase. The Magisterium of the Church expressed itself in this way on the point; the text of *Gaudium et Spes* quoted above concludes as follows:

"People should be wisely informed of scientific advances in research into methods of birth regulation, whenever the value of these methods has been thoroughly proved and their confrormity with the moral order established" (GS 87).

And in the same meaning we have this intervention of Paul VI during the World Population Year (1974):

"Some people are carried away by the temptation to believe that there is no other solution except to curb population growth by the use of radical measures, measures which are frequently in contrast with the laws implanted by God in man's nature, and which fall short of due respect for the dignity of human life and man's rightful liberty. Such measures are in some cases based upon a materialistic view of man's destiny.

"The true solutions to these problems—We would say the only solutions—will be those that take due account of all concrete factors as a whole: the demands of social justice along with respect for the divine laws governing life, the dignity of the human person as well as the freedom of peoples, the primary role of the family as well as the responsibility proper to married couples (see *Populorum Progressio* 37;

Humanae Vitae 23 and 31. . . .)." (Address of March 30, 1974 to the Executive Director of the UN Fund for Population Activities, and the Secretary General of the World Population Conference.)

For the rest the Encyclical *Humanae Vitae* has explicitly denounced the danger of contraception imposed by the state to control demographic growth as one of the "grave consequences of artificial methods of regulating births:"

"Consider also the dangerous weapon that would thus be placed in the hands of those public authorities who have no concern for the requirements of morality. Who could blame a government for applying, as a solution to the problems of the community, those means acknowledged to be permissible for married couples in solving a family problem? Who will stop rulers from favoring and from even imposing upon their peoples, if they should consider it necessary, the method of contraception that they judge to be most efficacious? In this way men, in wishing to avoid the individual, family or social difficulties which they encounter in observing the divine law, would come to place at the mercy of the intervention of public authorities the most personal and most reserved sector of conjugal intimacy" (HV 17).

2) Education toward a sense of responsibility and of social justice

After these clarifications have been made the first question arises again, namely what effectivity the natural regulation of births can claim toward a solution of the problem of demographic growth. The answer to this question depends upon the concept of effectiveness which is used, which is profoundly different when given a technological interpretation in regard to human existence, or a personalistic interpretation which is properly human and humanizing.

Now there is no doubt that Catholic moral teaching strongly stresses the way of responsibility of the couples, opposing this against the facile temptation to use technology to force a solution of the problems which are profoundly human by their very nature. The Church bears witness that, despite everything, she rests her confidence in man, making her appeal to that which constitutes his specific humanness: his responsibility. She contributes in this way to a restoration of a "civilization of love" and of a true and proper process of humanization. This is the conviction expressed frequently by Paul VI:

"In defending conjugal morality in its entirety the Church knows that she contributes to the establishment of a truly human society; she challenges man not to abandon his own responsibility in exchange for reliance on technical means; by this means she defends the dignity of husbands and wives" (HV 18).

Certainly this proposed means of the Church is a long road and a difficult one, one which perhaps not all can understand. And the effectiveness should be evaluated in terms of quality, in human profundity, and in durability. But there is no other direction that can respect and promote truly and fully man insofar as he is man.

There is another profound significance in the position of Catholic moral teaching: the reaffirmation of the moral illiceity of contraception also for the purposes of containing demography—contraception which is often associated with the very serious manipulation of sterilization and even abortion—constitutes a stimulus towards attacking the problem of demographic growth and resolving it on its true level, which is social justice by means of an equal distribution of goods. How can social justice be stimulated when contraception is permitted? The human answer to the problem of births consists, as Paul VI said to FAO on November 16, 1970, in "multiplying bread and sharing it" rather than in "decreasing the number of the guests invited." The Pontiff here repeated clearly what he had said at the Assembly of the United Nations on October 4, 1965:

"It is in your Assembly, even where the matter of the great problem of birth rates is concerned, that respect for human life ought to find its loftiest profession and its most reasonable defense. Your task is so to act that there will be enough bread at the table of mankind and not to support an artificial birth control that would be irrational, with the aim of reducing the number of those sharing in the banquet of life."

Conclusion

The moral illicitness of contraception is seen when we view it in its personalistic context. Use of artificial means and methods to regulate births distorts the conjugal act in its inner conjugal configuration, and offends the human dignity of the performers, because it unlawfully dissociates the human meanings of sexuality.[10] The use of contraceptives is a moral problem because it is an action of responsible human beings, attempting to use dominion in an area where this is not morally possible. The statement of Pope Paul VI, indicating that sexuality must be viewed in its proper context is to the point:

"The problem of birth, like every other problem regarding human life, is to be considered beyond partial perspectives—whether of the biological or psychological, demographic or sociological orders — in the light of the integral vision of man and his vocation, not only his natural and earthly, but also his supernatural and eternal vocation" (HV 7).

The present Pope, before he ascended to the throne of Peter, used an apt term to describe how man must always act as an integrated human if he is to maintain his dignity. Man should always act as *homo humanus* he said:

"Man in our day succumbs, in a manner that is not even perceptible to himself, to alienation from his own humanity and often, in the name of progress, becomes merely '*homo economicus*' or '*homo technicus*'. The author of the encyclical *[HUMANAE VITAE]* is aware that he has an obligation of bringing to man's attention, with all humility and firmness, the integral vision of man, for which Christ takes a stand, lives and dies; a vision in which man rediscovers and reaffirms himself as '*homo humanus*'."[11]

Footnotes:

1. Paul VI, *Allocution to Cardinals,* June 23, 1978. See commentary by E. Lio, *The Pope of Humanae Vitae:* L'Osservatore Romano, July 25, 1978.
2. Paul VI, *Allocution to Centro Italiano Femminile,* February 12, 1966.
3. Cardinal Karol Wojtyla, Keynote address to the International Congress on "Responsible Fruitful Love," Milan, June 21-25, 1978.
4. St. Thomas, *In III Sent.*, d. 33, q. 1, ad 2; q. 3, sol. 1.
5. "We owe to St. Thomas a precise and ever valid definition of what the substantial greatness of man consists in: 'Ipse est sibi providens' (*Contra Gentes,* III, 81). Man is master of himself, he is able to provide for himself and to project his own destiny . . ." (John Paul II, at the Angelicum University, November 17, 1979).
6. Cfr. the analysis of the conciliar text and of its successive interpretations in M. Zalba, "*Ex personae eiusdemque actuum natura*" (GS, 51, 3): Periodica de re morali canonica liturgica 68 (1979) 201-232.
7. Besides this explicit and specific affirmation of HV, there is the historical fact itself of the intervention of Paul VI. This intervention could not be adequately explained without admitting the existence of a specifically moral value of methods and means of regulating births. In fact, the encyclical was the Pope's reply to the theological debate in progress which was concerned with contraception and the manner of achieving responsible parenthood.
8. We are considering contraceptives only in the strict acceptance of the term, that is, all those modalities and/or instruments that prevent conception. We do not deal here with sterilization and abortion, whose moral character is well known.
9. The distinction between *using* and *making use of* is in HV 13: "To use this divine gift while at the same destroying, even if only partially, its meaning and its purpose is to contradict the nature both of man and of woman and of their most intimate relationship, and therefore it is to contradict also the plan of God and His will. On the other hand, to make use of the gift of conjugal love while respecting the laws of the generative process means to acknowledge oneself not to be the arbiter of the sources of human life, but rather the minister of the design established by the Creator."

10. It is well known that intervention on the reproductive faculties is morally licit in therapeutic cases (cfr. HV 15). Cfr. B. Honings, *Il principio di inscindibilità.* Un segno per due significati: Lateranum 44 (1978) 169-194.
11. Cardinal K. Wojtyla, *La visione antropologica della Humanae Vitae*: Lateranum 44 (1978) p. 129.

The problem of birth regulation and population growth is vast and complex, and is treated more precisely and amply in CATHOLIC VIEWPOINT ON OVERPOPULATION, by Fr. Anthony Zimmerman, SVD (New York: Doubleday, 1961; also in his doctoral dissertation "OVERPOPULATION" A Study of Papal Teachings on the Problem, with Special Reference to Japan, The Catholic University of America, Washington, 1957; 4th printing.

Bibliography:

Introduction to the Encyclical "HUMANAE VITAE" in "Notificationes" e Curia Metropolitana Cracoviensi, A.D. 1969 (Ianuarius — Aprilis) N. 1-4. Tipografia Poliglotta Vaticana 1969.

G. MARTELET, *L'esistenza umana e l'amore*, Cittadella Editrice, Assisi 1970.

L. CICCONE, *Humanae Vitae. Analisi e orientamenti pastorali,* Edizione Pastorali, Roma, 1970.

J. DE FINANCE, *La determination de la norme morale. Quelques reflexiones:* Gregorianum 57 (1979) 702-739.

J. BONOMI, *La differenza essenziale tra metodi artificiali e metodi naturali:* Lateranum 44 (1978) 146-168.

THE MORAL DISORDER OF CONTRACEPTION

Carlo Caffarra

One of the essential points of the teaching of *HUMANAE VITAE* is expressed in these words: ". . . Ecclesia . . . id docet necessarium esse, ut quilibet matrimonii usus ad vitam humanam procreandam per se destinatus permaneat" (HV 11). (The Church . . . teaches that each and every marriage act must remain open to the transmission of life.)

The theological debate which followed after *HUMANAE VITAE* was issued went through two phases which are logically connected. The first phase was characterized chiefly by a pastoral concern about the best manner to instruct the consciences of married couples, especially those who are beset with particular difficulties in accepting and carrying out this teaching. The second phase was and still is concerned with the theological problem of establishing the basis for the directives given, or to be given, in the above-mentioned circumstances. In both fields a novel concept about the goodness or the malice of the contraceptive act has been proposed by some moralists; this concept now constitutes one of the knots of the present problem.

In this study we aim to explain what this new concept proposes, both in regard to its meaning and its application to *HUMANAE VITAE*. We will try to be concise. Next we will criticize the new concept, testing its inner logic and the attempt to apply this in reference to the doctrine of *HUMANAE VITAE*.

1. The "new" concept of the moral disorder of the contraceptive act

The theological debate that arose from HV has been focusing more and more on the concept of the goodness or malice of the human act, considered in itself. This is one of the essential moments of every ethical reflection.

1) *The definition of the "new" concept.* The "new" concept states

CARLO CAFFARRA teaches fundamental moral theology at the School of Theology of the University of the Sacred Heart in Milan. He is a member of the editorial board of Medicina e Morale, a review of the School of Medicine of that University, and of the review Communio (Italian edition). He has published studies on fundamental moral theology and on moral problems arising from the development of human genetics. He is a past member of the International Theological Commission.

that the morality of an act connotes the relation of the act to practical reason, and it is this relation which constitutes the act in its moral nature. In what does this relation consist? And when is an action justified rationally? These moralists answer: firstly, all of the goods at issue, and all of the circumstances which surround the act must be taken into account; then the good which is perceived in the act imposes itself on the reason as the *preponderant value,* prevailing over all others and demanding a *preferential choice,* is what justifies the action.

To grasp the meaning of this answer (according to these moralists), the following elements must be kept in mind:

First. The goods at issue in interhuman relations, which alone concern us here,[1] are always of a contingent, limited, and competitive nature, according to the proponents of this theory. *Contingent:* this amounts to their nature as created beings, on account of which the good does not necessarily (hence not always and everywhere) demand to be performed under penalty of renouncing one's rationality. *Limited:* consequently the obligation to achieve this good and to shun the evil that contradicts it does not bind human free will to the point of never being able (or obliged) to undergo an exception. *Competitive:* given the human condition, a free decision inevitably entails a choice among the goods present in the various possible courses of action; the choice is made on the basis of preference, choosing one (or some) and excluding others.

Second. A moral judgment, according to this theory, consists essentially in weighing on the balance of reason the various contingent, limited, and competitive goods, with a view to the preferential choice of that good which, all things considered, must be looked upon as having the greatest claim to be chosen over the other contingent, limited, and competitive goods.

Third. The moral value of the choice would, according to this theory, emerge only within this judgment, and not previous to it. In other words, a distinction of supreme importance, so they say, must be made between a *pre-moral* good and a *moral* good. A *pre-moral* good signifies the propriety of the act considered in isolation, outside the context of other competing goods. A *moral* good signifies the propriety of the act after consideration of this good within the context of competing goods and in conjunction with the judgment that this choice *must be preferred* over the others. A moral obligation arises from a perception of this *oughtness.*

Fourth. The judgment of reason and the preferential choice that it makes must indeed be regulated by the moral law, say these moralists. But the nature of this regulation by the moral law must be considered carefully, they say. A moral norm expresses the fact that something which is already accepted as good in the light of reason and experience, must *generally* be preferred over competing goods. Decisions should not be reckless or unreasonable, but must be justified on the basis of objectivity. The norm is not just a recommendation which one is free to follow if he so wishes. It has a binding force, so no one who intends to act reasonably is free to ignore it.

Nevertheless, they say, *no norm is so absolute as never to admit of an exception.* Every finite good is limited, and so we can always conceive of a competing good which would outrank it. Should we wish to endow a norm with absolute binding force which excludes exceptions, our knowledge would have to span the horizon of *all* possible situations. We would have to cogitate all possible situations in which this good sanctioned by the norm now in force, would compete against other goods, and conclude serenely that it always and everywhere *outweighs all competitors.* But such a capacity is obviously beyond the power of human reason.

Therefore, say these moralists, existing norms are valid in general, but they do not apply in every case *(valent ut in pluribus, non autem semper et pro semper).* Norms are aids to assist reason in the difficult task of evaluating various goods. But such norms do not exempt reason, so it is asserted, from considering whether the general value of the norm perdures in the case at hand. The perdurance must be verified by the subject in each and every case.

Fifth. The judgment with which one denies the validity of the norm for one's own case ought not be characterized as the judgment of an (invincibly) erroneous conscience, say these moralists. On the contrary, it is a true judgment inasmuch as the good sanctioned by the norm does not outweigh competing goods in this particular case.

By combining the five elements described above we can now form an idea of what these moralists consider to be the nature of the morality of an action, and what they think of the term inherently evil *(intrinsece inhonestum).*

According to their theory, the morality of an action would consist formally in its relation to reason insofar as reason judges correctly that one act must be performed (a good act) whereas another must be avoided (a bad act). Reason judges that the good which an act achieves must be preferred to other goods which compete with it; this judgment of preference makes the act a good one. Or, if reason perceives that the good achieved by the act is outweighed by competing goods, the act is a bad one.

The intrinsic goodness or malice of an act, therefore, could mean one of two things: it could denote an act's quality by which the act adduces a so-called pre-moral good or pre-moral evil, that is, without reference to the context in which that good or evil is found; or it could denote the quality of an act by which the act adduces a good or evil which, weighed carefully by the reason against competing goods, is found to be either preferable or non-preferable. The intrinsic goodness or malice in the first meaning does not necessarily establish the intrinsic goodness or evil in the second meaning. There is no identity between the two concepts either in meaning or in application.

2) *Application to HUMANAE VITAE.* That HUMANAE VITAE judges a contraceptive act intrinsically evil (cfr. #14) is beyond dispute. Now let us see the interpretation this papal text undergoes when the "new" concept of goodness or evil is applied to it.

Let us begin with the definition of the contraceptive act as the papal document presents it in #14. We find there that a contraceptive act is defined as one which deprives sexuality of its procreative capacity; the good at issue, therefore, is that a man accepts his sexuality in its integrity, as it is.

Some moralists now claim that this good, like every other, is contingent, limited, and competitive. Goods which compete with it may be the physical or spiritual good of the spouses together, or of one or the other of the two; or the good of an adequate education to which the children who are already born have a previous right; and so forth.

These moralists say that the couple is called upon to make a rational judgment, weighing all the competing goods against each other carefully in their concrete circumstances; from this process the couple will understand which of the goods *must* be preferred.

What the norm of HV presents, according to these moralists, is a pre-moral good: it is the exercise of sexuality which remains open to procreation, but this has not yet been placed into the context of competing goods. This norm of HV has binding force, one which must guide the rational judgment, but only *in general (valet ut in pluribus).* It means that the good sanctioned by the norm of HV is, in general, preferable to the others. Nevertheless, this general validity of the norm of HV does not exclude exceptions which are either permitted, or even indicated. It is the duty of the couple to make a judgment by weighing the various goods at issue in their case; they must conclude from this which of the goods must be preferred. The conclusions of their search will not necessarily agree with the norm of HV.

If the conclusion of the couple disagrees with the norm of HV, this judgment of their conscience must not be characterized as erroneous (invincibly so). Rather, it should be characterized as a true conclusion, assuming that the good sanctioned by the norm of HV is not the preferred good in this case.

To be consistent, one must take one further step, following this theory of the moralists in question: if a careful analysis of the present existential situation were to show that conditions have changed to such an extent that contraception ought to be preferred not as an exception to the norm, but as the norm itself, then it is time to change the norm. The reason is not a denial of the pre-moral evil of contraception, but a recognition of the changed historical situation, which now calls for reformulation. Instead of stating, as *HUMANAE VITAE* does: "... excluded is every action which ... proposes ... to render procreation impossible" we should change the text to read: "allowed is every action which . . . for just and proportionate reasons" and so forth (cfr. #14).

Let us conclude our review of the theory of these moralists by posing the question: if we were to accept their explanation, then how would we describe the intrinsic malice of contraception? According to their theory there are *two* qualities of contraception which are formally distinct. *One* is the fact that contraception hinders the realization of a *pre-moral* good, and in this sense it is always bad. *Two,* it hinders the realization of a good which is considered in context and which is found to be preferable over competitive goods; in this sense contraception is a *moral* evil. Nevertheless, the latter does not always apply, hence contraception is *not always* a moral evil. In this second sense, intrinsic evil is not considered by these theologians to be identical with what is absolutely and unconditionally evil. This follows from their reasoning that a contraceptive act is not objectively evil in all situations.

2. Criticism of the "new" concept of the moral disorder of a contraceptive act, and of its application to HUMANAE VITAE

1) *Criticism of the definition.*

If I am not mistaken, the real knot of the problem is an inadequate concept of the absoluteness of moral values. An ethical absolute (a moral good) is one which must be willed unconditionally, not only in relation to some competitive good. It must be willed in its own right, without need of reference to another good.

For the sake of brevity we will omit detailing various theoretical steps which must be presupposed, and go right to the core of the matter: in the Christian vision the ultimate ethical absolute, the *Absolute Good,* is *God Himself.* God is the subsistent Being who wills Himself (loves Himself) absolutely by reason of His infinite Goodness. His act of will is identical with His Being. In the case of created spirits, these must also will God absolutely; that is, they must love Him for His own sake.

What is meant by saying that created spiritual beings must will God absolutely? Does it perhaps mean that only the love of God is an absolute and unconditional value? The matter calls for rigorous examination.

Every created being *(esse creatum)* is a participation in the subsistent Being of God, and stands in relation to Him. At the peak of creation stands the spiritual creature, who is a true and proper "image of God." God shares Himself with a created spiritual being in an essentially superior degree; a rational creature is capable of contacting the Absolute Himself by acts of intellect and will. The creature is capable of willing the Absolute for His own sake, being an image of God and sharing the Love with which God loves Himself (cfr. ST I, q. 93, a.4c).

When making an ethical judgment, a human person perceives an absolute oughtness which challenges freedom in its own name. There is no reference here to some other thing, no relation to a competing good. This quality of absoluteness is proper to God alone; better, it exists in the Divine Being as the demand for our unconditional obedience. That is why, whenever and wherever he makes an ethical judgment, man perceives God as an end of intention, (though not as an object of intuition, let us state this clearly). And so, when a man acts contrary to the injunctions of practical reason, he offends *God Himself*, not some immanent, created order: man thereby refuses to acknowledge God as God.

If participation in God's knowing and loving of Self is what being a spiritual creature means, and if this participation is exercised in practical judgments and in fidelity to the light of reason, it then follows that a person fulfills himself as person and as image of God through the fulfillment of moral values; and vice versa, the fulfillment of moral values consists properly in the fulfillment of the person as such. Consequently the love of friendship by which a person loves God as God, necessarily includes love of self and of other persons by reason of being persons.[2] There are not two loves, but one love which extends to different objects.[3]

Let us try to encapsulate the concept of absoluteness. The love with which God loves Himself and His own absolute necessity, is the source from which the whole hierarchy of values and duties flows; this love is the archetype of every obligation. When God wills and loves spiritual subjects other than Himself, these share formally in the act of love with which God loves them for His own sake and for their sake *(propter Se et propter seipsos):* the two targets are not opposed and not juxtaposed. This sharing is the basis of the absoluteness of moral Value. This participating in God's action also indicates the content of moral Value to be recognition of God as God and, in an inseparable act, of person as person (one's own and that of others).

From this concept flow three corollaries, which constitute the reasons for our complete rejection of the "new" definition of moral evil as described above.

Corollary one: A distinction between pre-moral goods and moral goods is not admitted

Our first corollary rejects the distinction which the moralists attempted to find between *pre-moral* goods and *moral goods.*

As we were saying above, ethical obligation is the "expression" in our moral conscience and the "impress' in our spirit of the divine Will. When God's Will calls us into being, He wills that we fulfill ourselves. But, given the human person's various dimensions, goods that fulfill his person are arranged on various levels. There are, first of all, *infra-human* goods, not in the meaning that they are of no value to the person, but in the sense that they do not relate to person as such (for example, biological values). Then there are *infra-moral human goods,* meaning that these fulfill the person in what is proper to him (intelligence and will), but not in an absolutely and perfect manner (for example, noetic and esthetic values). Finally, there are *moral goods,* by which a person fulfills himself simply as such, in the sense that they constitute an opening to the Absolute Himself.

Given man's substantial unity, which means that *that by which* he is man is identically *that by which* he is animal, namely a living being, a body, a substance (St. Thomas: cfr. Quest disp. de spiritualibus creaturis, a. 3), we have the following situation: the first two levels of human goods are oriented toward the third and demand to be integrated into it. By this integration the lower values are drawn up, as it were, into the moral Value and share in its absoluteness. In fact, integration consists in placing them into relation to the demands of practical reason as a faculty of the axiological Absolute, and in evaluating them in the light of this relationship.

What is more, this relationship is demanded by the nature of the person as person. The integration of which we speak here constitutes that "living according to reason" which is fulfilling oneself as a person, that is as an image of God. The goods on the infra-human and infra-moral human levels are still found in their identity (materially considered) on the level of moral goods. Nevertheless, in this third area they have changed "form", in the profoundest meaning of that term: they have become *moral* goods, even while retaining their entity as biological goods, and so forth. That is to say, they now connote a relationship with that which constitutes a person as such, his capacity for the Absolute (cfr. a beautiful application of this in IIa, IIae, q. 141. a. 1, ad 1um).

The passage from the level of infra-human goods to that of infra-moral human goods is not of the same order as the next passage into moral goods. The relationship to the Absolute, established on the third level, introduces a radical discontinuity.

In the area of the first two levels and in their comparison, competition is possible. It is not always reasonable to prefer an infra-moral human value to an infra-human value. Since it is a question here of *relative values,* not one of them can demand preference over others as a matter of principle. But when it is a question of moral goods, this situation ceases to apply. How can it be good to prefer anything to the Good? Or — what amounts to the same thing — how can the fulfillment of the person call for an act that does not fulfill him?

At this point one can see that the distinction between pre-moral goods and moral goods, in the meaning given to it by certain moralists today, is untenable. The reasons are various. It is beyond discussion, of course, that human goods are arranged on various levels. Nevertheless *the person is a subject endowed with substantial unity.* If consideration of the *distinction* among the various human goods results in their separation, our theorizing becomes abstract, that is, false. The distinction is not a separation of static goods. Rather, a single polarizing movement crosses the first two levels, orientating and transignifying them towards the Good as such (God who shares Himself with man, man the image of God), without thereby losing their proper nature and consistency.

Moreover, if we admit that man is a substantial unity, and that practical reason is a faculty of the Absolute, as participating in the divine Reason itself, then we also realize that the goods situated on the first two levels cease being mere contingent and relative goods by their integration into the third level. The infra-human and infra-moral human goods become moral goods; they now are necessary and absolute. Competition between them is no longer conceivable, since all are absolute. In short, the substantial unity of man, and the orientation of practical reason towards the Absolute, towards God, exclude the concept of actual pre-moral goods.[4]

Corollary two: The "new" concept of intrinsic good and evil falls short of the real thing

From what has preceded, it follows that the more an act belongs to the subject by reason of its inner, inborn teleology and the more it is part of his spiritual, psychical, and vital "self," so much the more does it reveal itself to the practical reason as either congenial or uncongenial to it. The intrinsic malice of an act consists in its relation of incompatibility with reason; reason is consciously oriented towards Being, which reflects the countenance of absolute Value. This relation is therefore based on the inner and inborn teleology of the act in question *(finis operis).* Hence that act ought never be done. Intrinsically evil, absolutely evil, and unconditionally evil are identical concepts.[5]

At this point one can see the whole equivocation of the position under criticism: the position confuses the concept of *objective malice* with that of *natural malice;* similarly, it confuses the concept of *"finis operis"* of an act with the concept of that act's *"finis naturalis."*

Objective malice, however, is a specifically moral qualification inasmuch as it connotes the ethical impossibility of being performed by a will which is acting rationally; the act is disorderly by reason of its internal teleology. Whereas natural malice would connote only the incapacity of an act to fulfill a faculty of the person understood as nature *(finis naturalis)*, prescinding from its relation to the rational will. Hence, in order that the definition under criticism maintain consistency, it must either deny the existence of *objectively* evil acts, and by doing so fall into the trap of moral relativism; or, to escape this trap, it must reduce objective malice to natural malice. In that case ethics becomes on the one hand a subsidiary of biology, psychology, and sociology, and on the other it becomes an exercise of mere abstractionism; that is, it enunciates only principles that are ultimately no more than abstractions (one must achieve this *natural* good which outweighs the others: *this* is what the activity of the practical reason amounts to).

Corollary three: The meaning of the moral law

With this third corollary we must reject the concept of the moral norm as presented by the moralists cited above. The real moral law constitutes the statement of the relations existing between human acts and the person-image of God; these relations are based on the inner, inborn teleology of the acts themselves. For this reason the moral law is the work of reason as sharer in the eternal Law of God (cfr. Ia IIae, q. 91, a. 2). We can then understand the validity and the profound meaning of an ancient axiom. The relationship of congruence (objectively good act) does not of itself render an act obligatory in a concrete case: *lex positiva valet semper sed non pro semper* (the act must always be judged as good in itself, but that does not mean that one must perform the act; other factors must be taken into account). Quite to the contrary, however, is the case of an incongruent act. The relationship of incongruence (objectively evil act), by itself alone requires that the act must never be performed: *lex negativa valet semper et pro semper.* The moral law, therefore is always valid but it does not always require performance of an action (*valet semper sed non pro semper*); the theorizers are mistaken when they say *ut in pluribus* (in general).

2) *Criticism of the interpretation of the encyclical HUMANAE VITAE*

Sexual activities are actions which possess an objective intentionality of their own, apart from the intention of the subject and the evaluation of public opinion. Were one to deny this, he would implicitly deny the substantial unity of man, through which man's biological faculties are integrated with his spirit, reflecting its demands, and being interiorly regulated by it. Objective intentionality does not of itself and directly mean that the sexual act is *biologically* ordered to a certain end. By affirming this arrangement one merely states a fact. Objective intentionality signifies that a relation exists between the act considered in itself and the practical reason of man. *Insofar as* participating in God's eternal Law, it enjoins on the will the fulfillment of the person as such. The concept of objective intentionality does not signify directly a relation inscribed in the purely biological; rather it signifies a relation, based on the internal teleology of the act, to the practical reason. And it is precisely in this that the intrinsic malice of the contraceptive act consists. It is not precisely a malice of preventing the realization of a biological end (relative good); rather, it is the negative relation existing between this act of impeding and the demands of reason, as understood above (moral evil).

We therefore have a kind of circularity which recurs in the way of knowing peculiar to man, an embodied spirit. The contraceptive act is not congruent with human nature because it is not congruent with reason; but reason does not judge it congruent with itself because it does not perceive it congruent with human nature. Recognizing as incompatible with itself this incongruence with human nature, reason transforms it and turns it into moral incongruence: the infra-moral good (or natural good, or *secundum genus naturae*) enters with the aid of reason into the sphere of morality and becomes endowed with absoluteness because it is a good of the person as such. This is the teaching of *GAUDIUM ET SPES* (51, 3: "from the nature of the human person and human action" *(ex personae eiusdemque actuum natura)*.

From this it follows that the "new" concept which we are criticising must by inner logic either deny the substantial unity of the corporality (sexuality) and spirituality of man, or it must affirm a concept of an autonomy of human reason which is not founded upon its theonomy. Both positions are contrary to ecclesial tradition. The conclusion is clear. If we admit these two theses and consider them jointly, it follows that the contraceptive act is unconditionally, absolutely and intrinsically evil. If we reject both theses or even one of them, it follows that the contraceptive act is conditionally and relatively and only naturally bad.

On the other hand, we cannot conclude from the intrinsic malice of the contraceptive act that conception would be good unconditionally and in every case. Circumstances, as perceived by reason, can forbid its actuation *(lex positiva valet semper, sed non pro semper)*.

One can also see the theoretical inconsistency of the concept of *competitiveness* in this context. If the exercise of sexuality with full respect for its biological finality were only a natural and therefore relative good, such a concept would be correct. But since we are dealing with a formally moral good, we can never affirm that it is competing with another good. One ethical value can never require the sacrifice of another. Since it is a value by reason of the Good as such, it would be like saying that the Good demands that one do evil. This would amount to saying: the Truth demands that reason contradict itself so that reason may know the truth.

Conclusion

The theological theory which we are rejecting takes its start from a real problem: the reality of the difficulties which couples have to face. The right solution, however, is to be sought in the classical theology of conscience, honestly and profoundly understood. But this will be the object of another study.

Footnotes:

1. This clarification is essential. The limits of the discussion are determined solely by inter-human relations and by man's relations with himself. The relation of man to God is excluded, insofar as its value can never be placed below other values.
2. The creative will of God is impressed and expressed in the will by which the spiritual creature wills itself. But, being an image of God, the spiritual creature wills *as* God wills, that is, as a being and insofar as it is a being which shares in His divine Goodness. This means that the will to fulfill oneself coincides with the will to do the good as such (the moral good). The spiritual will truly expresses itself by doing good for goodness's sake (the Christian concept of freedom).
3. The reason for this identity is the identity of the motive or formal object: the divine Being as infinite Goodness, considered in itself and insofar as it communicates itself formally to the spiritual creature (cfr. II, IIae, q. 25, a. 1 et 4). Note that it was an idea dear to the Greek Fathers (cfr., e.g., St. Basil, *Regulae fusius tractatae,* Resp. 2,1; PG 31, 908-910) and to St. Thomas that man is naturally *"capax Summi Boni"* that is, he is oriented towards loving God and others with a love of friendship. "Alioquin," he adds with profound insight, "sequeretur quod naturalis dilectio esset perversa et quod non perficeretur per caritatem, sed destrueretur" (I, q. 60, a. 5c).
4. Let us clarify this thought further. Are human goods, and the person also, contingent and limited? I reply by making a distinction. If the word "good" connotes ontological goodness *(ens et bonum convertuntur),* I agree. If it connotes ethical goodness, I disagree. Assuming that God freely chose to create man, metaphysically we have a contingent good; ethically we have an absolute and unlimited good. The person cannot but be willed for his own sake (a good of absolute value), in the sense that he cannot be an "image of God", "capax Dei" (a good of unlimited value). All the paradoxical greatness of man consists in this: *creatura* (ontologically contingent and limited) – *capax Dei* (ethically absolute and unlimited). That is the

central thesis of Ia IIae Qq. 1-3. This thesis, together with that on the substantial unity of man, is the foundation of all Thomistic ethics.

5. To be more precise, I should say: "Intrinsically" means that the foundation of the relationship lies in the nature of the act. "Absolutely" means that malice does not relate to anything else but the demands of reason as a faculty of the Absolute. "Unconditionally" means that in no case can the action be justified by reason as such.

Bibliography:

J. De FINANCE, *Ethique generale,* Rome, 1962. *Essai sur l'agir humain,* Rome, 1962. *La determination de la norme morale,* Gregorianum 57 (1976) 702-739.

Th. G. BELMANS, *La specification de l'agir humain par son objet chez Saint Thomas,* Excerpta ex dissertatione ad Doctoratum in Fac. Theol. Univ. Gregorianae, Vatican City, 1979.

D. TETTAMANZI, *La H.V. nel decennio 1968-1978. Continuita' di Magistero e riflessione teologica,* La Scuola Cattolica 107 (1979) 3-61.

CHRISTIAN CONSCIENCE AND *HUMANAE VITAE*

Boniface Honings

Because of her stand on grave moral problems in our day such as birth control, access to the sacraments by divorced persons who have remarried, and abortion, the Church is accused of "not being a credible sign of the merciful love which God bears all without exception, and of not living her motherhood of grace toward her most suffering and needy children."[1]

So far as *HUMANAE VITAE* is concerned – and that is precisely what interests us here – such an accusation is baseless. Indeed the very contrary is true.

"The Church, in fact, cannot act differently toward men than does the Redeemer," wrote Pope Paul VI in *HUMANAE VITAE*, 19. "She knows their weakness, has compassion on the multitude, welcomes sinners. But she cannot renounce teaching the law that in reality is proper to human life restored in its original truth and led by the Spirit of God."

In these few pages I shall try to highlight this papal document's pastoral concern for safeguarding the personal responsibility of married couples. I shall deal with the demands of conscience for autonomy and for theonomy; that is, for personal judgment but on the basis of information which agrees with God's norms. The treatment covers theory as well as application to practical life. Finally, I will emphasize participation in the life of the Church, especially in her sacraments, by couples who are "moving gradually" towards the goal of Christian perfection.

1. Autonomous decision and theonomous information

With this title I wish to indicate from the start how conscience is an eminently personal act which binds man, finally, before God. As *GAUDIUM ET SPES* expresses it: "His conscience is man's most secret core and his sanctuary. There he is alone with God whose voice echoes

Boniface Honings, age 58, is professor of moral theology and dean of the Faculty of Theology at the Pontifical Lateran University. He has written numerous articles on sexuality, both general and particularized: on HUMANAE VITAE, divorce, abortion, premarital sex, etc. He contributes to several international scientific reviews and is a consultor of the Pontifical Commission on Justice and Peace.

in his depths" (GS 16). A person who loves God cannot fail to want to know His will *here and now,* in order to commit himself to carry out in the best way possible what he has understood he should do, or to shun what he should not do: "Deep within his conscience man discovers a law which he has not laid upon himself but which he must obey. Its voice, ever calling him to love and to do what is good and to avoid evil, tells him inwardly at the right moment: do this, shun that" (GS 16).

In the depths of his heart man formulates a judgment on the moral value of acting or not acting. He holds what he should do to be in accord with the divine will, and what he should shun to be contrary to the divine will. He decides how he should behave, in the concrete, in order that what he does or does not do may express his desire to obey God.

From this sincere desire to discover and acknowledge the imperatives of the divine law through one's own conscience stems, for everyone, the obligation to respect the decision of conscience. Man is bound to follow it "faithfully in all his activity so that he may come to God, who is his last end. Therefore he must not be forced to act against his conscience. Nor must he be hindered from acting according to it . . . ."[2]

Note that the key expression of the discussion about conscience is *conformity between personal decision and divine will.* The decision is indeed autonomous in the sense that it is the final subjective standard of practical behavior. However this autonomous decision is the final practical norm in the measure in which it correctly interprets the objective moral order established by God. Here we are at the root of the relation between conscience and the Magisterium, and hence of possible difficulties between them.

When Pope Paul VI dealt with responsible parenthood, he specified that it "also and above all implies a more profound relationship to the objective moral order established by God, and of which a right conscience is the faithful interpreter" (HV 10). The privilege of conscience to be autonomous must not be confused with a decision depending solely upon one's own free will. Rather it is conditioned upon, because measured by, the normative will of God. Moreover, Christ has ordained that the divine will find in the Church's Magisterium its only authentic interpreter:

"In the task of transmitting life, they (couples) are not free, therefore, to proceed at will, as if they could determine with the complete autonomy the right paths to follow; but they must conform their actions to the creative intention of God, expressed in the very nature of marriage and of its act, and manifested by the constant teaching of the Church" (HV 10).

Conscience, then, is at once *autonomous and theonomous;* or rather, it is *autonomous because it is theonomous.* From this it follows that the personal decision, besides having subjective qualities such as sincerity and certainty, also and above all has an objective quality: truth. It is precisely this quality, intrinsic to the personal decision, that engages the magisterial mission of the very Church of Christ. In fact, the Catholic Church is by the will of God the teacher of truth. It is her duty to proclaim and to teach with authority the truth which is Christ and, at the same time, to declare and confirm by her authority the principles of the moral order which spring from human nature itself.[3]

It is not the Church's role, therefore, to displace the autonomous decision of conscience. Rather, the Church helps conscience by manifesting authentically the will of God, so that that decision of conscience can be truly ruled by the Wisdom of God.

2. Difficulties of accepting HUMANAE VITAE, and of applying its doctrine

As Christ mediated the knowledge of God's will in the order of the concrete moral decision, so also does the Church. On the occasion of the encyclical of Pope Paul VI on the proper regulation of the transmission of life, various problems of conscience arose concerning this mediating mission of the Magisterium. The various conferences of bishops dealt with them expressly, some more than others. It seems to me that the Bishops of England and Wales present a very precise and complete picture in their document:

"At one time not only Catholics but all Christians held contraception to be abhorrent. In recent years, however, doubts have been expressed about the Church's interpretation of the moral law. The very fact that the Pope created a commission to review the question tended to confirm their doubts. It was soon widely believed that a change in the Church's attitude would be announced. Understandably many wives and husbands, anticipating the promised statement of the Pope, have come to rely on contraception. In this they have acted conscientiously and often after seeking pastoral advice. They may now be unable to see that, at least in their personal circumstances, the use of contraception is wrong. A particular difficulty faces those who after serious thought and prayer cannot as yet understand or be fully convinced of the doctrines as laid down. This is not surprising in view of the discussions of recent years which have resulted in the present controversy. For others the problem of putting the doctrine into practice in their lives seems insuperable because of ill-health or other serious obstacles, sometimes because of a conflict of duties."[4]

The above presents a good characterization of types of persons in difficulties of conscience. After pointing out the climate of openness in regard to methods of regulating births, the document distinguishes two classes of persons: those with *theoretical difficulties*, that is, of acceptance of the moral norm stated by the Magisterium; and those with *practical difficulties,* namely the application of the moral norm to their own conjugal situation. Both classes of people have a right to be taken seriously, precisely because they are not wanting in the religious respect due to the teaching authority of the Church. They fully admit the right and duty of the Magisterium to mediate doctrine about the norms for the moral behavior proper to Christians authentically. Neither the Pope's authority nor the validity of the doctrine taught by him are challenged.

1) *Difficulties of acceptance in regard to theory*

If one starts with the premise that *HUMANAE VITAE* is not an infallible *ex cathedra* declaration, and then goes on to conclude from this that it is not binding absolutely and unconditionally,[5] he may then be able to theorize that a person, especially if he is well informed and competent, may with due reflection in God's sight, adopt a personal judgment which does not agree with that of the Pope. In such a case he would supposedly have a right to follow his own conviction, provided he remain disposed to continue his search honestly.

It is extremely important, however, to clarify terms and conditions in regard to the above theory, in order to avoid simplistic mistakes.

It should be kept in mind, first of all, that a lack of an infallible declaration does not at all mean that the doctrine of *HUMANAE VITAE* lacks binding force upon the consciences of the faithful. Thus the Belgian Episcopal Conference, basing itself on No. 25 of *LUMEN GENTIUM*, writes:

". . . Even in the case where the Pope . . . does not make use of the fullness of his teaching powers, the doctrines prescribed by him, in virtue of the power entrusted to him, demand in themselves on the part of the faithful a religious submission of will and intellect, sustained by the spirit of faith. This adhesion depends not so much on the arguments invoked in the pronouncement as on the religious motive appealed to by the authority sacramentally instituted in the Church."[6]

Furthermore, the conditions needed in order to have a right to follow one's own conviction include sufficient competence and information, a serious examination of conscience before God, a disposition to continue honestly the search for truth, and care to avoid endangering the common good, and others. The Bishops of West Germany wrote as follows in regard to this question:

"One who believes that he should depart from a non-infallible teaching of the Church, both in regard to personal theory and private practice – such a possibility is basically conceivable – must ask himself reflectively and with a critical sense, whether he can do this in a responsible manner before God . . . . One who believes that he may think in this way should examine his conscience to ascertain whether he is free of presumption and superficial concent, and whether he can sustain his point of view responsibly before God. When defending his view he must respect the laws of internal dialogue in the Church, taking care to avoid any scandal. One who proceeds in this way avoids opposition to the properly constituted authority of the Church and to the duty of obedience. Only by proceeding in this way do they contribute to their Christian thinking and manner of life."[7]

The right to follow one's conviction does not at all mean that the conviction is in agreement with objective truth. More: the presumption of truth certainly stands on the side of the Pope, who proposes his doctrine as the constant teaching of the Church. I would therefore venture to state that the convictions of our inquirer, no matter how competent and well informed he may be, rather are mistaken, objectively speaking. Nevertheless, since he has reached his conclusion with honesty and conviction, this conclusion is the basis for his right. Here one applies the principle already formulated by St. Thomas: "Although the judgment of erroneous reason does not derive from God, nevertheless such reason presents the judgment as true and therefore as derived from God on whom all truth depends."[8]

The Church, then, respects the personal decision of conscience. At the same time she enjoins on conscience the duty to continue its search so that it may arrive at objective conformity to the divine will, as the Magisterium of the Church authoritatively manifests it.

From what has been said thus far, it follows that non-acceptance in conscience of *HUMANAE VITAE* is to be judged with pastoral prudence. Certainly, non-acceptance is most often not founded on specific competence in the matter and on adequate information. But even if it were solidly founded, non-acceptance remains subject to the obligation of being questioned by the search for objective truth mediated by the Magisterium.

By this I do not mean to underestimate the effort these believers must make, but I think it is a question of the attitude most proper to a believing Catholic. It is reasonable, in fact, to apply the principle: "I am not convinced by the arguments used, but it is the Church which proposes the teaching to me. For this reason I conduct myself according to the teaching of the Church." The Bishops of West Germany gave directions according to this line:

"A sincere effort to discover the value of a teaching of the Church, also of a temporary one, and to internalize it, is a necessary duty arising from the right attitude of faith in a Catholic. Just as in secular life profound decisions are made on the basis of a sincere but fallible knowledge of another person, so also no one in the Church should feel ashamed or think himself harmed when he prefers the doctrine of the

Church to his own, even though he knows from the beginning that it does not have definitive value . . . ."[9]

2) *Difficulties in regard to practice*

Even where difficulties of a theoretical nature may not exist, or are overcome easily, practical difficulties arising from various reasons may pose obstacles to applying the norms of the encyclical.

The discussion goes into various directions at this point because the factors which can render the application of *HUMANAE VITAE* difficult are of different kinds, and they may affect the subjective "responsibility" of the couple. Such are: a culture excessively preoccupied with sex which strongly conditions persons whose critical judgment has not been developed sufficiently or who are still on the road towards maturity (perhaps they received only minimal instructions before marriage or none at all); the pull of instinct and of contracted habits may be strong; also temptations, moral weakness, a lack of accord between spouses on this question, and similar factors come to mind. In addition to subjective difficulties, spouses frequently face objective difficulties, whether individual or social; and here the discussion becomes even more subtle and delicate.

First of all, we must make clear that the difficulties do have characteristics of an objective nature. Insofar as they are situations in which the couples find themselves, the difficulties are *subjective.* On the other hand, we must take into consideration that they are real, that is *objective* difficulties. "Where the intimacy of married life is broken, it often happens that faithfulness is imperiled and the good of the children suffers: then the education of the children as well as the courage to accept more children are both endangered" (GS 51). In these cases it is customary to speak of a *conflict of duties:* on the one hand, the spouses would fail in their duty to avoid or to postpone a new birth; on the other hand, they would fail in their duty to preserve the stability of their union. To break out of this dilemma the solution proposed is recourse to the principle of *preferential choice* before God. The spouses are supposedly the ones who have to decide, in a particular case, which of the duties is greater.[10]

Certainly, traditional wisdom is acquainted with the principle at issue; it suffices to recall the classic example of the mother facing the dilemma of Sunday Mass and caring for a child who is gravely ill. The mother can perform only one of these duties; by doing one she necessarily omits the other. But she thinks that she sins, whichever choice she makes. Actually, in this so-called situation of perplexity, the mother sins neither subjectively nor objectively. What she does is to make a choice of one over the other, and this in the sight of God. Perplexity exists only in the erroneous conscience, not in any will of God. Since the two values can be separated one from the other, the one which

God wills is the one which a rightly formed conscience chooses in His presence.

Our case concerning difficulties about applying the norm of conjugal morality is different, however. But even here – and this must be said at once – *there is no conflict of duties on the objective level,* that is on the level of God's will. As the Fathers of Vatican II taught: "The Church calls to mind once more that there can be no real contradiction between the divine laws governing the transmission of life on the one hand, and the fostering of a genuine married love on the other" (GS 51). The conflict, however real, is found only on the *subjective level,* that is, in the minds of the spouses. Now, if the solution of preferential choice were valid, the spouses would then be allowed to choose a "unitive" act which, from the point of view of its "procreative" meaning, would be either irresponsible because open to conception, or intrinsically evil because of contraceptive measures. In either case they would be choosing in the sight of God to sin, at least objectively; and even intrinsically if they use a contraceptive measure. The point at issue here is not the ability to achieve one of two values or meanings, the unitive or the procreative; the point is the duty to mean both those values in one and the same act of mutual love, and that is the very conjugal act itself. Only "by so doing, (do) they give proof of love that is truly and fully virtuous" (HV 16). "Consequently it is an error to think that a conjugal act which is deliberately made infertile and so is intrinsically wrong, could be made right by a fertile conjugal life considered as a whole" (HV 14).

The same holds true for all the other reasons which support the various difficulties of applying the moral norms of *HUMANAE VITAE.* There the so-called solution of preferential choice is not acceptable, in our case, because it is in opposition to the basic moral principle: *Bonum est faciendum, malum autem vitandum; non sunt facienda mala ut eveniant bona.*[11] (Do good, but avoid evil; do not perform what is evil in order to achieve a good result.)

It may happen, however, that even while spouses know the objective law of God and therefore the objectivity of sin, they may think that in their own particular subjective situation God does not charge them with sin; or at least that He does not charge them with a serious or mortal sin ("fault"). Not every objective disorder is necessarily, by the very fact of objectivity, a subjective fault. There can be various factors which decrease – or in the extreme case remove entirely – personal responsibility, and therefore moral imputability. "Particular circumstances of *a human act which is objectively evil,* though they cannot transform it into an objectively virtuous act, can render it *inculpable, or less culpable, or subjectively defensible.*"[12] The principle emerges, then, which must guide us in the solution of difficulties in the application of the moral norms of *HUMANAE VITAE:* a lessening of the gravity of the sin is possible.

Obviously, it can happen here, as in other areas, that there is a *"de facto"* case of an erroneous judgment of conscience. A shepherd of souls is obliged to respect this, if the error is invincible. There remains, however, an obligation to look for a way of conduct that will permit adapting one's behavior to the norm willed by God and manifested by the Church.

3. Participation in sacramental life

What we have said until now has application especially in the administration of the sacraments. As the Bishops of West Germany wrote:

"Therefore the shepherds of souls will respect the personal decisions of the consciences of the faithful in their ministry, and especially in the administration of the sacraments."[13]

The point is brought home by Pope Paul VI:

"The Church, while teaching the inviolable demands of divine law, announces the tidings of salvation, and by means of the sacraments opens up the paths of grace, which makes of man a new creature, capable of corresponding in love and authentic freedom to the design of his Creator and Savior, and of experiencing the gentleness of the yoke of Christ" (HV 25).

The problem of recourse to the sacraments is to be resolved not only with the criterion of the possible lessening of grave guilt (not to be confused with the principle of the lesser evil), but also with the criterion of the *gradualness of progress towards the ideal of Christian perfection.* The Conference of the Bishops of France observes:

"It may happen that some Christian spouses admit that they are guilty of not responding to the demands explained by the encyclical. Let their faith and their humility help them not to become discouraged. Let them be convinced that the failings of spouses, who are otherwise generous in their personal and apostolic life, are not comparable in gravity to the failings of couples who scorn this teaching and who allow themselves to be dominated by selfishness and the search for pleasure. They must not keep away from the sacraments, but should do quite the contrary."[14]

So Pope Paul VI writes to priests:

"Teach married couples the indispensable way of prayer; prepare them to have recourse often and with faith to the sacraments of the Eucharist and of Penance, without ever allowing themselves to be discouraged by their own weakness" (HV 29).

At this point I think I should clarify what is meant by an authentic pastoral program based on the principle of "gradualness" with reference to the reception of the sacraments.

1) *The Principle of "Gradualness"*

The principle of gradualness applies to all sectors of moral life, and therefore to the sexual life of spouses too. We find rhythms of growth here which vary from couple to couple, and from time to time in the same couple. A statement by the Bishops of Italy is appropos:

"Finally, a special and fatherly invitation must be extended to Christian spouses .... They should not feel downhearted because of any failures. The Church, whose duty it is to teach goodness in its totality and perfection, is aware that there are *laws of growth in goodness,* and that now and then a person may be moving ahead through still imperfect degrees, but aiming sincerely to move beyond them in a constant striving toward the 'ideal'."[15]

And the Bishops of France:

"The encyclical stimulates us to set out on the road. Man moves forward on the path of holiness only with patient steps, now falling, now rising again. Every day is a little battle, sustained by hope. Every existence is intermingled with good and evil. What is essential is that, despite this ambiguity, the sense of life and of love move ahead in sincere fidelity to truth."[16]

However even this principle of gradualness must be rightly understood. What it requires, first of all, is that a couple really "set out on the journey." Then, the couple must travel toward a goal which is clearly defined. Finally, the couple must take steps which are possible for them in their concrete situation. What finally characterizes gradualness is not so much the weaknesses or the failures, or even the difficulties to overcome along the way, as perseverance in efforts to move forward along the way of the Lord.

The criterion in judging gradualness is of a positive nature:

"For this reason spouses are fortified and, as it were, consecrated for the duties and dignity of the state by a special sacrament; fulfilling their conjugal and family role by virtue of this sacrament, spouses are penetrated with the spirit of Christ and their whole life is suffused with faith, hope, and charity; thus they increasingly further their own perfection and their mutual sanctification, and together they render glory to God" (GS 48).

In other words, the spouses should find "in sacramental participation in the love of the Lord Jesus not only the sublime model but also the effective stimulus so that their life be shaped day by day as a following and imitation of Christ, as growth in mutual communion and in dedication to their children, in service and mission within the Church, in love and concern for everyone, and in desire and hope for the glory of God."[17]

Thus gradualness embraces the vast gamut of commitments belonging to a communion of life and Christian love, and modeled on the spousal love between Christ and the Church. Here it is obvious that not all duties are fulfilled with the same perfection and the same intensity, and so there is really room for failing in one or more duties. It will be up to the spiritual shepherd to evaluate prudently to what extent the spouses' judgment of conscience conforms to objective truth where they do not feel themselves separated from God's love.

2) *Sacramental Life*

In the light of the principle of gradualness, in the positive sense set forth above, we can also face the problem of the spouses' participation in the Church's sacraments. We know that the sacraments are not concessions meant only for such of the faithful who do not sin gravely because of their weakness; nor are they mere aids to overcome certain difficulties of life. The sacraments are, more than anything else, peak moments of encounter with Christ to actuate His work of redemption. And so they are important moments in the process of moral and spiritual growth in the Christian life, both personal and ecclesial.

This applies basically to the Eucharist. The Church desires of the faithful: "Offering the immaculate victim, not only through the hands of the priest, but also together with him, they should learn to offer themselves. Through Christ, the Mediator, they should be drawn day by day into ever more perfect union with God and each other, so that finally God may be all in all."[18] Participation in the Eucharistic Sacrifice means, for the spouses, a perfecting of their unity, which could be better expressed and effected if they would nourish themselves with the Body of Christ.[19] This explains why Paul VI, addressing himself to Christian spouses, writes: "Let married couples, thus face up to the efforts needed, supported by faith and hope . . . . Let them implore divine assistance by persevering prayer; *let them, especially in the Eucharist, draw from the source of grace and charity*" (HV 25).

Of course, the spouses need to be in the state of grace in order to be able to express and effect their communion of life and love through the Eucharist. And here we come to the Sacrament of Reconciliation. Returning with humble perseverance to God's mercy, they can realize the fulness of conjugal life as the Apostle describes it in the fifth chapter of the Letter to the Ephesians, in terms of mutual love. The spouses, while they make of their lives the experience of God's mercy and proclaim it, celebrate with the priest the liturgy of the Church, which is continually converting and renewing herself:

"Therefore the celebration of this sacrament is always an act of the Church, by it the Church proclaims her faith, gives thanks to God for the freedom with which Christ has freed us, offers her life as a spiritual sacrifice to the praise and glory of God, and hastens to meet Christ the Lord."[20]

Conclusion

Such is the pastoral stance of *HUMANAE VITAE.* It is a positive perspective of sacramental life that permits all Christian spouses and, in particular, those who are coping with difficulties in accepting or applying, in conscience, the moral norm willed by God and manifested by the authentic Magisterium of the Church, to pursue an authentic route of the Christian life, marked by a gradualness that is lived sincerely.

Without diminishing in any way the saving doctrine of Christ, Pope Paul VI wants spouses to be accompanied by the understanding and patience of which the Redeemer Himself gave an example in dealings with men. Though intransigent against evil, He was certainly patient and merciful towards sinners (Cf. HV 29).

Hence, the Congregation of the Clergy stipulates:

"While the counselor has the obligation of giving an objective judgment on the data at hand, he should not presume too hastily, on the one hand, that the person is completely innocent; nor should he, on the other hand, judge too hastily that the person is deliberately refusing the divine commandment of love, in the case of a person who is honestly trying to lead a good Christian life."[21]

Footnotes:

1. Conference of the Bishops of Italy, *Pastoral Letter concerning those divorced and remarried, and those who live in irregular marriages, and difficult situations,* (1979) No. 30.
2. *Declaration on Religious Liberty* (DH) No. 3.
3. *Ibid.* No. 14.
4. Declaration of the Conference of Bishops of England and Wales, concerning *HUMANAE VITAE and the Episcopal Magisterium.* L. SANDRI, Bologna 1969, No. 148. We will give the reference according to the numbers of this collection in the notes about statements of Bishops Conferences which follow.
5. Bishops of Belgium, No. 80.
6. Bishops of Belgium, No. 81.
7. Bishops of West Germany, No. 46 and 59.
8. St. Thomas, *Summa Theologica* I-II, 19, 5, ad 1.
9. Bishops of West Germany, *Letter to those who have received from the Church the commission to announce the Gospel*, September 22, 1967.
10. Bishops of France, No. 263.
11. "In truth, if it is sometimes licit to tolerate a lesser evil in order to avoid a greater evil or to promote a greater good, it is not licit, even for the gravest reasons, to do evil so that good may follow therefrom; that is, to make into the object of a positive act of the will

something which is intrinsically disorder, and hence unworthy of the human person, even when the intention is to safeguard or promote individual, family or social well-being" (HV 14).

12. *Declaration of the Congregation for the Clergy*, April 26, 1971, II, 4.
13. Bishops of West Germany, No. 63.
14. Bishops of France, No. 262
15. Bishops of Italy, No. 103.
16. Bishops of France, No. 258.
17. Bishops of Italy, Pastoral Document, *Evangelization and the Sacrament of Matrimony* (1975) No. 52.
18. *Sacrosanctum Concilium (Constitution on the Sacred Liturgy)* No. 48.
19. Cfr. Bishops of Italy, Document cited, No. 37 and 86.
20. *Ordo Poenitentiae, Praenotanda*, No. 7.
21. *Document of the Congregation for the Clergy*, April 26, 1971, III, 2.

Bibliography:

D. CAPONE, *La coscienza morale nelle discussioni sulla HUMANAE VITAE*, Rome, 1969.

E. QUARELLO, *La HUMANAE VITAE: le conferenze episcopali e l'obiezione di coscienza:* Rivista di Teologia Morale 1 (1969) 63-83.

D. TETTAMANZI, *Sacramenti e spiritualita conjugale*, Roma 1967.

B. HONINGS, *Il principio de inscindibilita. Un segno per due significati:* Lateranum 44 (1978) 169-194.

J. VISSER, *La coscienza e l'enciclica HUMANAE VITAE:* Lateranum 44 (1978) 228-242.

THE ROLE OF CONTINENCE IN CONJUGAL LIFE

Edouard Hamel

Spouses are surely aware of the inevitability of periodic continence in their conjugal life, that is of periods of time during which sexual intercourse is either not possible or not advisable. Circumstances frequently impose a genital pause. Such are, for example, times of illness, the period of the immediate postpartum, periods of physical separation (because of travelling, for example) and times for spacing births. Even if such situations are not always ideal (cf. *GS* 51, 1), they must be foreseen and accepted.

Furthermore, spouses can agree to observe such periods of sexual abstinence, either for religious and spiritual motives (1 Cor 7, 5), or for the sake of improving the marriage; for example, to acquire an increasingly deep understanding of each other. Total mutual knowledge of the spouses is not identified with sexual experience alone, nor can it be reduced to it. The life-story of a couple is not made up exclusively of their sexual life. If it were, everything would happen on the superficial level of a corporal component which would be detached, almost, from the rest of personhood. The couple is capable of a language of love not confined to the sexual act. Unfortunately, some people seem to have no other way of knowing each other than through sexual relations. "Adam knew Eve his wife, and she conceived" (Gn 4, 1). Is this the only way husbands can know their wives?

Once sexual abstinence is agreed upon by the spouses, however, they ought to transform it into a positive experience. Abstinence as such does not possess any sanctifying virtues. It necessarily leaves a void which cries to be filled and compensated for on other levels, by some sort of activity in the family, or apostolic or spiritual activity.

EDOUARD HAMEL, S.J., was born in Quebec in 1920. Since 1962 he has been teaching moral theology at the Gregorian University in Rome. Among his publications are the following: Loi naturelle et loi du Christ, Bruges, 1964; Les dix paroles, Bruges, 1969. He has also contributed to the following collections: Fondamenti biblici della teologia morale, Brescia, 1973; Ortodossia e revisionismo, Rome, 1974; Christlich Glauben und Handeln, Duesseldorf, 1977; In libertatem vocati estis, Rome, 1977; Problèms doctrinaux du marriage chrétien, Louvain-la-Neuve, 1979. Father Hamel is a past member of the International Theological Commission.

St. Paul, speaking of times of sexual abstinence in the lives of married couples, says that these periods should be decided upon "by mutual consent for a time, to devote themselves to prayer" (1 Cor 7, 5). To designate such *time* he does not use the word *kronos,* meaning mere chronological succession, but *kairos,* which indicates a time of salvation. Through docility to the Holy Spirit, a couple will be able to discern these moments of grace and, according to the advice of the Apostle, they will establish a link between sexual abstinence and religious activity.

Periods of sexual abstinence also serve to intensify the so-called love of affection. During these times, the spouses can rediscover the meaning of interpersonal relations, achieved through words, gestures, tenderness, and other manifestations of affection, each spouse being ever more attentive to the other, speaking heart to heart till they touch one another's heart.

Human sexuality and its dynamics are not limited to genital activities. If a couple desire to space births for reasons of the marriage, and so abstain during the days when the two organisms are ready to cooperate with God the Creator, they can learn to love each other in a different way, and to become more humane in their most instinctive responses. To the question: "How much body is needed for an *optimum* of spirit?" Teilhard de Chardin replied: "A gradual increase in affective love with a gradual decrease in sexual relations."

In fact, as some psychologists have shown, sexual pleasure is not the only guarantee of conjugal happiness. Even to renounce the use of sexuality, when freely accepted and properly motivated, can create a period of interpersonal growth, a deepening of the couple's relationship, perhaps even its purification (through control over addiction to sexual pleasure).

Affective love, which is different from physical genital love, is a basic requirement of marriage, and perhaps its strongest bond. It enables the couple to overcome crises and difficulties, and it appears to be the secret of happy marriages. If the two partners are full of affection for each other and know how to show it by meaningful gestures, and if they are happy to be together as human persons for reasons other than simple erotic stimulus, they will reach an understanding of each other that goes deeper than the one deriving from mere physical union.

According to John Paul II, continence in marriage is an indispensable condition not only for responsible parenthood, but also for conjugal love:

"On this plane (of responsible parenthood) the spouses, the parents, may meet with a certain number of problems which cannot be solved without deep love, a love which comprises also an effort of continence. These two virtues, love and continence, appeal to a common decision of the spouses and to their will to submit to the doctrine of the Faith, to the teaching of the Church" (Oss. Rom. Nov. 4, 1979).

Unfortunately, in the consumer society in which we live today, the body is facilely considered an unlimited source of sexual pleasure, to be used as freely and intensely as possible. People speak of the *right* to sexual pleasure, which is vaunted as the great secret of a happy marriage. With this orientation the sexual relation runs the risk of being no longer an interpersonal relation, but of taking on all the characteristics of an economic exchange: sexuality becomes a consumer item, and the person a thing.

Against this, Freud understood quite well that sexual life cannot be reduced to the mere search for pleasure. Frankl wrote: "For one who seeks sexual pleasure as if it were an end in itself, pleasure departs." It is a law of psychology. People today are frightened by the words *chastity*, *continence*, and *self-control*. As a result many find themselves in the situation of the governor Felix before the prisoner Paul: "As Paul talked on about continence and the coming judgment, Felix became frightened and exclaimed: 'That's enough for now! You can go!' " (Acts 24, 25)

Self-giving and continence in marriage

The full realization of sexual communion supposes in the couple the capacity for self-giving in the fullness of one's person. Two persons who are not fully integrated or unified can only with difficulty be united, since the unintegrated sectors of their persons, that is, the sectors which are not fully possessed, are not included in the gift of self. When it is a question of interpersonal giving, the juridical axiom, "*nemo dat quod non habet*" (no one gives what he doesn't have), changes to "*nemo dat quod non est*" (no one gives what he isn't). What we *have* we can divide among many; but when a person gives himself in his corporality, he gives what he *is*, and his gift is indivisible and therefore exclusive. Now, dominion over self, which is required for authentic interpersonal giving, can be helped by periods of sexual abstinence, to the great advantage of love itself.

A condition for the giving of self is possession of self. Self-dominion is possible to the human person by reason of his being able to stand at a distance from what is immediate: man can distance himself from his own impulses and desires; he can create a space between a desire and its fulfillment. This capacity is a condition for all genuine spiritual and human understanding.

Man's behavior, unlike that of animals, is not predetermined by instinctual patterns. While the rule of the animal is momentary satisfaction, the human person possesses a stupendous capacity to temper his genital reactions and his instincts, so as to place them at the service of his vocation and mission.

While animals are like machines with an automatic pilot, the human person instead possesses a great ability to modify his sexual behavior, to organize and to change it according to his plans. But the animal is sure of itself, while the human person lacks that sureness which would come from a strict determinism. For a person the difficulties are greater than for an animal; but the possibilities are also greater.

But does not continence risk creating tensions and frustrations that dehumanize the couple? Harmful frustrations will occur only if the various needs and impulses are simply repressed, forced underground, so to speak, into a subconscious life. This will not happen if they are integrated into a plan of life. To be sure, renouncing one's desires and demands will provoke a certain amount of tension. But the mature person is able to transform it into *tension of growth,* accepting it, giving it positive orientation towards progressive growth, and connecting it with the fulfillment of his ideals. In other words, there are "normal," constructive conflicts which, if accepted and properly resolved, cause the person to grow in humanity.

The more mature the couple, the more they will know how to accept tensions that are at once unavoidable and indispensable to growth. Conjugal chastity is not given to spouses whole and entire on their wedding day. Like the other moral virtues, chastity is the result, never fully achieved, of a slow, gradual and at times difficult process, that must always forge ahead: *castitas semper maior.* The human person is capable of transforming instinctive pleasures into higher forms, no longer dominated by *libido,* but inspired by loftier sentiments. Even the human spirit and the heart have their pleasures! There is in every person a love for the moral good, an affective force prompting the person from within to temper and check his instincts and desires, to keep his distance from them. This allows him to achieve growth towards maturity and to free himself from selfish ways. The more one forgets himself and makes a gift of himself, the more does he fulfill himself: "Man truly discovers his true self only in a sincere giving of himself," as Vatican II declares (*GS* 24, 4). There is a footnote to this passage which quotes the text of Luke 17, 33: "Whoever seeks to gain his life will lose it, but whoever loses his life will preserve it." In marriage the tension rising from sexual renunciation can help the couple overcome certain selfish attitudes which impede the perfect integration of the person and consequently his capacity to give himself fully.

Continence and the grace of Christ

On their journey towards conjugal chastity, a journey that is long and strenuous but unifying and integrating, the couple find help in a final dynamic element, the grace of Christ, which operates also in the psychic structures of persons, provided they are open to its liberating action. Christ comes to meet the spouses through the Sacrament of Matrimony and remains with them, pledging to help them. In this way they are strengthened and, as it were, consecrated (*GS* 50, 3). Helped by Christ, they find the strength to be fully human even in the sexual area. The "You must" becomes a "You can." The ability of the spouses to conduct a human sexual life that includes periodic continence is enhanced by their relationship with Christ.

When St. Thomas, along with other theologians, asked himself whether marriage is a sacrament, he objected: "The sacraments receive their efficacy from the passion of Christ. But in marriage, which involves pleasure, man is not conformed to the passion of Christ, which was painful." He replies as follows: "Although marriage does not conform one to the passion of Christ as regards suffering, nevertheless this conformity is produced *as regards charity,* by which He accepted the passion in order to unite the Church to Himself as His spouse" (*Suppl.* 42, 1 ad 3um). Marriage is not the sacrament of sexual pleasure but of love. Spouses cannot give themselves to each other completely, with respect for each other, without dying to themselves, that is, without renunciation: love and sacrifice are intimately connected.

A glance at history

One cannot deny that in the history of Western Christianity there are currents of Platonic spirituality hostile to the body. Underlying these currents is a non-biblical dualism which sees in the genital expression of human sexuality a kind of structural defect in man, originally not foreseen by the Creator. In this perspective of sexual pessimism the word *chastity* can easily be considered not as integration but as rupture or evasion. Conquering sexual allurement is the supreme expression of the triumph of spirit over flesh. The expression "perfect chastity" denotes exclusively virginity or consecrated celibacy, as if chastity had no place in the lives of married people.

But one must admit honestly that the sexual pessimism encountered in history depends also on non-Christian or outright non-religious elements. When the Church announced the message of salvation in the Greco-Roman world, she found secular currents that attacked sexuality as demeaning to man. Theories hostile to the body and to the exercise of sexuality derived from Persian dualism, the mystery cults, and Stoicism. Paul found, especially in Corinth, an asceticism which held in contempt the body and the world. Precisely in response to this dualistic anthropology, Paul gave us his theology on the vocation of the human body and proclaimed the nobility of the human person in his body and his consecration in Christ.

Later, with the arrival of bourgeois society, a sexual pessimism arose that was in no way inspired by religious motives. It suffices to think of the great influence of J.J. Rousseau and of the Philanthropists of the eighteenth century, when a climate hostile to sexuality spread in Europe. In the nineteenth century A. Comte justified the sexual act solely by generation. It is not surprising that the use of sexuality, always a problem in the history of cultures, of moral systems and of religions, has given rise to problems in Christianity also.

The Church has been able to emphasize in an original way the fundamental and transcultural ambiguity inherent in the use of sexuality. This she has done by sustaining a permanent tension and a constant dialectic between the value of marriage willed by the Creator and sanctified by Christ, and the value of continence in imitation of Christ. The simultaneous affirmation of the goodness of marriage and continence underlines – *but does not create* – the fundamental ambiguity linked to sexuality, and as a result it relativizes its exercise even in marriage itself. From this flow the possibility and the positive meaning of periodic continence. The tension between marriage and continence has succeeded in creating unilateral exaggerations in the past, and it can still do so today, but it must be maintained since it is a specific element of the Christian message.

The two vocations or choices of life – marriage and continence for the kingdom of heaven – aid each other, each helping the other to a better understanding of the other's deep roots. That a vocation be genuine, there must be a choice, and that is possible at least between two paths. Continence sheds light on the value of marriage as a responsible choice willed by the Creator and sacramentalized by Christ, but not a norm obliging everyone. Marriage sheds light on continence, which is not a rejection of, nor contempt for, a depreciated state of life, but a conscious and free renunciation of a desirable value that is accessible to all; nor is continence a dehumanizing failure, but a personal choice permitting openness and availability.

Moreover, when the vocation to continence is despised, so too is the vocation to marriage. If the response to the vocation to continence becomes rare, marriage faces the risk of being reduced to the merely natural or material level. On the other hand, spouses who are faithful to their pledge of love and who have experienced in their marriage the value of periodic continence practiced in a certain sense "for the kingdom of heaven" (cf. 1 Cor 7, 5), often become in their children the source of consecrated virginity: "He who is able to receive this, let him receive it" (Mt 19, 12).

Bibliography:

A. CHAPELLE, *Sexualité et sainteté*, Brussels, 1977.
A. PLE, *Vita affettiva e castità*, Rome, 1965.

D. TETTAMANZI, *La visione cristiana della castità*, Presenza Pastorale, 46 (1976) 455-477.
W.P. CUNNINGHAM, *Abstinence: compatible with married love*, Homiletic and Pastoral Review, 76 (1975) 23-29.
E. POUSSET, *Union conjugale et liberté*, Paris, 1970.
PAUL VI, *Address to the Equipes Notre Dame*, AAS 62 (1970) 428-437.

THE MAGISTERIUM OF THE POPE AND OF THE EPISCOPAL CONFERENCES; THE THEOLOGICAL QUALIFICATION OF THE DOCTRINE EXPRESSED IN THE ENCYCLICAL *HUMANAE VITAE*

Marcellino Zalba

Debate over the doctrinal value of Paul VI's encyclical *HUMANAE VITAE* on methods of regulating birth loses none of its interest and contemporaneity with the passing of time. Its interest is explained by the document's implications for the behavior of the faithful. It remains to the fore, perhaps because neither theologians nor spiritual shepherds who have discussed it are convinced by its argumentation, while the faithful who follow them do not feel easy in conscience, and continue to confess their way of behaving.

It is a delicate problem to seek to attach a *theological note* (qualifying the doctrinal value) of the teaching which affirms the essential immorality of contraceptive practices. In fact, one will have to analyze what some conferences of bishops have formulated (or are said to have formulated) in doubtful harmony with the encyclical. Besides, one cannot avoid taking into account the diverse (and at times contrasting) arguments presented by theologians who have criticized the encyclical, however hasty some of their positions, and however well-founded the suspicion that a good number of them wanted chiefly to excuse contraception in some cases on grounds of the circumstances and the honest purpose of the person acting, and sought arguments where they could find them.

We shall consider first the alleged difference between the Pope's doctrinal magisterium (abstract and theoretical, which points out the

MARCELLINO ZALBA, a native of Spain, was born in 1908. Entered the Society of Jesus in 1924; obtained a licentiate in philosophy in 1932; a licentiate in theology in 1938; a doctorate in theology from the Gregorian University in 1941. He taught moral theology in the Jesuit school of theology in Oña (Burgos) from 1941 to 1960. He has been teaching at the Gregorian University since 1960. As professor emeritus he taught special courses in 1978 and 1979. His works are as follows: Theologiae Moralis Summa, 3 vol.; Theologiae Moralis Summarium (auctore olim P. Arregui), revised from the 13th to the 23rd edition; Compendio de Teologia Moral (an adaption of the Summarium), 6th edition from 1945 to 1965); Regulacion de la Natalidad (Madrid, 1968); Las Conferencias Episcopales ante la Humanae Vitae (Madrid, 1971). He has also written 173 articles.

ideal to be achieved by the spouses) and the pastoral magisterium of the episcopal conferences (concrete and practical, which realistically declares what the situations in conjugal life demand). We shall then present what refers not to the encyclical and to the magisterial act of Paul VI, but to the traditional doctrine of the Church reaffirmed in that act, and to the characteristics with which that doctrine presents itself for the purpose of eliciting our assent. Finally, we shall propose the *theological note* which, in the light of the data available for determining it, seems to apply to the doctrine.

1. Alleged contrast between the encyclical and the collective pastoral letters

The bishops received in the encyclical a pressing invitation to work "zealously and incessantly . . . to safeguard marriage and keep it holy, so that it may ever be lived more and more in all its human and Christian fullness" (*HV* 30). At the request of the Pope the Cardinal Secretary of State asked of them "that in this circumstance they should stand beside him as never before, to present to the Christian people this delicate subject of the Church's doctrine, explaining and justifying its profound reasons." He added that it was "necessary to make spouses understand all the spiritual riches brought by the effort at renunciation demanded of them . . .; to persuade them that it is possible, with the grace of God which never puts man to a test beyond his strength, to progress in chastity and in the other virtues . . . . You must finally make every pastoral effort so that there remain no ambiguity either among the faithful or in public opinion on the Church's position in this grave matter" (July 20, 1968).

Most conferences of bishops were able without difficulty to follow these recommendations in presenting the encyclical to their respective flocks. A small number of them found themselves facing the danger of a strong reaction against the encyclical on the part of many of the faithful, with the risk that the refusal would spread massively by contagion, The Pope vigorously disowned the rash opinion which, with the approval of some theologians and confessors, was asserted in certain countries; and he condemned the practice which was taking root in various countries, especially in Central Europe and in America. For this reason many conferences felt bound to speak on the possibility of "dissent" with the non-fallible magisterium by members of the Church *competent* in the matter; on the primacy of conscience in final decisions; on the practical difficulties that can cloud judgment when real conflicts of value seem to be conflicts of duties; and on a certain feeling of helplessness in fulfilling immediately the Christian ideal. In all this they demonstrated a reasonable understanding of human frailty, even though many times they did not make sufficient mention of the supernatural aids that strengthen human weakness, as the Pope and his Secretary of State had done.

All this the bishops recalled in accordance with traditional doctrine, even though to ardent souls their statements seemed to bear a tone of novelty and to go beyond the limited field attributed to the encyclical. What may have contributed to this interpretation were the dissenting attitude of theologians searching for differences in language and concepts, and the not entirely happy and clear formulation of some sensitive points of the pastoral letters. This, however, was quite understandable, since the bishops could not in a matter of weeks weigh expressions with the same accuracy as the encyclical had through years of preparation. In fact, some conferences (Canada, Australia, Indonesia, Mexico at a later date) subsequently explained their thinking when faced with mistaken interpretations.

We must, then keep these considerations in mind while attempting a fair assessment of the episcopal magisterium on the encyclical. But to discover the truth about the alleged divergence between the pastoral magisterium of the conferences of bishops and the doctrinal magisterium of the encyclical, other considerations must be brought forward. Among these are the following:

As Paul VI pointed out to Archbishop Marcel Lefebvre,[1] there can be no adequate distinction between dogmatic doctrine and pastoral doctrine by differentiating the nature (not the degree) of the assent due to the faith to be professed and to the faith to be applied to life (*Lumen Gentium* 25, 1).

To maintain that there is real disagreement between the Pope and the bishops, especially in view of the preceding observations, valid proofs would be needed. In our judgment they do not exist, or at least have never been produced. On the contrary, there exist very meaningful counterproofs:

The great majority of conferences stated either explicitly or in a manifestly implicit way their total agreement with the Pope. Some also expressed their profound gratitude for the support he gave to their concerns (Latin America and the Third World in general). Others assured the Pope of their firm support and urged the faithful to do so (United States, Mexico, Poland, East Germany, southern Europe). Others were concerned about restraining and remedying the resistance they feared would follow, without, however, calling in doubt the validity of the papal document (Belgium, Austria, Scandinavia, England, Canada). Some were at least ambiguous or confusing on certain points, but without claiming to disagree (France, Austria, Indonesia, South Africa).

In fact, it should be noted that even in those pastoral letters that are cited as disagreeing with the encyclical, there is acknowledgment of its doctrine.[2] Some letters deplore "the criticisms full of rancor and the erroneous interpretations of the encyclical" (cf. Switzerland 303), or they recall the duty of listening to the Pope's appeal "with the interior disposition of assent" (West Germany 32).

When we consider these endorsements dispassionately and we take into account the circumstances leading to the drafting of the pastoral letters, we think it impossible to find any real divergences between the papal teaching and that of the bishops. Neither is it possible to discover in the latter a departure from the clear and unconditional affirmations of the former regarding their application to help married people in the concrete; nor can any valid evidence by found that some pastoral letters threw a damper on the encyclical. In the majority of cases the letters only tried to render the encyclical accessible and acceptable by explaining its contents in greater depth and by supporting it with considerations of their own. In general, they wished to take into account theoretical and practical difficulties, thus demonstrating an understanding which, in our view, has been erroneously interpreted, partly because of the infelicitous phrasing of this or that passage of some pastoral letters, which happened to contradict statements found in the same letter.

Apart from this, it comes as a surprise to note the generalization of the alleged difference between the doctrinal magisterium of the Pope and the pastoral magisterium of the bishops. The entire third part of the encyclical (19 to 31) is as pastoral as are the episcopal documents, a fact which many bishops acknowledge; and the pastoral applications made by the bishops are based on the teaching of the encyclical. It could not be otherwise if the Gospel "is the source of every saving truth and of the entire discipline of morals" (Denzinger-Schönmetzer 1501). Moreover, if we look at the number of pastoral letters and of bishops, the group openly declaring that they support the encyclical is by far the larger.

2. Doctrine of the Church on the artificial regulation of birth

Against the claim, contrary to reality, that some conferences went beyond the limits set by the Pope to the licit exercise of marriage, there is need here of calling to mind the Catholic teaching, so that no one may remain confused or deceived by a supposed disagreement between the papal intransigence that pointed out the essential order based on absolute moral norms and the episcopal openness that attributed objective validity to certain exceptions in the existential order.

By their consecration bishops receive the office of teaching authentically in the Church (*Lumen Gentium* 21, 2) and are sacramentally strengthened with the "sure charism of truth" (*Dei Verbum* 8, 2): thus their teaching ministry is given the presumption of truth. But diocesan bishops feed their flocks *under the authority of the Roman Pontiff* (*LG* 11, 2), even when they do so on their own authority (*LG* 27, 2). It follows that they must be respected as witnesses of the divine and Catholic truth when they teach *in union with the Roman Pontiff* (*LG* 25, 1). For this reason, in gauging the authenticity or the value of their teaching, we cannot prescind from the phrases underlined. To be heedworthy, bishops must teach in communion with the Pope,[3] since "the body of bishops has no authority unless united with the Roman Pontiff" (*LG* 22, 2).

In light of this indisputable doctrine all arguments fail which attempt to set up the pastoral letters against the encyclical or to diminish the value of the encyclical by the fact that it has taken a stand on a topic debated by theologians and bishops. Such attempts would fail even if we acknowledged a basis for certain distinctions made by theologians, but which seem to us indefensible, between the merely prudential magisterium regarding the non-revealed natural law (a magisterium exercised by virtue of the power to govern, and valid only insofar as its reasons are valid), and the doctrinal magisterium deriving from the power to teach, and valid on the basis of the guarantee given to reason by the assistance of the Holy Spirit.

In conclusion, where there is a hypothetical discordance between the papal magisterium and the episcopal magisterium, the former should prevail as the teaching of the Church.

On the other hand, it must also be clearly stated that what the encyclical proposes is not only the teaching of Paul VI, but the teaching professed by the faithful and traditionally proclaimed by the magisterium of the Holy See and of the bishops of the Church "with constant firmness" (*HV* 6).

In the title, I have intentionally referred to the doctrine *expressed in the encyclical*, not to the doctrine *of the encyclical*. Actually, there can be a great difference between the formulation of a doctrine and the mode of formulation. The encyclical, as a document of the ordinary magisterium, is undoubtedly fallible by itself. This was pointed out by several conferences (e.g., France 240, Scandinavia 212) in statements which in some cases (cf. Austria 121) could have been more exactly worded to avoid erroneous interpretations on the part of the faithful. But from this it does not follow that the encyclical could not express a doctrine that is infallibly true and irreformable for another reason. One can hardly find an encyclical that does not contain some infallible proposition. Such can be case with *Humanae Vitae*; not only when it affirms, for example, that Christ made the Apostles the authentic interpreters of the law of the Gospel (4, 2), but also when it declares intrinsically and objectively immoral every act which is directly or indirectly contraceptive (14, 3-4).

Right in this line, two outstanding American professors, Ford and Grisez,[4] well known as experts on the subject, published on the tenth anniversary of the encyclical a documented article. Their discussion, pursued with clear and well-weighed reasoning, focuses on the conditions laid down by Vatican II[5] for teachings on faith and morals to be held infallibly true. They conclude in a convincing manner that such conditions are present in the Catholic tradition expressed in No. 14 of the encyclical, referring to the artificial regulation of birth.

These authors found a first proof in the doctrine presented in 12, 1 of the constitution *Lumen Gentium,* containing an idea from St. Robert Bellarmine, a Doctor of the Church. This idea, which was being prepared for definition in Vatican I, is that in a *Church* established to profess truth and to sanctify itself through doing good, it is not possible over a long period of time and throughout the world for a notable error to prevail among the People of God in a matter of faith and morals. (We would add: especially when the matter is one of great importance and of constant application, as in the case under discussion.) The Council says: "The whole body of the faithful, who have the anointing of the Holy Spirit, cannot err in matters of belief. This characteristic is manifested by the supernatural *appreciation of the faith of the entire people* when, 'from the bishops to the last of the faithful,' they manifest a universal consent in matters of faith and morals."

What is stressed is the value of the *sensus fidelium,* which today is frequently invoked inopportunely, but which here finds its real application; not a *sensus* which constitutes truth, but which *manifests* it. It is also clear that once the truth is professed by the People of God (not because of the opinion of men of good will nor because of an opinion deriving from an ecclesial source, even though supported by the theologians), of necessity it remains substantially true for all times.

The second reason is found by the above-mentioned authors in 25, 2 of the same Constitution: "Although the bishops, taken individually, do not enjoy the privilege of infallibility, they do, however, proclaim infallibly the doctrine of Christ on the following conditions: namely, when, even though dispersed throughout the world but preserving nonetheless amongst themselves and with Peter's successor the bond of communion, in their authoritative teaching concerning matters of faith and morals they are in agreement that a particular teaching is to be held definitively and absolutely."

To maintain that the moral doctrine presented by Paul VI on contraception is infallible, it will be necessary to demonstrate with certainty that the bishops by their moral unanimity, in union with the Pope, have held it as certain and definitive.

Now, this demonstration appears very clear during the pontificates of Pius XI and Pius XII, and is sufficiently documented during one and a half centuries, since 1816 when the Holy See had to concern itself with guiding bishops and confessors on the abuse of marriage.

The Holy See intervened at least nineteen times to condemn this abuse under various forms of onanism, approving instead periodic continence, before Pius XI promulgated once more and in a very serious tone "the Christian doctrine taught from the beginning and handed down uninterruptedly down through the centuries," according to which "every marriage act which is deliberately deprived of its natural procreative power is against the law of God and against the natural law; and those who act thus are guilty of a serious crime."[6] Pius XII confirmed this doctrine by condemning "every attempt of spouses to prevent procreation in the exercise of the conjugal act." He added that such a "prescription is as fully valid today as it was yesterday, and will be valid tomorrow and always, because it is the expression of a natural and divine law."[7]

It must be observed that both passages received the endorsement of the Council when it referred to them as texts which indicate the means of birth control disapproved by the magisterium (*GS* 51, 3 and footnote 14).

History offers no doubts about the fact that the body of the faithful has given its assent to this doctrine during the past one and a half centuries. This fact is also admitted by those who try to interpret it as an indication of a lack of freedom of opinion. That the episcopal magisterium has professed and upheld in general the same doctrine throughout this period of time is demonstrated by the textbooks of moral theology used in their seminaries, as well as by a large number of individual and collective pastoral letters of this century.[8] That the condemnation of onanism includes the condemnation of any action that attempts to frustrate the generative power of the conjugal act is clear from the expressions: "every marriage act," "every attempt on the part of the spouses," and also from several pastoral letters referred to in note 8.

Consequently Paul VI was well able to appeal to the doctrine which "the Church has always provided" (*HV* 4, 3), doctrine "manifested by the constant teaching of the Church" (*HV* 10, 6), "proposed with constant firmness' (*HV* 6, 1), as part of "the saving teaching of Christ" (*HV* 29, 1), which the magisterium cannot change but only safeguard and interpret (*HV* 18, 1), presenting it virtually as irreformable.[9]

To claim that the encyclical was dealing with a temporary solution to prevent public authorities from intervening in the sector of conjugal intimacy (cf. *HV* 17); to maintain that it was not a question of affirming a truth in a definitive way (cf. *HV* 6), but of proposing a safe doctrine amid the various ongoing debates; to try to interpret the indicted intrinsic disorder as a mere ontic or pre-moral evil, a distinction never recognized by the magisterium; to suggest that according to the encyclical the moral disorder can be classified as objectively venial (cf. *HV* 25, 3) – these and other considerations, at times fetched from afar to construe obscurely positions that are clear, not only forget the circumstances of the promulgation of the encyclical but even overlook many expressions of the papal document which deny all such considerations.

The most serious difficulty against the encyclical would be that of demonstrating its disagreement with the Council. But if one takes into account the part of the encyclical which in exposing the doctrinal principles (*HV* 7-13) describes conjugal love and its characteristics in an integral vision of man, the various aspects of responsible parenthood and its relation to conjugal love, one will admit how rightly Paul VI (the only interpreter authorized by the Council) concluded that, feeling "obliged to make our own the Council's doctrine promulgated by us," he had followed "the personalistic concept proper to the conciliar teaching,"[10] and that, as he repeated shortly before his death, the encyclical was "the reaffirmation of the important principles which, in keeping with the recently concluded Council, he had put forward *with a more careful formulation*."[11]

This was admitted by various conferences, but it is especially clear from a comparison of the two documents. These documents refer to the Church's magisterium, and concretely to the passages of Pius XI and Pius XII which we have already mentioned, for a norm of behavior on responsible parenthood and on the manner of harmonizing love with the responsible transmission of life. Moreover, the Council announced beforehand that the Holy See would in due time issue a declaration on moral questions.

3. Theological note of the doctrine expressed in the encyclical Humanae Vitae

There is no doubt that the doctrine expressed in the encyclical is susceptible of theological qualification. "No one of the faithful will want to deny that the magisterium of the Church is competent to interpret even the natural moral law," the Pope remarked at the beginning of his encyclical, referring to important papal documents (*HV* 4, 2 and note 1).

Although this law is theoretically accessible to human reason, man's intelligence needs the help of revelation in numerous cases of application in order to formulate its conclusions without error (cf. D.S. 3004/5). Today this happens in many fields because of the enormous influence of "public opinion" on the superficial judgment of people, especially with regard to issues dealt with passionately, such as sexuality, which itself can easily cloud our mind to the point of preventing us from seeing the truth.[12] On this particular question the Council quite suitably referred twice to the interpretation of the natural and divine law given by the Church in the light of the Gospel, and to the submission in ecclesiastical faith which the faithful owe to that interpretation (*GS* 50, 2; 51, 3).

From the very first centuries the Church pronounced herself on this doctrine when and in the manner the times required. We have made reference to statements made by the Holy See and the episcopate when doubts began to arise at the beginning of the last century concerning the value of the traditional doctrine. Their decisions, universally accepted up to a couple of decades ago, have all the value of a universal and definitive magisterium (all one need do is consider the formulas used) and of an equally universal *sensus fidelium,* with all that this signifies for a theological qualification of the doctrine. It is impossible for the Holy Spirit to permit, in a question of such transcendence and of constant application, an error of long duration in the Church and in the world.

In previous periods of history following the first centuries we do not have as many explicit documents on this doctrine as we have on fundamental dogmas of our faith. The reason for this is clear: the Church calls men back to the truth insistently, when truth is in danger. Now with regard to the moral disorder of contraception, there was no danger of an eclipse of the truth up to the nineteenth century, if we make an exception for the early periods of Christianity and for some chance discussions between rigorists and laxists. During the first centuries, contrariwise, it was necessary to call to mind the demands of Christian morality threatened at times by pagan behavior. That is why, beginning with the second century (Minucius Felix, Hyppolitus, Epiphanius) up to the Fathers of the fifth century (Chrysostom, Jerome, Augustine) and the bishops during the time of the barbarian invasions (Cesarius of Arles, the Penitentials, some Descretals), we find increasingly clear allusions to contraception, to the "poisons of sterility" which kill the seed of life or which, if ineffective, provoke the "cruel lasciviousness" leading to abortion.[13]

A reading of the expressions of the Fathers leaves no doubt about the idea of perversity which the People of God recognized in anticonceptive practices; and this, long before the theological doctrine on the primary end of marriage took shape, with the obvious implication for the morality of the conjugal act.

One might think that the doctrine of the magisterium presents the requisites for infallibility with respect to onanism, but not with respect to contraception in particular. Now, not only does the basic reason for condemning onanism find its full application in contraception, but it is also manifest that the condemnatory texts of Pius XI and Pius XII are sufficiently alike in their moral reach to that of Paul XI, to enable them to be applied to contraception just as much as his; in fact, he cites them on this point. On the other hand, the Popes appeal to the living tradition of the Church from the beginning. But from the beginning, even before the onanistic use, anticonceptive practice was condemned. Finally, during the period between the encyclicals of Pius XI and Paul VI, the four collective pastoral letters of India, Formosa, Canada, and France, proceed without interruption from the condemnation of onanism to that of contraception, making explicit mention of contraceptive practices.[14]

"Your first task . . . is to expound without ambiguity the Church's teaching on marriage," is the charge given by Paul VI to priests and especially to theologians (*HV* 28).

If we proceed without ambiguity, without searching for dark avenues of escape from the clear and precise statements of this doctrine, we think the following conclusions must be drawn:

– There is a clear teaching of the universal magisterium which condemns conjugal onanism in the strongest language, from the beginning of the nineteenth century. This condemnation was also applied in an explicit way to contraception in the early centuries. The same condemnation, without any reasonable doubt, was issued by Pius XI, Pius XII and Paul VI: Pius XI characterized onanism explicitly as an objectively serious moral disorder, Paul VI only implicitly although unequivocally.

– There is no doctrinal disagreement between Paul VI and the pastoral constitution *Gaudium et Spes,* according to the judgment of the Pope, the only person competent to make such a judgment, who felt it his duty to conform his teaching to that document. The Constitution itself referred to the magisterium of the Church which had already pronounced or was about to pronounce itself on this matter.

– There is no foundation for the alleged divergence between the Pope and the conferences of bishops. In fact, the majority of the conferences undertook the task of presenting that doctrine to the Christian people, explaining it and justifying its profound roots, as they had been urged to do. Moreover, the slender number of conferences mentioned as disagreeing were in reality referring to individual situations of some of their people (the manner of expression did not even remotely allow the generalizations attributed to them), and in general they were clearly referring to the *subjective* order of conscience (as did subsequently the Congregation of the Clergy, which was so poorly interpreted). Besides, among the statements that could have created difficulties, some were explained later; other have a correct and true meaning different from what was attributed to them; while others may seem to contest the teaching of the papal and universal magisterium and by that very fact lack authenticity for the faithful. In some cases the ambiguity that some claim to interpret as the admission of an *objective* conflict of duties to be resolved in conscience can be explained by consulting other statements made by the same conferences of bishops[15] and comparing them with the statement of the Council: "There can be no conflict between the divine laws governing the transmission of life and the fostering of authentic married love" (*GS* 51, 2: *HV* 24).

– Finally, the central teaching of the encyclical (11-16), having been affirmed and reaffirmed as the traditional, firm, and constant teaching of the Church, is proposed *ex professo* and is therefore no longer a matter to be debated freely among theologians (cf. *D.S.* 3885). There is no doubt that the latest Popes present it as definitive (there was even talk of an ex cathedra definition in 1930). Its definability was upheld by a theologian of the authority of Charles Journet; and, in the light of the two passages of *Lumen Gentium* which we have quoted, there appears to be a solid fundation for the opinion of respectable theologians (Ciappi, Guzzetti, etc.) who hold this doctrine to be irreformable and infallible, even if each one of the papal documents expounding it is fallible.

In any case, one thing is certain. Aside from the theological discussion about the precise doctrinal value of *HUMANAE VITAE,* there can be no doubt about the grave moral obligation of everybody, pastors and faithful, to accept its teaching as indeed an expression of an act of the authentic magisterium as well as of a traditional doctrine of the Church. As the Bishops of Spain wrote: "The doctrinal value of this encyclical must be contemplated in the light of the faith. It confronts a subject which is not mere science, but is intimately and directly connected with faith and morals. The Pope speaks as the Supreme Shepherd of the Church, not as a private teacher . . . . He expressly wanted to settle a grave question which concerns the faith and morals of the faithful, availing himself of his supreme teaching authority . . . . He proposes a true doctrine which may not rightfully be presented as something provisional from the moment it possesses that stability on which the future of his supreme teaching authority depends. It adds a new and more solemn testimony to the numerous ones given previously and 'proposed with constant firmness by the Magisterium of the Church' (*HV* 6)" (351-352).

Footnotes:

1. Oct. 11, 1976, cf. Insegnamenti di Paolo VI, 14 (1976) 812.
2. "Needless to say, we welcome with filial respect the document of the Holy Father as it has been written and in the meaning he has given it." (Bishops of Belgium, 68. The quotations are taken from *Humanae Vitae e magistero episcopale,* Bologna 1969, indicating the page). "First of all, we express full communion of faith and intentions with the Vicar of Christ and profound gratitude for his

pondered and enlightening decision" (Bishops of Italy, 94). "We make our own the doctrine of the Holy Father on the lofty dignity of marriage and on the necessity of a truly Christian union between conjugal love and responsible parenthood . . . . Faith in the Church . . . demands that her teaching be accepted willingly" (Canada, 158, 167). "The acknowledgment of faith in the authority of the Pope . . . implies that no one should allow himself to doubt the content of the encyclical without considering his responsibility before God" (Scandinavia, 214). "The bishops have received this encyclical in a spirit of faith, according to the will of the Lord who entrusted to Peter the daily care of the whole Church" (France, 240). "The teaching of the encyclical . . . basically calls for its acceptance on the part of Catholic Christians" (Germany, 28).

3. *Nota praevia,* in *LG,* observatio 4a.
4. John C. Ford and Germain Grisez, *Contraception and the Infallibility of the Ordinary Magisterium,* Theological Studies, 39 (1978) 258-312.
5. *Lumen Gentium,* 25, 2 and note 40, which shows agreement with Vatican I.
6. Encyclical *Casti Connubii,* A.A.S., 22 (1930) 560.
7. A.A.S., 43 (1951) 843.
8. Belgium, 1909; Germany, 1913; United States, 1919; India, 1957; Canada, 1958; Formosa, 1961; France, 1919 and 1961.
9. Cf. A.A.S., 58 (1966) 219.
10. A.A.S., 60 (1968) 528, 529.
11. A.A.S., 70 (1978) 432.
12. Cf. *Casti Connubii,* A.A.S., 22 (1930) 579.
13. St. Augustine presented the well-known description of the three ways to destroy unborn life; quoted by Pius XI in his encyclical, A.A.S., 22 (1930) 563.
14. Cf. M. Zalba, *Circa ordinem rectum in usu matrimonii episcopi per orbem quid tradiderint,* in Per. Mor. Can. Lit., 56 (1967) 61-87.
15. "It is never permitted, not even to achieve a good end, to use an essentially evil procedure, because it is directly contrary to the profound meaning of a human function." (Assembly of Cardinals and Archbishops of France, March 3, 1961. Cf. Docum. Cath., 58 (1961) 371.)

APPENDIX

PONTIFICAL DOCUMENTS CONCERNING THE NATURAL REGULATION OF BIRTHS

A selection of pontifical statements on the regulation of births is presented here. Our aim is to select statements which are most directly concerned with the problem, rather than to attempt complete coverage. The statements chosen deal with moral, social, demographic, and scientific aspects of the problem of regulating births.

Although a number of statements were made by Conferences of Bishops on the subject, especially after HUMANAE VITAE was issued in 1968, we confine ourselves here to a bird's eye view of pontifical statements only, due to limitations of space.

1. SACRED PENITENTIARY, March 2, 1853 (eighteen fifty three)

The Sacred Penitentiary responded to a question of the Bishop of Amiens, who asked whether there is a duty to give instructions to those who are convinced about the existence of a certain number of infertile days during the woman's cycle, and who confine conjugal intercourse exclusively to those days. The Sacred Penitentiary answered as follows: "Those who inquire about this should not be disturbed, provided they do nothing to impede conception. *("Non esse inquietandos illos de quibus in precibus, dummodo nihil agant per quod conceptio impediatur.")*

2. SACRED PENITENTIARY, June 16, 1880

To an inquiry similar to the one documented above, the Sacred Penitentiary again answered: "Spouses who use the matrimonial right in the manner described in the inquiry, [namely only on the days which are considered to be infertile] should not be disturbed. The Confessor may prudently suggest this method to spouses if he has tried in vain to persuade them with other arguments to stop the detestable crime of Onanism." *("Coniuges praedicto modo matrimonio utentes inquietandos non esse, posseque confessarium sententiam, de qua agitur, illis coniugibus, caute tamen, insinuare, quos alia ratione a detestabili onanismi crimine abducere frustra tentaverit.")*

3. PIUS XI, ENCYCLICAL *CASTI CONNUBII* (On Christian Marriage) December 31, 1931

"Nor are those considered as acting against nature who in the married state use their right in the proper manner, although on account of natural reasons either of time or of certain defects, new life cannot be brought forth. For in matrimony as well as in the use of matrimonial rights there are secondary ends, such as mutual aid, the cultivation of mutual love, and the quieting of concupiscence which husband and wife are not forbidden to consider so long as they are subordinated to the primary and so long as the intrinsic nature of the act is preserved" (No. 59).

4. PIUS XII, *ADDRESS TO ITALIAN CATHOLIC UNION OF MIDWIVES*, October 29, 1951

Use of Sterile Period

29. Then, there is the serious question today as to whether and how far the obligation of ready disposition to serve motherhood can be reconciled with the ever more widely diffused recourse to the periods of natural sterility (the so-called agenetic periods of the woman) which seems to be a clear expression of the will contrary to that disposition.

Be Informed Scientifically and Morally

30. It is rightly expected that you be well informed from the medical point of view about this theory and of the progress that is likely to be made in it. It is also expected that your advice and aid be not based on popular publications but founded on scientific objectivity and the authoritative judgment of specialists in medicine and biology. It is your office, not that of the priest, to instruct married people either when they come for private consultations or through serious publications on the biological and technical aspects of the theory, without, however, allowing yourselves to be let in for propaganda that is neither right nor decent. In this field, too, your apostolate demands of you as women and Christians that you know and defend the norms of morality to which the application of this theory is subordinated. Here it is the Church that is the competent judge.

31. There are two hypotheses to be considered. If the carrying out of this theory means nothing more than that the couple can make use of their matrimonial rights on the days of natural sterility too, there is nothing against it, for by so doing they neither hinder nor injure in any way the consummation of the natural act and its further natural consequences. It is in this respect that the application of the theory of which we have spoken differs from the abuse already mentioned which is a perversion of the act itself. If, however, it is a further question – that is, of permitting the conjugal act on those days exclusively – then the conduct of the married couple must be examined more closely.

Invalidity of Marriage Possible

32. Here two other hypotheses present themselves to us. If at the

time of marriage at least one of the couple intended to restrict the marriage right, not merely its use, to the sterile periods, in such a way that at other times the second party would not even have the right to demand the act, this would imply an essential defect in the consent to marriage, which would carry with it invalidity of the marriage itself, because the right deriving from the contract of marriage is a permanent, uninterrupted and not intermittent right of each of the parties, one to the other.

33. On the other hand, if the act be limited to the sterile periods insofar as the mere use and not the right is concerned, there is no question about the validity of the marriage. Nevertheless, the moral licitness of such conduct on the part of the couple would have to be approved or denied according as to whether or not the intention of observing those periods constantly was based on sufficient and secure moral grounds. The mere fact that the couple do not offend the nature of the act and are prepared to accept and bring up the child which in spite of their precautions came into the world would not be sufficient in itself to guarantee the rectitude of intention and the unobjectionable morality of the motives themselves.

Fulfillment of a Positive Work

34. The reason for this is that marriage obliges to a state of life which, while conferring certain rights also imposes the fulfillment of a positive work in regard to the married state itself. In such a case, one can apply the general principle that a positive fulfillment may be omitted when serious reasons, independent from the good will of those obliged by it, show that this action is not opportune, or prove that a similar demand cannot reasonably be made of human nature.

35. The marriage contract which confers upon husband and wife the right to satisfy the inclinations of nature, sets them up in a certain state of life, the married state. But upon couples who perform the act peculiar to their state, nature and the Creator impose the function of helping the conservation of the human race. The characteristic activity which gives their state its value is the *bonum prolis.* The individual and society, the people and the state, the Church itself depend for their existence in the order established by God on fruitful marriage. Therefore, to embrace the married state, continuously to make use of the faculty proper to it and lawful in it alone, and, on the other hand, to withdraw always and deliberately with no serious reason from its primary obligation, would be a sin against the very meaning of conjugal life.

Grave Reasons Necessary

36. There are serious motives, such as those often mentioned in

the so-called medical, eugenic, economic, and social "indications," that can exempt for a long time, perhaps even the whole duration of the marriage, from the positive and obligatory carrying out of the act. From this it follows that observing the non-fertile periods alone can be lawful only under a moral aspect. Under the conditions mentioned it really is so. But if, according to a rational and just judgment, there are no similar grave reasons of a personal nature or deriving from external circumstances, then the determination to avoid habitually the fecundity of the union while at the same time to continue fully satisfying their sensuality, can be derived only from a false appreciation of life and from reasons having nothing to do with proper ethical laws.

5. PIUS XII, *ADDRESS TO THE NATIONAL CONGRESS OF THE FAMILY FRONT AND THE ASSOCIATION OF LARGE FAMILIES*, November 26, 1951

Regulation of Offspring

21. On the other hand, the Church knows how to consider with sympathy and understanding the real difficulties of the married state in our day. Therefore, in Our last allocution on conjugal morality, We affirmed the legitimacy and, at the same time, the limits – in truth very wide – of a regulation of offspring, which, unlike so-called "birth control," is compatible with the law of God. One may even hope (but in this matter the Church naturally leaves the judgment to medical science) that science will succeed in providing this licit method with a sufficiently secure basis, and the most recent information seems to confirm such a hope.

6. JOHN XXIII, ENCYCLICAL *MATER ET MAGISTRA*, May 15, 1961

Population Increase and Economic Development

185. More recently, the question often is raised how economic organization and the means of subsistence can be balanced with population increase, whether in the world as a whole or within the needy nations.

Imbalance Between Population and Means of Subsistence

186. As regards the world as a whole, some, consequent to statistical reasoning, observe that within a matter of decades mankind will become very numerous, whereas economic growth will proceed much more slowly. From this some conclude that unless procreation is kept within limits, there subsequently will develop an even greater imbalance between the number of inhabitants and the necessities of life.

187. It is clearly evident from statistical records of less developed countries that, because recent advances in public health and in medicine are there widely diffused, the citizens have a longer life expectancy consequent to lowered rates of infant mortality. The birth rate, where it has traditionally been high, tends to remain at such levels, at least for the immediate future. Thus the birth rate in a given year exceeds the death rate. Meanwhile the productive systems in such countries do not expand as rapidly as the number of inhabitants. Hence, in poorer countries of this sort, the standard of living does not advance and may even deteriorate. Wherefore, lest a serious crisis occur, some are of the opinion that the conception or birth of humans should be avoided or curbed by every possible means.

The Terms of the Problem

188. Now to tell the truth, the interrelationships on a global scale between the number of births and available resources are such that we can infer grave difficulties in this matter do not arise at present, nor will in the immediate future. The arguments advanced in this connection are so inconclusive and controversial that nothing certain can be drawn from them.

189. Besides, God in His goodness and wisdom has, on the one hand, provided nature with almost inexhaustible productive capacity; and, on the other hand, has endowed man with such ingenuity that, by using suitable means, he can apply nature's resources to the needs and requirements of existence. Accordingly, that the question posed may be clearly resolved, a course of action is not indeed to be followed whereby, contrary to the moral law laid down by God, procreative function also is violated. Rather, man should, by the use of his skills and science of every kind, acquire an intimate knowledge of the forces of nature and control them ever more extensively. Moreover, the advances hitherto made in science and technology give almost limitless promise for the future in this matter.

190. When it comes to questions of this kind, we are not unaware that in certain locales and also in poorer countries, it is often argued that in such an economic and social order, difficulties arise because citizens, each year more numerous, are unable to acquire sufficient food or sustenance where they live, and peoples do not show amicable cooperation to the extent they should.

191. But whatever be the situation, we clearly affirm these problems should be posed and resolved in such a way that man does not have recourse to methods and means contrary to his dignity, which are proposed by those persons who think of man and his life solely in material terms.

192. We judge that this question can be resolved only if economic

and social advances preserve and augment the genuine welfare of individual citizens and of human society as a whole. Indeed, in a matter of this kind, first place must be accorded everything that pertains to the dignity of man as such, or to the life of individual men, than which nothing can be more precious. Moreover, in this matter, international cooperation is necessary, so that conformably with the welfare of all, information, capital, and men themselves may move about among the peoples in orderly fashion.

Respect for the Laws of Life

193. In this connection, we strongly affirm that human life is transmitted and propagated through the instrumentality of the family which rests on marriage, one and indissoluble, and, so far as Christians are concerned, elevated to the dignity of a sacrament. Because the life of man is passed on to other men deliberately and knowingly, it therefore follows that this should be done in accord with the most sacred, permanent, inviolate prescriptions of God. Everyone without exception is bound to recognize and observe these laws. Wherefore, in this matter, no one is permitted to use methods and procedures which may indeed be permissible to check the life of plants and animals.

194. Indeed, all must regard the life of man as sacred, since from its inception, it requires the action of God the Creator. Those who depart from this plan of God not only offend His divine majesty and dishonor themselves and the human race, but they also weaken the inner fiber of the commonwealth.

Education toward a Sense of Responsibility

195. In these matters it is of great importance that new offspring, in addition to being very carefully educated in human culture and in religion — which indeed is the right and duty of parents — should also show themselves very conscious of their duties in every action of life. This is especially true when it is a question of establishing a family and of procreating and educating children.

7. PAUL VI, *ALLOCUTION TO CARDINALS,* June 23, 1964

Birth Control

The problem, which is on everyone's lips, goes by the name of birth control. It is, in other words, the problem of population increase on the one hand, and family morality on the other. It is an extremely grave problem. It touches upon the wellsprings of human life. It touches upon the most intimate sentiments and interests in the experience of man and woman. It is an extremely complex and delicate problem.

Many Aspects

The Church recognizes its manifold aspects, that is to say, the multiple spheres of competence. Certainly pre-eminent among these is that of the spouses – of their freedom, their conscience, their love, their duty. But the Church must also affirm her proper competence here – that of the law of God which she interprets, teaches, promotes, and defends. She will have to proclaim this law of God in the light of the scientific, social, and psychological truths that have been the subject of extensive new studies and publications in recent times. It will be necessary to take a careful look at the practical and theoretical development of this question.

Study under Way

This is precisely what the Church is in the course of doing. The question is under study, a study as extensive and intensive as possible, that is to say, as serious and as forthright as it ought to be in a matter of such great importance. Again We say that the question is under study. And We hope to conclude this study soon with the help of many eminent scholars. So in a short time We shall present the conclusions in the form that will be judged most fully suited to the subject under consideration and the goal being sought.

Existing Norms Still in Force

Meanwhile let Us say in all frankness that so far We do not have sufficient reason to regard the norms laid down by Pius XII on this matter as superseded and therefore no longer binding. So these norms must be considered valid, at least until We may feel obliged in conscience to modify them. In a matter of such importance it seems right that Catholics desire to follow one single law propounded authoritatively by the Church. So it seems advisable to recommend that for the present no one should arrogate to himself the right to take a stand differing from the norm now in force.

8. VATICAN COUNCIL II, *PASTORAL CONSTITUTION GAUDIUM ET SPES (CHURCH IN THE MODERN WORLD)* December 7, 1965

The Fruitfulness of Marriage

50. Marriage and married love are by nature ordered to the procreation and education of children. Indeed children are the supreme gift of marriage and greatly contribute to the good of the parents themselves. God himself said: "It is not good that man should be alone" (Gen. 2:18), and "from the beginning (he) made them male and female" (Mt. 19:4); wishing to associate them in a special way with his own creative work, God blessed man and woman with the words: "Be fruitful

and multiply" (Gen. 1:28). Without intending to underestimate the other ends of marriage, it must be said that true married love and the whole structure of family life which results from it is directed to disposing the spouses to cooperate valiantly with the love of the Creator and Saviour, who through them will increase and enrich his family from day to day.

Married couples should regard it as their proper mission to transmit human life and to educate their children; they should realize that they are thereby cooperating with the love of God the Creator and are, in a certain sense, its interpreters. This involves the fulfilment of their role with a sense of human and Christian responsibility and the formation of correct judgments through docile respect for God and common reflection and effort; it also involves a consideration of their own good and the good of their children already born or yet to come, an ability to read the signs of the times and of their own situation on the material and spiritual level, and, finally, an estimation of the good of the family, of society, and of the Church. It is the married couple themselves who must in the last analysis arrive at these judgments before God. Married people should realize that in their behavior they may not simply follow their own fancy but must be ruled by conscience – and conscience ought to be conformed to the law of God in the light of the teaching authority of the Church, which is the authentic interpreter of divine law. For the divine law throws light on the meaning of married love, protects it and leads it to truly human fulfilment. Whenever Christian spouses in a spirit of sacrifice and trust in divine providence[12] carry out their duties of procreation with generous human and Christian responsibility, they glorify the Creator and perfect themselves in Christ. Among the married couples who thus fulfil their God-given mission, special mention should be made of those who after prudent reflection and common decision courageously undertake the proper upbringing of a large number of children.[13]

But marriage is not merely for the procreation of children: its nature as an indissoluble compact between two people and the good of the children demand that the mutual love of the partners be properly shown, that it should grow and mature. Even in cases where despite the intense desire of the spouses there are no children, marriage still retains its character of being a whole manner and communion of life and preserves its value and indissolubility.

Married Love and Respect for Human Life

51. The Council realizes that married people are often hindered by certain situations in modern life from working out their married love harmoniously and that they can sometimes find themselves in a position where the number of children cannot be increased, at least for the time

being: in cases like these it is quite difficult to preserve the practice of faithful love and the complete intimacy of their lives. But where the intimacy of married life is broken, it often happens that faithfulness is imperiled and the good of the children suffers: then the education of the children as well as the courage to accept more children are both endangered.

Some of the proposed solutions to these problems are shameful and some people have not hesitated to suggest the taking of life: the Church wishes to emphasize that there can be no conflict between the divine laws governing the transmission of life and the fostering of authentic married love.

God, the Lord of life, has entrusted to men the noble mission of safeguarding life, and men must carry it out in a manner worthy of themselves. Life must be protected with the utmost care from the moment of conception: abortion and infanticide are abominable crimes. Man's sexuality and the faculty of reproduction wondrously surpass the endowments of lower forms of life; therefore the acts proper to married life are to be ordered according to authentic human dignity and must be honored with the greatest reverence. When it is a question of harmonizing married love with the responsible transmission of life, it is not enough to take only the good intention and the evaluation of motives into account; the objective criteria must be used, criteria drawn from the nature of the human person and human action, criteria which respect the total meaning of mutual self-giving and human procreation in the context of true love; all this is possible only if the virtue of married chastity is seriously practiced. In questions of birth regulation the sons of the Church, faithful to these principles, are forbidden to use methods disapproved of by the teaching authority of the Church in its interpretation of the divine law.[14]

Let all be convinced that human life and its transmission are realities whose meaning is not limited by the horizons of this life only: their true evaluation and full meaning can only be understood in reference to man's eternal destiny. . . .

87. . . . The government has, assuredly, in the matter of the population of its country, its own rights and duties, within limits of its proper competence, for instance as regards social and family legislation, the migration of country-dwellers to the city, and information concerning the state and needs of the nation. Some men nowadays are gravely disturbed by this problem; it is to be hoped that there will be Catholic experts in these matters, particularly in universities, who will diligently study the problems and pursue their researches further.

Since there is widespread opinion that the population expansion of the world, or at least some particular countries, should be kept in check by all possible means and by every kind of intervention by public authority, the Council exhorts all men to beware of all solutions, whether uttered in public or in private or imposed at any time, which transgress the natural law. Because in virtue of man's inalienable rights to marriage and the procreation of children, the decision regarding the number of children depends on the judgment of the parents and is in no way to be left to the decrees of public authority. Now, since the parents' judgment presupposes a properly formed conscience, it is of great importance that all should have an opportunity to cultivate a genuinely human sense of responsibility which will take account of the circumstances of the time and situation and will respect divine law; to attain this goal a change for the better must take place in educational and social conditions and, above all, religious formation or at least full moral training, must be available. People should be discreetly informed of scientific advances in research into methods of birth regulation, whenever the value of these methods has been thoroughly proved and their conformity with the moral order established.

Footnotes:

12. Cf. 1 Cor. 7:5.
13. Cf. Pius XII, Allocution, *Tra le verità*, 20 Jan. 1958: *AAS* 50 (1958), p. 91.
14. Cf. Pius XI, Litt. Encycl. *Casti Connubii: AAS* 22 (1930), pp. 559-561; *Denz.* 2239-2241 (3716-3718); Pius XII, *Allocution to the Congress of Italian Midwives,* 29 Oct. 1951: *AAS* 43 (1951), pp. 835-54; Paul VI, *Allocution to the Cardinals,* 23 June 1964: *AAS* 56 (1964), pp. 581-9. By order of the Holy Father, certain questions requiring further and more careful investigation have been given over to a commission for the study of populations, the family, and births, in order that the Holy Father may pass judgment when its task is completed. With the teaching of the magisterium standing as it is, the Council has no intention of proposing concrete solutions at this moment.

9. PAUL VI, ENCYCLICAL *HUMANAE VITAE*, July 25, 1968

HUMANAE VITAE

Encyclical Letter of His Holiness Pope Paul VI
On the Regulation of Births

To the venerable patriarchs and archbishops, to the bishops and other local ordinaries in peace and communion with the Apostolic See, to the clergy, to the faithful, and to all men of good will.

Venerable brothers and beloved sons:

The Transmission of Life

1. The very serious duty of transmitting human life, by reason of which married persons are free and responsible collaborators with God the Creator, has always been for them a source of great joys – joys, however, sometimes accompanied by not a few difficulties and sufferings.

In all ages the fulfillment of this duty has posed serious problems to the conscience of married persons. But with the recent evolution of society, changes have taken place that raise new questions which the Church cannot ignore, since they have to do with matters touching so closely the life and happiness of men.

I. NEW ASPECTS OF THE PROBLEM AND THE COMPETENCY OF THE MAGISTERIUM

2. The changes that have taken place are in fact noteworthy and of various kinds. In the first place, there is rapid population growth, which causes many to fear that world population is growing more rapidly than available resources, with the consequence of growing distress for so many families and developing countries. Therefore, authorities are greatly tempted to counter this danger with radical measures. Moreover, conditions of work and of housing as well as increased demands both in the economic field and in the field of education, today often make the adequate support of a large number of children difficult.

There has also been a change in how people consider the person of woman and her place in society. There has been a change, too, in the value attributed to conjugal love in marriage and to the meaning of conjugal acts in relation to that love.

Finally and above all, man has made stupendous progress in the mastery and rational organization of the forces of nature, so that he tends to extend this mastery to his own total being: to the body, to psychic life, to social life and even to the laws that regulate the transmission of life.

3. This new state of things gives rise to new questions. Given the conditions of life today, and given the importance that conjugal relations have for harmony between husband and wife and for their mutual fidelity, would not a revision of the ethical norms in force up to now be perhaps advisable, especially when one considers that they cannot be observed without sacrifices, sometimes heroic sacrifices?

Or else, by extending to this field the application of the so-called "principle of totality," could one not admit that the intention of a less abundant but more rationally controlled fertility transforms a materially sterilizing intervention into a permissible and wise control of births? Could one not admit, in other words, that the procreative finality pertains to conjugal life considered as a whole, rather than to its single acts? It is also asked whether, in view of the increased sense of responsibility of modern man, the moment has not come for him to entrust the objective of birth regulation to his reason and to his will, rather than to the biological rhythms of his organism.

Competency of the Magisterium

4. Questions of this sort required from the Magisterium (the teaching authority) of the Church a new and deeper reflection upon the principles of the moral teaching on marriage; a teaching founded on the natural law, illuminated and enriched by divine Revelation.

No one of the faithful will want to deny that the Magisterium of the Church is competent to interpret also the natural moral law. It is, in fact, indisputable, as our predecessors have on numerous occasions declared,[1] that Jesus Christ, when communicating to Peter and to the Apostles his divine authority and sending them to teach his commandments to all nations,[2] constituted them guardians and authentic interpreters of the whole moral law, that is to say, not only of the law of the gospel, but also of the natural law. For the natural law, too, is an expression of the will of God, and it likewise must be observed faithfully to obtain salvation.[3]

In keeping with this mission of hers, the Church has always provided – and more amply in recent times – a coherent teaching on the nature of marriage as well as on the correct use of conjugal rights and on the duties of husbands and wives.[4]

Special Studies

5. It was out of awareness of this very mission that we confirmed and enlarged the Study Commission that our predecessor John XXIII of venerated memory had established in March, 1963. This Commission, which included married couples along with numerous experts from the various relevant disciplines, had as its purpose to gather opinions on the new questions concerning married life, and in particular concerning birth regulation, and to furnish useful data so that the Magisterium could give an adequate reply to the expectations not only of the faithful but also of world public opinion.[5]

The labors of these experts, as well as the judgments and counsels later sent to us spontaneously or expressly requested from a good number of our brothers in the episcopate, have permitted us to weigh more accurately all the aspects of this complex matter. Hence, we most sincerely express to all of them our lively gratitude.

Reply of the Magisterium

6. And yet the conclusions reached by the Commission could not be considered by us as final, nor dispense us from a personal examination of the serious question; and this also because, within the

Commission itself, no full agreement of judgments concerning the moral norms to be proposed had been reached, and above all because certain criteria for resolving the question had emerged that departed from the moral teaching on marriage proposed with constant firmness by the Magisterium of the Church.

Therefore, having attentively sifted the documentation offered us, after mature reflection and assiduous prayers, we now intend, by virtue of the mandate entrusted to us by Christ, to give our reply to these grave questions.

II. DOCTRINAL PRINCIPLES

A Total Vision of Man

7. In considering the problem of birth regulation, as in the case of every other problem regarding human life, one must look beyond partial perspectives – whether biological or psychological, demographic or sociological – and make one's consideration in the light of an integral vision of man and of his vocation, not only his natural and earthly vocation, but also his supernatural and eternal one. And since, in the attempt to justify artificial methods of birth control, many have appealed to the demands both of conjugal love and of "responsible parenthood," it is good to state very precisely the true concept of these two great realities of married life, recalling principally what was recently set forth in this regard in a highly authoritative form by the Second Vatican Council in the Pastoral Constitution *Gaudium et Spes.*

Conjugal Love

8. Conjugal love reveals its true nature and nobility when it is considered in its supreme source, God, who is Love,[6] "the Father, from whom all fatherhood in heaven and on earth receives its name."[7]

Marriage is not, then, the effect of chance or the product of the evolution of blind natural forces; it is a wise institution of the Creator to realize in mankind His design of love. By means of the reciprocal personal gift which is proper and exclusive to them, husband and wife tend toward that communion of their beings whereby they help each other toward personal perfection in order to collaborate with God in the begetting and rearing of new lives.

For baptized persons, moreover, marriage takes on the dignity of a sacramental sign of grace, inasmuch as it represents the union of Christ and the Church.

Its Characteristics

9. In this light, one sees clearly the characteristic marks and requirements of conjugal love. It is of the highest importance to have an exact understanding of these marks and requirements.

This love is first of all fully *human;* that is to say, it pertains at the same time to both sense and spirit. It is not, then, a simple transport of instinct and feelings but also, and principally, an act of the free will, destined to endure and to grow by means of the joys and sorrows of daily life, in such a way that husband and wife become one heart and one soul, and together attain their human perfection.

And this love is *total;* that is to say, it is a very special form of personal friendship, in which husband and wife generously share everything, without undue reservations or selfish calculations. Whoever truly loves his spouse, does not love her only for what he receives from her, but for herself, happy to be able to enrich her with the gift of himself.

This love is also *faithful* and *exclusive* until death. Such in fact do bride and groom conceive it to be on the day when they freely and with full awareness assume the duty of the marriage bond. A fidelity, this, that can at times be difficult, but which is always possible, always noble and meritorious, as no one can deny. The example of so many married persons down through the centuries shows not only that fidelity is according to the nature of marriage but also that it is a source of profound and lasting happiness.

Finally, this love is *fruitful,* for it is not exhausted by the communion between husband and wife, but is destined to perpetuate itself, bringing new lives into existence. "Marriage and conjugal love are by their nature ordained to the begetting and rearing of children. Indeed, children are the most precious gift of marriage and contribute immensely to the good of the parents themselves."[8]

Responsible Parenthood

10. Hence, conjugal love requires in both husband and wife an awareness of their mission of "responsible parenthood," which today is rightly insisted upon, and which also must be correctly understood. It must be considered under its various legitimate and interrelated aspects.

In relation to the biological processes, responsible parenthood means knowing and respecting the functions of these processes; the intellect discovers in the power of giving life biological laws that are part of the human person.[9]

In relation to the tendencies of instinct and of the passions, responsible parenthood means the necessary mastery that reason and will must exercise over them.

In relation to physical, economic, psychological and social conditions, responsible parenthood is exercised either by the thoughtfully made and generous decision to raise a large family, or by the decision, made for grave motives and with respect for the moral law, to avoid a new birth for the time being, or even for an indeterminate period.

Responsible parenthood also and above all implies a more profound relationship to the objective moral order established by God, and of which a right conscience is the faithful interpreter. The responsible exercise of parenthood implies, therefore, that husband and wife recognize fully their duties toward God, toward themselves, toward the family and toward society, in a correct hierarchy of values.

In the task of transmitting life, they are not free, therefore, to proceed at will, as if they could determine with complete autonomy the right paths to follow; but they must conform their actions to the creative intention of God, expressed in the very nature of marriage and of its acts, and manifested by the constant teaching of the Church.[10]

Respect for the Nature and Finality of the Marriage Act

11. These acts, by which husband and wife are united in chaste intimacy and by means of which human life is transmitted, are, as the Council recalled, "good and honorable,"[11] and they do not cease to be legitimate if, for causes independent of the will of husband and wife, they are foreseen to be infertile, because they remain ordained to expressing and strengthening their union. In fact, as experience bears witness, not every act of marital intercourse is followed by a new life. God has wisely arranged natural laws and rhythms of fertility, which already of themselves bring about a separation in the succession of births. But the Church, calling men back to the observance of the norms of the natural law, interpreted by her constant teaching, teaches that each and every marriage act must remain open to the transmission of life.[12]

Two Inseparable Aspects: Union and Procreation

12. This teaching, set forth by the Magisterium on numerous occasions, is founded upon the inseparable connection, willed by God and which man may not break on his own initiative, between the two-fold significance of the conjugal act: the unitive significance and the procreative significance.

Indeed, by its intimate structure, the conjugal act, while closely uniting husband and wife, makes them apt for the generation of new lives, according to laws inscribed in the very being of man and woman. By safeguarding both these essential aspects, the unitive and the procreative, the conjugal act preserves in its fullness the sense of true mutual love and its ordination to man's most high vocation to parenthood. We think that men of our day are particularly capable of confirming the deeply reasonable and human character of this fundamental principle.

Faithfulness to God's Design

13. It is in fact justly observed that a conjugal act imposed upon one's partner without regard for his or her conditions and legitimate desires is not a true act of love, and therefore denies a requirement of the right moral order in the relations between husband and wife. Hence, one who reflects carefully must also recognize that an act of mutual love that prejudices the capacity to transmit life that God the Creator has inserted therein, according to particular laws, is in contradiction with the design constitutive of marriage, and with the will of the Author of Life. Those who make use of this divine gift while destroying, even if only partially, its significance and its finality, act contrary to the nature of both man and woman and of their most intimate relationship, and therefore contradict also the plan of God and His will. On the other hand, those who enjoy the gift of conjugal love while respecting the laws of the generative process show that they acknowledge themselves to be not the masters of the sources of human life, but rather the ministers of the design established by the Creator. In fact, just as man does not have unlimited dominion over his body in general, so also, with particular reason, he has no such dominion over his generative faculties as such, because of their intrinsic ordination to the bringing into being of life, of which God is the principle. "Human life is sacred," John XXIII recalled; "from its very inception it directly involves the creative action of God."[13]

Unlawful Means of Birth Regulation

14. In conformity with these fundamental elements of the human and Christian vision of marriage, we must once again declare that the direct interruption of the generative process already begun, and, above all, directly willed and procured abortion, even if for therapeutic reasons, are to be absolutely excluded as lawful means of birth regulation.[14]

Also, to be excluded, as the Magisterium of the Church has on a number of occasions declared, is direct sterilization, whether perpetual or temporary, whether of the man or of the woman.[15]

Similarly excluded is every action that, either in anticipation of the conjugal act or in its accomplishment or in the development of its natural consequences, would have as an end or as a means, to render procreation impossible.[16]

And to justify conjugal acts made intentionally infertile one cannot invoke as valid reasons the lesser evil, or the fact that when taken together with the fertile acts already performed or to follow later, such acts would coalesce into a whole and hence would share in one and the same moral goodness. In truth, if it is sometimes permissible to tolerate a lesser moral evil in order to avoid a greater evil or to promote a greater good,[17] it is not permissible, not even for the gravest reasons, to do evil so that good may follow therefrom.[18] One may not, in other words, make into the object of a positive act of the will something that is intrinsically disordered and hence unworthy of the human person, even when the intention is to safeguard or promote individual, family or social goods. Consequently it is an error to think that a conjugal act which is deliberately made infertile and so is intrinsically wrong could be made right by a fertile conjugal life considered as a whole.

Lawfulness of Therapeutic Means

15. The Church, on the other hand, does not at all consider unlawful the use of those therapeutic means truly necessary to cure diseases of the organism, even if an impediment to procreation, which may be foreseen, should result therefrom, provided such impediment is not, for whatever motive, directly willed.[19]

16. In our day, as we observed above (no. 3), the objection is made against this teaching of the Church on conjugal morality that it is the prerogative of human intelligence to master the energies made available by irrational nature and to direct them toward an end that is in conformity with the good of man. In consequence, some ask, concerning the case at hand, is it not perhaps reasonable in many circumstances to have recourse to artificial birth control if thereby are secured the harmony and tranquility of the family, and conditions more favorable to the education of children already born? To this question it is necessary to reply with clarity: the Church is the first to praise and recommend the intervention of intelligence in a work that so closely associates the rational creature with his Creator; but she affirms that this must be done with respect for the order established by God.

If, then, there are serious motives for spacing births, motives deriving from the physical or psychological condition of husband or wife, or from external circumstances, the Church teaches that it is then permissible to take into account the natural rhythms immanent in the generative functions and to make use of marriage during the infertile times only, and in this way to regulate births without offending the moral principles that we have just recalled.[20]

The Church is consistent when she considers recourse to the infertile times to be permissible, while condemning as being always wrong the use of means directly contrary to fertilization, even if such use is inspired by reasons that can appear upright and serious. In reality, there is an essential difference between the two cases. In the first case, the husband and wife legitimately avail themselves of a natural condition; in the second case, they impede the working of natural processes. It is true that in both cases the married couples agree in positively willing to avoid children for plausible reasons, seeking to be certain that offspring will not result; but it is likewise true that only in the first case do they prove able to abstain from the use of marriage during the fertile times, when for proper motives procreation is not desirable, then making use of it during the infertile times to manifest affection and to safeguard mutual fidelity. By so doing, they give proof of a love that is truly and fully virtuous.

Serious Consequences of the Methods of Artificial Birth Regulation

17. Responsible persons can be still more easily convinced of the solid grounds on which the teaching of the Church in this field is based, if they stop to reflect upon the consequences of the methods of artificial birth regulation. Let them consider, first of all, how wide and easy a road would thus be opened to conjugal infidelity and to a general lowering of morality. One does not need much experience to know human weakness and to understand that human beings — especially the young, who are so vulnerable on this point — have need of encouragement to be faithful to the moral law, and must not be offered an easy means to evade its observance. It can also be feared that the man who becomes used to contraceptive practices, may finally lose respect for the woman, and no longer caring about her physical and psychological equilibrium, come to the point of considering her as a mere instrument of selfish enjoyment, and no longer as his respected and beloved companion.

Consider also the dangerous weapon that would thus be placed in the hands of those public authorities who have no concern for the requirements of morality. Who could blame a government for applying, as a solution to the problems of the community, those means acknowledged to be permissible for married couples in solving a family problem? Who will stop rulers from favoring and from even imposing upon their peoples, if they should consider it necessary, the method of contraception that they judge to be most efficacious? In this way men, in wishing to avoid the individual, family or social difficulties which they encounter in observing the divine law, would come to place at the mercy of the intervention of public authorities the most personal and most reserved sector of conjugal intimacy.

Consequently, if one does not want to see the mission of generating life exposed to the arbitrary decisions of men, one must of necessity recognize certain absolute limits to the possibility of man's dominion over his own body and its functions; limits that no one, whether a private individual or someone invested with authority, has any right to exceed. And such limits cannot be determined otherwise than by the respect owed to the integrity of the human organism and its functions, according to the principles recalled above and according to the correct understanding of the "principle of totality" explained by our predecessor Pius XII.[21]

The Church, Guarantor of Authentic Human Values

18. One can foresee that this teaching will perhaps not be easily received by all: too numerous are the voices — amplified by today's communications media — which disagree with the voice of the Church. To tell the truth, it does not surprise the Church that she becomes, like her divine Founder, a "sign of contradiction";[22] yet because of this she does not cease to proclaim with humble firmness the entire moral law, both the natural law and the law of the Gospel. The Church was not the author of the moral law and therefore cannot be its arbiter; she is only its depository and its interpreter, and can never declare to be permissible that which is not so by reason of its intimate and unchangeable opposition to the true good of man.

In defending conjugal morality in its entirety the Church knows that she contributes to the establishment of a truly human civilization. The Church challenges man not to abandon his own responsibility in exchange for reliance on technical means; by this very fact she defends the dignity of husbands and wives. Faithful to both the teaching and the example of the Savior, she shows herself to be the sincere and disinterested friend of men, whom she wishes to help, even now during their earthly sojourn, "to share as sons in the life of the living God, the Father of all men."[23]

III. PASTORAL DIRECTIVES

The Church, "Mother and Teacher"

19. Our words would not be an adequate expression of the mind and of the solicitude of the Church, Mother and Teacher of all peoples, if, after having recalled men to the observance and respect of the divine law regarding matrimony, we did not encourage them in the way of proper birth regulation, even amid the difficult conditions that beset families and peoples today. The Church, in fact, cannot act differently toward men that does the Redeemer: she knows their weakness, has compassion on the multitude, welcomes sinners; but she cannot renounce teaching the law that in reality is proper to human life restored in its original truth and led by the Spirit of God.[24]

Possibility of Observing the Divine Law

20. The teaching of the Church on birth regulation, which is a promulgation of the divine law, will easily appear to many to be difficult or even impossible to put into practice. And certainly, like all great and beneficial realities, it calls for serious commitment and many efforts on the part of individuals, of families and of society. More than that, it would not be livable without the help of God, who upholds and strengthens the good will of men. Yet to anyone who weighs the matter well, it must be clear that such efforts ennoble man and are beneficial

to the human community.

Mastery of Self

21. A proper practice of birth regulation requires first and foremost that a husband and wife acquire and possess solid convictions about the authentic values of life and of the family, and that they tend toward the achievement of perfect self-mastery. To dominate instinct by means of one's reason and free will undoubtedly demands asceticism in order that the affective expressions of conjugal life be according to right order. This is particularly necessary for the observance of periodic continence. Yet this discipline, which is proper to the purity of married couples, far from harming conjugal love, rather confers upon it a higher human value. It requires continual effort, but thanks to its beneficent influence husband and wife fully develop their personalities and are enriched with spiritual values. Such discipline bestows upon family life fruits of serenity and peace, and facilitates the solution of other problems; it fosters attention to one's partner, helps both spouses drive out selfishness, the enemy of true love; and it deepens their sense of responsibility. By its means, parents become capable of a deeper and more efficacious influence in the education of their offspring; children and young people grow up with a correct appreciation of human values, and enjoy a serene and harmonious development of their spiritual and sense faculties.

Creating an Environment Favorable to Chastity

22. On this occasion, we wish to draw the attention of educators and of all those who occupy positions of responsibility for the common good of human society, to the need of creating a climate favorable to the development of chastity, favorable that is, to the triumph of healthy liberty over license by means of respect for the moral order.

Whatever in the communications media today leads to overstimulation of the senses, to the loosening of morals, as well as every form of pornography and licentious performances, must provoke the open and unanimous reaction of all persons who are deeply concerned for the progress of civilization and the defense of the highest values of the human spirit. It is futile to allege artistic or scientific needs as justification for such depravity,[25] or to deduce an argument in their favor from the freedom allowed in this sector by public authorities.

Appeal to Public Authorities

23. To those who govern in civil society and who are principally responsible for the common good, and can do so much to safeguard morality, we say: Do not allow the morality of your peoples to be degraded; do not accept that by legal means practices contrary to the

natural and divine law be introduced into that fundamental cell which is the family. Quite other is the way in which public authorities can and should contribute to the solution of the demographic problem: namely, by way of a provident policy for the family, of a wise educational program that is respectful of the moral law and the liberty of the citizens.

We are well aware of the serious difficulties experienced by public authorities in this regard, especially in developing countries. We devoted our encyclical *Populorum Progressio* to these legitimate concerns of theirs. Nevertheless we repeat the words of our predecessor John XXIII: "These difficulties are not to be overcome by having recourse to methods and means that are unworthy of man and that are based solely on a purely materialistic concept of man himself and of his life. The true solution is found only in economic development and in social progress that respect and promote authentic human individual and social values."[26] And it would be a serious injustice to blame divine Providence for what could be due, instead, to insufficient wisdom in government, to an inadequate sense of social justice, to selfish monopoly, or again to culpable indolence in putting forth the efforts and the sacrifices necessary to insure a rise in the standard of living for an entire people.[27] Let all responsible public authorities generously redouble their efforts, as some are already laudably doing. And may mutual aid continue to increase between members of the great human family. This opens up an almost limitless field to the activity of the great international organizations.

To Men of Science

24. We now wish to express our encouragement to men of science, who "can accomplish much for the benefit of marriage and the family and for the peace of consciences, if by uniting their efforts they seek to shed more light on the various conditions that make possible a proper regulation of human procreation."[28] It is particularly desirable that, according to the wish expressed by Pius XII, medical science succeed in providing a sufficiently secure basis for a regulation of births based on the observance of natural rhythms.[29] In this way, scientists and especially Catholic scientists will contribute evidence to demonstrate that, as the Church teaches, "a true contradiction cannot exist between the divine laws pertaining to the transmission of life and those pertaining to the fostering of authentic conjugal love."[30]

To Christian Husbands and Wives

25. And now we turn our attention more directly to our own sons and daughters, to those especially whom God calls to serve him in marriage. The Church, while teaching the inviolable demands of the

divine law, announces the tidings of salvation, and by means of the sacraments opens up the paths of grace, which makes of man a new creature, capable of corresponding in love and authentic freedom to the design of his Creator and Savior, and of experiencing the gentleness of the yoke of Christ.[31]

Christian married couples, then, docile to the voice of the Church, should recall that their Christian vocation, which began at Baptism, was further specified and strengthened by the sacrament of Matrimony. By means of this sacrament husband and wife are strengthened and, as it were, consecrated for the faithful fulfillment of their specific duties, for the living out of their own vocation unto perfection, and for bearing their own particular Christian witness before the world.[32] To them the Lord entrusts the task of making visible to men the holiness and gentleness of the law that unites the mutual love of husband and wife to their cooperation with the love of God, the author of human life.

We do not at all intend to hide the sometimes serious difficulties inherent in the life of Christian married persons; for them as for anyone else, "the gate is narrow and the way is hard that leads to life."[33] But hope in that life must illumine their way, as with courage they strive to live with wisdom, justice, and piety in the present time,[34] knowing that the form of this world passes away.[35]

Let married couples, then, face up to the efforts needed, supported by the faith and the hope that "does not disappoint because God's love has been poured into our hearts through the Holy Spirit, who has been given to us."[36] Let them implore divine assistance by persevering prayer; let them, especially in the Eucharist, draw from the source of grace and charity. And if sin should still keep its hold over them, let them not be discouraged, but rather let them have recourse with humble perseverence to the mercy of God, which is poured forth in the sacrament of Penance. In this way they will be able to achieve the fullness of married life described by the Apostle: "Husbands, love your wives, as Christ loved the Church . . . . Husbands should love their wives as they do their own bodies. In loving his wife a man loves himself. For no one ever hates his own flesh, but nourishes and cherishes it, as Christ does the Church . . . . This is a great mystery, and I mean in reference to Christ and the Church. But in what concerns you, let each one of you love his wife as himself, and let the wife respect her husband."[37]

Apostolate of Couples

26. Among the fruits that result from a generous effort of fidelity to the divine law, one of the most precious is that married couples themselves not infrequently feel the desire to communicate their experience to others. Thus a new and most noteworthy form of the

apostolate of like towards like comes to be included in the vast field of the vocation of the laity: it is married couples themselves who become apostles and guides to other married couples. Among so many forms of apostolate, this is assuredly one of those that seem most opportune today.[38]

To Doctors and Medical Personnel

27. We hold in the highest esteem those physicians and medical personnel who, in the exercise of their profession, value above every human interest the higher demands of their Christian vocation. Let them persevere, therefore, in promoting on every occasion the solutions inspired by faith and right reason; and let them strive in their various contacts to convince others and win their respect for these solutions. Let them also consider as their proper professional duty the task of acquiring all the knowledge necessary in this delicate sector, so as to be able to give to the married persons who consult them the wise counsels and sound directives that these have a right to expect.

To Priests

28. Beloved sons who are priests, by vocation you are the counselors and spiritual guides of individual persons and of families. We now turn to you with confidence. Your first task — especially in the case of those who teach moral theology — is to expound without ambiguity the Church's teaching on marriage. Be the first to give, in the exercise of your ministry, the example of loyal internal and external submission to the Magisterium of the Church. Such submission, as you well know, obliges not only because of the reasons adduced, but much more on account of the light of the Holy Spirit, which is given in a particular way to the pastors of the Church in order that they may explain the truth.[39] You know, too, that it is of the utmost importance, for peace of consciences and for the unity of the Christian people, that in the field of morals as well as in that of dogma, all should attend to the Magisterium of the Church, and should speak the same language. Hence with all our heart we renew to you the heartfelt plea of the great Apostle Paul: "I entreat you, brethren, by the name of Our Lord Jesus Christ, that all of you agree and that there be no divisions among you, but that you be united in the same mind and the same judgment."[40]

29. Not to compromise in any way the saving teaching of Christ is an eminent form of charity for souls. But this must ever be accompanied by patience and goodness, such as the Lord himself gave the example of in dealing with men. Having come not to condemn but to save,[41] he was indeed intransigent with evil, but merciful toward individuals.

In their difficulties may married couples always find in the words and in the heart of the priest, the echo of the voice and love of the Redeemer.

And speak with confidence, beloved sons, fully convinced that the Spirit of God, while assisting the Magisterium in proposing doctrine, illumines internally the hearts of the faithful, inviting them to give their assent. Teach married couples the indispensable way of prayer; prepare them to have recourse often and with faith to the sacraments of the Eucharist and of Penance, without ever allowing themselves to be discouraged by their own weakness.

To Bishops

30. Beloved and venerable brothers in the episcopate, with whom we share more closely in caring for the spiritual good of the people of God, our reverent and affectionate thoughts turn to you as we conclude this Encyclical. To all of you we extend an urgent invitation. Work zealously and incessantly with the priests your collaborators and with your faithful people to safeguard marriage and keep it holy, so that it may ever be lived more and more in all its human and Christian fullness. Consider this mission one of your most urgent responsibilities at the present time. As you know, this involves concerted pastoral action in all the fields of human activity, the economic, the cultural and the social: for, in fact, only a simultaneous improvement in these various sectors will make it possible to render the life of parents, and of the children within their families, not only tolerable, but easier and more joyous, to render our common existence in human society more fraternal and peaceful, in faithfulness to God's design for the world.

Final Appeal

31. Venerable brothers, most beloved sons, and all men of good will, great indeed is the work of education, of progress and of love to which we call you, upon the foundation of the Church's teaching, of which the successor of Peter, together with his brothers in the episcopate, is the depository and interpreter. We are deeply convinced that this is truly a great work, both for the world and for the Church, since man cannot find true happiness, toward which he aspires with all his being, other than by respecting the laws inscribed by God in his very nature, laws which he must observe with understanding and love. Upon this work, and upon all of you, and especially upon married couples, we invoke God's abundant graces of holiness and mercy, and in pledge thereof, we impart to you our apostolate blessing.

Given at Rome, from St. Peter's, on the 25th day of July, the feast of St. James the Apostle, in the year 1968, the sixth of our pontificate.

Footnotes:

1. See Pius IX, Encyclical *Qui Pluribus,* Nov. 9, 1846: *Pii IX P.M. Acta* 1, pp. 9-10; St. Pius X, Encyclical *Singulari Quadam,* Sept. 24, 1912: *AAS* 4 (1912), p. 658, Pius XI, Encyclical *Casti Connubii,* Dec. 31, 1930: *AAS* 22 (1930), pp. 579-81; Pius XII, Allocution *Magnificate Dominum* to the Episcopate of the Catholic World, Nov. 2, 1954: *AAS* 46 (1954), pp. 671-72; John XXIII, Encyclical *Mater et Magistra,* May 15, 1961: *AAS* 53 (1961), p. 457.
2. See Mt. 28:18-19.
3. See Mt. 7:21.
4. See *Roman Catechism of the Council of Trent,* Part II, ch. 8; Leo XIII, Encyclical *Arcanum,* Feb. 10, 1880: *Acta Leonis XIII,* 2, (1880), pp. 26-29; *Code of Canon Law:* Canon 1067; Canon 1068, §1; Canon 1076 §§1-2; Pius XI, Encyclical *Divini illius Magistri,* Dec. 31, 1929: *AAS* 22 (1930), pp. 58-61; Encyclical *Casti Connubii: AAS* 22 (1930), pp. 545-46; Pius XII, Allocution to the Italian Medico-Biological Union of St. Luke, Nov. 12, 1944: *Discorsi e Radiomessaggi di S.S. Pio XII,* 6, pp. 191-92; to the Congress of the Italian Catholic Union of Midwives, Oct. 29, 1951: *AAS* 43 (1951), pp. 835-54; to the Congress of the Family Front and the Association of Large Families, Nov. 26, 1951: *AAS* 43 (1951), pp. 857-59; to the Seventh Congress of the International Society of Hematology, Sept. 12, 1958: *AAS* 50 (1958), pp. 734-35; John XXIII, Encyclical *Mater et Magistra: AAS* 53 (1961), pp. 446-47; Second Vatican Council, Pastoral Constitution *Gaudium et Spes,* nn. 47-52: *AAS* 58 (1966), pp. 1067-74.
5. See Paul VI, Allocution to the Sacred College of Cardinals, June 23, 1964: *AAS* 56 (1964), p. 588; to the Commission for the Study of the Problems of Population, Family and Births, March 27, 1965: *AAS* 57 (1965), p. 388; to the National Congress of the Italian Society of Obstetrics and Gynecology, Oct. 29, 1966: *AAS* 58 (1966), p. 1168.
6. See 1 Jn. 4:8.
7. Eph. 3:15.
8. Second Vatican Council, Pastoral Constitution *Gaudium et Spes,* no. 50: *AAS* 58 (1966), pp. 1070-72.
9. See St. Thomas *Summa Theologica,* I-II, p. 94, art. 2.
10. See Second Vatican Council, Pastoral Constitution *Gaudium et Spes,* nn. 50-51: *AAS* 58, (1966), pp. 1070-73.
11. See *ibid,* no. 49: *AAS,* 58 (1966), p. 1070.
12. Cf. Pius XI, encyc. *Casti Connubii,* in *AAS* XXII (1930), p. 560; Pius XII, in *AAS* XLIII (1951), p. 843.
13. Cf. John XXIII, encyc. *Mater et Magistra,* in *AAS* LIII (1961) p. 447.

14. Cf. *Catechismus Romanus Concilii Tridentini,* part. II, Ch. VIII; Pius XI, encyc. *Casti Connubii,* in *AAS* XXII (1930), pp. 562-564; Pius XII, *Discorsi e Radiomessaggi,* VI (1944), pp. 191-192; *AAS* XLIII (1951), pp. 842-843; pp. 857-859; John XXIII, encyc. *Pacem in Terris,* Apr. 11, 1963, in *AAS* LV (1963), pp. 259-260; *Gaudium et Spes,* No. 51.
15. Cf. Pius XI, encyc. *Casti Connubii,* in *AAS* XXII (1930), p. 565; decree of the Holy Office, Feb. 22, 1940, in AAS XXXII (1940), p. 73; Pius XII, Allocution to the Congress of the Italian Catholic Union of Midwives, AAS XLIII (1951), pp. 843-44; to the Seventh Congress of the International Society of Hematology. *AAS* L (1958), pp. 734-735.
16. Cf. *Catechismus Romanus Concilii Tridentini,* part. II, Ch. VIII; Pius XI, encyc. *Casti Connubii,* in *AAS* XXII (1930), pp. 559-561; Pius XII, *AAS* XLIII (1951), p. 843; *AAS* L (1958), pp. 734-735; John XXIII, encyc. *Mater et Magistra,* in *AAS* LIII (1961), p. 447.
17. Cf. Pius XII, alloc. to the National Congress of the Union of Catholic Jurists, Dec. 6, 1953, in *AAS* XLV (1953), pp. 798-799.
18. Cf. Rom. 3:8.
19. Cf. Pius XII, alloc. to Congress of the Italian Association of Urology, Oct. 8, 1953, in *AAS* XLV (1953), pp. 674-675; *AAS* L (1958), pp. 734-735.
20. Cf. Pius XII, *AAS* XLIII (1951), p. 846.
21. Cf. *AAS* XLV (1953), pp. 674-675; *AAS* XLVIII (1956), pp. 461-462.
22. Cf. Luke 2:34.
23. Paul VI, Encyclical *Populorum Progressio,* March 26, 1967: n. 21, *AAS* 59 (1967), p. 268.
24. See Rom. 8.
25. See Second Vatican Council, Decree *Inter Mirifica,* nn. 6-7, *AAS* 56 (1964), p. 147.
26. Encyclical *Mater et Magistra, AAS* 53 (1961), p. 447.
27. See Encyclical *Populorum Progressio,* nn. 48-55, *AAS* 59 (1967), pp. 281-84.
28. Second Vatican Council, Pastoral Constitution *Gaudium et Spes,* n. 52: *AAS* 58 (1966), p. 1074.
29. See Allocution to the Congress of the Family Front and the Association of Large Families, *AAS* 43 (1951), p. 859.
30. Second Vatican Council, Pastoral Constitution *Gaudium et Spes,* n. 51: *AAS* 58 (1966), p. 1072.
31. See Mt. 11:30.
32. See Second Vatican Council, Pastoral Constitution *Gaudium et Spes,* n. 48: *AAS* 58 (1966), pp. 1067-69; Dogmatic Constitution *Lumen Gentium,* n. 35: *AAS* 57 (1965), pp. 40-41.

33. Mt. 7:14; see Heb. 12:11.
34. See Tit. 2:12.
35. See 1 Cor. 7:31.
36. Rom. 5:5.
37. Eph. 5:25, 28-29, 32-33.
38. See Second Vatican Council, Dogmatic Constitution *Lumen Gentium*, nn. 35 and 41: *AAS* 57 (1965), pp. 40-45; Pastoral Constitution *Gaudium et Spes*, nn. 48-49: *AAS* 58 (1966), pp. 1067-70; Decree *Apostolicam Actuositatem*, n. 11: *AAS* 58 (1966), pp. 847-49.
39. See Second Vatican Council, Dogmatic Constitution *Lumen Gentium*, n. 25, *AAS* 57 (1965), pp. 29-31.
40. 1 Cor. 1:10.
41. See Jn. 3:17.

10. POPE PAUL VI, *ADDRESS TO 2000 COUPLES, EQUIPES NOTRE DAME*, 4 May 1970

13. Dear sons and daughters, as you well know, it is by living the graces of the Sacrament of Marriage that you journey with "untiring, generous love"[38] towards that holiness to which we are all called by grace.[39] It is not an obligation arbitrarily imposed that calls us to holiness, but rather the love of a Father who desires that His children attain their fullest potential and development and find total happiness. Moreover, to arrive at this goal, you have not been left to your own resources, since Christ and the Holy Spirit, "those two hands of God," as St. Irenaeus puts it, are unceasingly at work on your behalf.[40]

Do not therefore let yourselves be led astray by the temptations, difficulties and trials that arise along the way. Do not be afraid, when necessary, to go against the tide of thought and opinion in a world of paganized behavior. St. Paul warns us: "Be not conformed to this world, but be transformed in the newness of your mind."[41]

And do not be discouraged by your failures. Our God is a Father full of tenderness and goodness, filled with concern and overflowing with love for those of His children who have to struggle on their journey. And the Church is a mother who means to help you live to the fullest this ideal of Christian marriage. She reminds you, along with the beauty of this ideal, of all its demands.

14. Dear sons, chaplains of the Teams of Our Lady, you know by a long and varied experience that your consecrated celibacy makes you particularly available to couples, to be for them, on their journey towards holiness, active witnesses of the love of the Lord in the Church.

Day after day you help them "walk in the light."[42] You help them to think right, that is, to evaluate their behavior in the light of the truth. You help them to will right, that is, to direct their will, as responsible persons, towards what is really good and therefore desirable. You help them to act right, that is, gradually to bring their life, in spite of the risks inherent in human existence, into harmony with the ideal of Christian marriage that they are generously pursuing.

Who is unaware of the fact that it is only little by little that a human being succeeds in ordering and integrating his manifold drives and tendencies, until at length he harmonizes them in that virtue of married chastity wherein the couple find their full human and Christian fulfillment.

This work of liberation, for that is what it is, is the fruit of the true freedom of the children of God. Their conscience must be respected, and at the same time, educated and formed, in an atmosphere of confidence and not of anxiety. In such an atmosphere, the moral laws are not seen as coldly inhuman, abstractly objective and remote prescriptions; instead they serve to guide the couple on their journey. When husband and wife, in fact, strive patiently and humbly, and without allowing themselves to be discouraged by setbacks, to live in truth the deep demands of a sanctified love, then the moral laws, which are there to recall these demands, are no longer rejected as a hindrance but recognized as a powerful help.

15. The journey of husband and wife, like every human life, has many stages; and, as you know from your experience over the years, it also includes difficult and painful periods. But it must be said emphatically: never should anguish and fear find a place in souls of good will since, after all, is not the Gospel good news also for husbands and wives? And despite all its demands, is it not a profoundly liberating message?

One naturally is distressed to realize that he has not yet achieved his interior liberty, that he is still subject to the impulses of his instincts. He is distressed to discover himself almost incapable at a particular moment of respecting the moral law in such a fundamental area. Yet this is the decisive moment when the Christian in his disarray, instead of yielding to a sterile and destructive revolt, makes his way humbly to the staggering discovery of what it means to be a man before God, a sinner before the love of Christ the Savior.

16. All progress in the moral life starts with this radical awareness. The couple has thus been "evangelized" in the depths of their being. And "with fear and trembling,"[43] but also with a wondrous joy, husband and wife discover that in their marriage, as in the union of Christ and the Church, the Easter mystery of death and resurrection is being accomplished.

In the bosom of the great Church this little church then recognizes itself for what it is in reality: a community — weak, sometimes sinful and penitent, but forgiven — on the road towards holiness, "in the peace of God which surpasses all understanding."[44]

This does not all mean that the spouses are shielded against all failures: "let him who prides himself on standing take care lest he fall."[45] They are not dispensed from the need of persevering effort, sometimes in cruel circumstances that can only be endured by the realization that they are participating in Christ's Passion.[46] But at least they know that the demands of a moral married life, which the Church recalls to them, are not intolerable and impracticable laws but a gift of God to help them discover, by means of their own weaknesses and looking beyond them, the riches of a fully human and Christian love. Hence the spouses do not at all have the anguished feeling that they have in some way reached a dead end, that in some instances they are perhaps sinking into sensuality as they abandon all reception of the sacraments or even as they rebel against a Church they consider inhuman. Nor do they grow hardened by reason of an impossible effort that threatens their harmony and emotional balance or even the marriage itself. Instead husband and wife will open themselves to hope, in the certainty that all of the Church's resources of grace are available to help them on their journey towards the perfection of their love.

Footnotes:

38. Dogmatic Constitution on the Church, *Lumen Gentium*, no. 41.
39. See Mt 5, 48: 1 Thes 4, 3; Eph 1, 4.
40. St. Irenaeus, Adversus Haereses IV, 28, 4: PG 7, 1, 200.
41. Rom 12, 2.
42. See 1 Jn 1, 7.
43. Phil 2, 12.
44. Phil 4, 7.
45. 1 Cor 10, 12.
46. See Col 1, 24.

11. PAUL VI, *Allocution to the Executive Director of the UN Fund for Population Activities, and the Secretary General of the World Population Conference, March 30, 1974.*

RADICAL MEASURES. . . . Some people are carried away by the temptation to believe that there is no other solution except to curb population growth by the use of radical measures, measures which are frequently in contrast with the laws implanted by God in man's nature, and which fall short of due respect for the dignity of human life and man's rightful liberty. Such measures are in some cases based upon a materialistic view of man's destiny.

The true solutions to these problems — We would say the only solutions — will be those that take due account of all concrete factors as a whole: the demands of social justice along with respect for the divine laws governing life, the dignity of the human person as well as the freedom of peoples, the primary role of the family as well as the responsibility proper to married couples.

The Church's Position

We do not intend to repeat here in detail the principles that govern the Church's position in the matter of population. These principles have been clearly set forth in the Second Vatican Council's Constitution on the Church in the World of Today, and in Our encyclical letters *Populorum Progressio* and *Humanae Vitae.* These documents, whose contents are well known to you, demonstrate that the Church's teaching on population matters is both firm and carefully enunciated, respectful of principles and at the same time deeply human in its pastoral approach.

No pressure must cause the Church to deviate toward doctrinal compromises or short-sighted solutions.

12. PAUL VI *TO PARTICIPANTS IN THE TWENTY FIFTH GENERAL ASSEMBLY OF PHARMACOLOGY*, September 7, 1974

The Pope invited them to "deepen and broaden their knowledge about the Church's teachings on the grave questions which concern the concept of man. There is no lack of documents on the subject, including also Our Encyclical *HUMANAE VITAE,* which sheds light on the subject which you have chosen as one of the principle points of your labors . . . . This document casts into focus a vision of total man in his dependence on God the Creator, and in his supernatural vocation . . . . It treats of a proper way of responsible parenthood. In the document (cfr. HV 24) we invite men of science, as the Fathers of Vatican II had already done, to pool their efforts and knowledge to explain more thoroughly the various conditions favoring a wholesome regulation of births.

. . . Our delegation to the World Population Congress at Bucharest issued a clear declaration, reaffirming without ambiguity the refusal of the Church to accept practices which run contrary to the respect due to man, including abortion, sterilization, and contraception, means which transgress the laws of transmission of life. After all, it is our mission which calls us to defend without growing weary that inestimable gift of God which is human life, and the sacred laws that govern it."

13. *LETTER OF CARDINAL VILLOT IN THE NAME OF POPE PAUL VI,* to the Congress of the International Federation for Family Life Promotion (IFFLP) at Cali, Colombia, June 22-25,

1977

. . . The importance of the knowledge of the biological laws of human fertility which can enhance a healthy regulation of births by natural methods, requires that scientific research be intensified in this area. The work should also be coordinated and ought to be supported with funds which are proportionate to the issue in question and to the services rendered.

Pope Paul VI also feels that couples themselves can help other couples very well in the search to discover, accept, and experience the holiness and gentleness of the law which binds their mutual conjugal love to the law of God, the author of human life. By sharing their experiences they are in a good position to win the confidence of couples and to become their guides.

This work requires the concerted effort of numerous specialized educators, informed marriage counselors and spiritual advisors, including lay people, religious, and members of the clergy, to help couples to meet the full scope of the requirements of their love and of responsible parenthood. The Holy Father has often had the opportunity to express and to recall to all Catholics and men of good will the principles involved. What is involved here is the construction of a world which respects love and life as gifts from God . . . .

14. JOHN PAUL II, *ADDRESS TO PROMOTORS OF NATURAL FAMILY PLANNING*

Address to Delegates of Liaison Center of Research Teams (CLER) and Directors of the International Federation for Family Life Promotion, Rome, November 3, 1979.

. . . 5. *Responsible parenthood* must be viewed in this perspective (of specifically Christian values). On this plane, the spouses, the parents, may meet with a certain number of problems which cannot be solved without deep love, a love which comprises also an effort of continence. These two virtues, love and continence, appeal to a common decision of the spouses and to their will to submit to the doctrine of the Faith, to the teaching of the Church. On this vast subject, I will limit myself to three observations.

Church's Doctrine Clear

6. In the first place, there must be no cheating with the *doctrine of the Church,* as it has been set forth clearly by the Magisterium, by the Council, by my predecessors. I am thinking especially of the Encyclical *HUMANAE VITAE* of Paul VI, of his address to the Notre Dame Teams on May 4, 1970, and of his numerous other addresses. We must hold our course steadily by this ideal of conjugal relations, governed by and respectful of the nature and purposes of the conjugal

act. We should shun the concession — more or less broad, more or less avowed — to the principle and practice of contraceptive morals. God calls spouses to the holiness of marriage, for their own good and for the quality of their witness.

Extending Help to Others

7. This point being firmly established, out of obedience to the Church — it is to your honor to cling to it cost what it may — a no less important point is to help Christian couples, and others, to strengthen their own *convictions,* by seeking with them the deeply human reason for acting that way. It is good that they should catch a glimpse of how this natural ethic corresponds to what is most authentically human. Armed with such knowledge they can escape more easily the traps of permissive laws and public opinion, and even contribute their part to a correction of public opinion. . .

8. . . . It must even be added that the popularization of artificial contraception leads to abortion, for both lie — though at different levels — on the same line of fear of the child, rejection of life, lack of respect for the act or the fruit of the union, such as it is established between man and woman by the creator of nature . . .

Living Responsible Parenthood

9. Finally, all possible means should be employed to provide concrete help to couples so that they can live this responsible parenthood. Your contributions in this area are irreplaceable . . . I am happy to know that a growing number of persons and organizations at the inter national level appreciate these efforts for natural regulation. To these men of science, doctors and specialists, I address all my good wishes and encouragement, since at stake is the welfare of families and of societies in their legitimate concern to harmonize human fertility with their capabilities. Also, provided only that an appeal is always made to the virtues of love and continence, it is a question of progress in human self-mastery, in conformity with the Creator's plan.

I encourage also all qualified lay people, those married couples who provide spouses with assistance to live worthily their conjugal love and that responsibility as parents by counselling, teaching, and guiding them; and who help young people to prepare for this responsibility.

I assure each of you, your collaborators, families and dear children, of my prayer for your magnificent apostolate, and impart to you my fatherly Apostolic Blessing.

15. JOHN PAUL II, *ADDRESS TO MIDWIVES*, January 26, 1980

. . . . And how could I fail to recall also, in a broader view of your service for life, the important contribution of advice and practical guidance you can offer to individual married couples, who wish to carry out responsible procreation, while respecting the order established by God? To you, too, are addressed the words of my predecessor Paul VI, exhorting members of the medical profession to persevere "in promoting on every occasion solutions inspired by faith and upright reason" and to endeavor to "bring forth conviction and respect for these correct solutions in their environment" (Encyclical *HUMANAE VITAE, No. 27).*

16. JOHN PAUL II *TALK TO INDONESIAN BISHOPS*

Pope John Paul II's English-language address June 7, 1980 to the third group of Indonesian bishops making their "ad limina" (official five-year) visits to Rome to report on their diocese.

Venerable and Dear Brothers in Our Lord Jesus Christ

I am very grateful for your visit today, grateful for the greetings you bring me from your local churches, grateful for your own fraternal love in Christ Jesus, grateful for the ecclesial communion we celebrate together in Catholic unity. This ecclesial communion — this Catholic unity — was the theme of my address to your brother bishops from Indonesia who were here less than two weeks ago. It is likewise the basis for this "ad limina" visit and for every "ad limina" visit to Rome.

Precisely because of this ecclesial communion, I personally, as successor of Peter, experience deeply the need to make every effort to understand as fully as possible the problems of your local churches and to assist in solving these problems in accordance with the will of Christ for his church. The issues you have presented to me affect the well-being of your people. Some of them raise questions that touch the Catholic faith and Catholic life in general. All of them represent pastoral concerns that in differing ways are the object of your responsibility and mine, matters to be examined with the assistance of the Holy Spirit in the light of the perennial value of God's word, upheld by the magisterium of the church, and in the context of ecclesial communion . . . .

In moral questions as in doctrinal issues we must continue to proclaim the church's teaching "in season and out of season" (2 Timothy 4:2). Hence we urge our people to admit only one measure of Christian love: to love one another as Christ has loved us (cf. John 13, 34). We charge them to bear constant witness to Christ's justice and his truth.

In our ministry at the service of life we are called to testify to the fullness of the truth we hold so that all may know the stand of the Catholic Church on the utter inviolability of human life from the moment of conception. Hence we proclaim with deep conviction that any willful destruction of human life by procured abortion for any reason whatsoever is not in accord with God's commandment, that it is entirely outside the competence of any individual or group and that it cannot redound to true human progress.

In the question of the church's teaching on the regulation of birth we are called to profess in union with the whole church the exigent but uplifting teaching recorded in the encyclical, *Humanae Vitae,* which my predecessor Paul VI put forth "by virtue of the mandate entrusted to us by Christ" (AAS 60, 1968, p. 485). Particularly in this regard we must be conscious of the fact that God's wisdom supersedes human calculations and his grace is powerful in people's lives. It is important for us to realize the direct influence of Christ on the members of his body in all realms of moral challenges. On the occasion of the "ad limina" visit of another group of bishops I made reference to this principle, which has many applications, saying, "Let us never fear that the challenge is too great for our people. They were redeemed by the precious blood of Christ. They are his people. Through the Holy Spirit Jesus Christ vindicates to himself the final responsibility for the acceptance of his word and for the growth of his church. It is he, Jesus Christ, who will continue to give the grace to his people to meet the requirements of his word, despite all difficulties, despite all weaknesses. And it is up to us to continue to proclaim the message of salvation in its entirety and purity with patience, compassion and the conviction that what is impossible with man is possible with God. We ourselves are only part of one generation in salvation history, but 'Jesus Christ is the same yesterday, today, and for ever' (Hebrews 13, 8). He is indeed able to sustain us as we recognize the strength of his grace, the power of his word and the efficacy of his merits" (AAS 71, 1979, pp. 1,423 f.).

Christ's grace does not eliminate the need for compassionate understanding and increased pastoral effort on our part, but it does point to the fact that in the last analysis everything depends on Christ. It is Christ's word we preach. It is his church we construct day after day, according to his criterion. Jesus Christ has built his church on the foundation of the apostles and prophets (cf. Ephesians 2, 20) and in a special way on Peter (cf. Matthew 16, 18). But it remains his church, the church of Christ: ". . . and on this rock I will build my church." Our people are ours only because they are, above all, his. Jesus Christ is the good shepherd, the author of our faith, the hope of the world.

It is important for us to reflect on the mystery of the headship of Christ over his church. Through his Holy Spirit Jesus Christ gives grace and strength to his people and he invites all of them to follow him. At times, beginning with Peter, Christ calls his people to be led, as he himself explains, where they do not wish to go (cf. John 21:18).

Venerable brothers, my recent pastoral visits confirm something that we have all experienced. Our people are constantly turning to us with the expectation and the plea: Proclaim to us the word of God; speak to us about Christ. Their request is an echo of the request spoken of by St. John and made to the apostle Philip, "We wish to see Jesus" (John 12, 21). Truly the world entreats us to speak about Christ. It is he who will shape the new heavens and the new earth. It is he who by his word of truth fashions and controls the destinies of our people.

With renewed pastoral love and zeal let us proclaim his saving word to the world. Relying on the assistance of Mary, mother of the incarnate word, let us together commend our people and our ministry to him who alone has "the words of eternal life" (John 6, 68).

With these sentiments I send my greetings back to all the members of your local churches and especially to all the Christian families. I offer my encouragement and gratitude to the priests and Religious and to all who collaborate with you in the cause of the Gospel. To the sick and suffering goes my special blessing and to everyone the expression of my love in our Lord and Saviour Jesus Christ."

Sections of the 1951 Address to Midwives, and to the Family Front are from the National Catholic Welfare Conference version. Those of MATER ET MAGISTRA *are from the version of The Missionary Society of St. Paul the Apostle, New York, 1963.*

The translation of the sections from THE CHURCH IN THE MODERN WORLD *is that of Costello Publishing Company, Northport, New York, USA, Austin Flannery, O.P., General Editor. Permission obtained. The Address to Cardinals, June 23, 1964, is taken from* THE POPE SPEAKS. *The* HUMANAE VITAE *translation is published by Ignatius Press, San Francisco, 1978, used with permission. Other quotations were translated by the coordinator, or adapted by him from various sources, especially the* OSSERVATORE ROMANO, *English Weekly Edition.*

"God looked at everything

he had made, and he found it

very good."

Genesis 1, 31.